Joseph/Fillenz/Macdonald/Marsden

Monitoring Neurotransmitter Release During Behaviour

Ellis Horwood Health Science Series

Series Editor: Dr. Alan Wiseman, Department of Biochemistry, University of Surrey

Cholecystokinin (CCK) in the Nervous System: Current Developments in Neuropeptide Research
Editors: J. de Belleroche and G. T. Dockray

The Blood Brain Barrier in Health and Disease
A. T. Suckling, M. G. Rumsby and M. W. Bradbury

Chemiluminescence: Principles and Applications in Biology and Medicine.
A. K. Campbell

Steroid Hormone Receptors: Their Intracellular Localization
Editor: C. R. Clark

Neuropharmacology and Neurobiology: Molecular Basis, Biological Activity with Applications in Neurotoxicity and Pest Control
Editors: M. G. Ford, P. N. R. Usherwood R. C. Reay and G. G. Lunt

Biological Oxidation of Nitrogen in Organic Molecules:
Editors: J. W. Gorrod and L. A. Damani

Medical Applications of Biosynthetic Studies of Membrane Glycoproteins:
Proteolysis – Glycosylation – Acylation
M. F. G. Schmidt, H. D. Klenk and R. T. Schwarz

Interaction of Steroid Hormone Receptors with DNA
Editor: M. Sluyser

Monitoring Neurotransmitter Release During Behaviour

Edited by
M. H. Joseph, M. Fillenz,
I. A. Macdonald and C. A. Marsden

ELLIS HORWOOD
international publishers in science and technology
Chichester England

Dr. M. H. Joseph
Institute of Psychiatry, London

Dr. M. Fillenz
University of Oxford

Dr. I. A. Macdonald and Dr. C. A. Marsden
University of Nottingham

Deutsche Bibliothek Cataloguing-in-Publication Data

Monitoring neurotransmitter release during behaviour/ed. by M. H. Joseph...
– Weinheim; Deerfield Beach, Fl.: VCH; Chichester: Horwood, 1986.
  (Ellis Horwood health science series)
  ISBN 3-527-26222-9 (VCH, Weinheim)
  ISBN 0-89573-367-6 (VCH, Deerfield Beach, Fl.)
NE: Joseph, Michael. H. [Hrsg.]

British Library Cataloguing in Publication Data
Monitoring neurotransmitter release during behaviour.
– (Ellis Horwood health science series)
  1. Neurotransmitters
  I. Joseph, M. H.
  612'.82   QP 364.7
  ISBN 3-527-26222-9
  ISBN 0-89573-367-6 (U.S.: VCH)

Library of Congress Card No. 85-27020

Published jointly in 1986 by
Ellis Horwood Ltd., Chichester, England
and VCH Verlagsgesellschaft mbH, Weinheim, Federal Republic of Germany

Distribution:

VCH Verlagsgesellschaft, P.O.Box 1260/1280, D-6940 Weinheim
(Federal Republic of Germany)

USA and Canada: VCH Publishers, 303 N.W. 12th Avenue, Deerfield Beach,
FL 33442-1705 (USA)

Printed in Great Britain by The Camelot Press, Southampton.

Table of Contents

**PART IV: – WORKSHOP: RECENT DEVELOPMENTS IN HPLC
ANALYSIS OF TRANSMITTERS AND RELATED COM-
POUNDS**

PART V – WORKSHOP: IN VIVO TECHNIQUES FOR MEASURING TRANSMITTER RELEASE AND METABOLISM

Part

I

Introduction

The recent rapid development of neurochemistry is leading to an increasingly detailed picture of the chemical architecture of the nervous system; an example is the rapid growth of knowledge of the neuroanatomy of neuronal systems using peptides, and other non-classical transmitters. However, just as for other organs, important aspects of neurochemistry are only revealed by dynamic studies. Indeed, in a system whose function is so exquisitely dependent upon its organization, understanding the relation of function to transmitter chemistry is crucially dependent on dynamic studies in individual conscious animals.

Classical neurochemistry and histochemistry can give us information about the nervous system 'even to its uttermost detail' (Thuddicum), but in general will tell us about only one point in time. In order to understand the relation between chemical changes in the brain or in the peripheral nervous system, and function, techniques are required that enable repeated observations to be made in individual subjects, while imposing physiological or psychological or pharmacological inputs and observing physiological, behavioural or endocrine outputs.

With regard to the autonomic nervous system the major approach has been to measure plasma catecholamines, though it is only recently that techniques have been developed that have made this a real possibility. These methods (HPLC with electrochemical detection and radioenzymatic assay) are discussed by Dr Hjemdahl together with the problems of interpreting changes in plasma adrenaline and noradrenaline. The second approach to the assessment of sympathoadrenal function is the measurement of catecholamine turnover. Again there are problems both with the design of the experiments and interpretation of the results obtained. Dr Landsberg and his colleagues describe their experiments in which they have made important steps in elucidating the various factors that may influence results obtained using turnover measurements. One of these factors, the importance of which is so far relatively unexplored, is the discovery of several neuropeptides associated with the autonomic nervous system, Dr Allen describes the current status of neuropeptide Y, suggesting it may have a role independent of noradrenaline as a peripheral vasoactive agent. Functional aspects of neuropeptides in both peripheral and central neural control will be a major feature of research in the future. With the establishment of techniques for monitoring sympathoadrenal neurochemical function, the next stage is to relate these measurements to changes in physiological status, as described by Dr Macdonald.

The second aspect of this book is the application of *in vivo* sampling techniques to monitor transmitter release and metabolism in the brain. The classical approach of using push—pull cannulae or cortical cups has in recent years yielded new information due to the development of new and more sensitive assays for amines and amino acids. Professor Bradford provides examples of the measurement of amino acid release using a modified closed cortical cup approach permitting chronic superfusion in the unrestrained animal. The more recent developments of intracerebral dialysis, in which the extracellular fluid is sampled using a closed dialysis system, and chronic CSF sampling are discussed by Dr Sharp and Professor Curzon respectively.

A major strand of the work discussed in this volume has come from the application of electrochemistry to neurochemical problems. The electrochemical activity of the amines and related metabolites has been turned to advantage in two ways, both originating in Ralph Adams's laboratory in Kansas. Firstly, electrochemical detection combined with HPLC separation provides a very sensitive technique for the analysis of amines and metabolites in plasma, in brain samples and in the CSF or the perfusates obtained from push–pull or *in vivo* dialysis experiments. The main current trends in the analytical aspects of electrochemical detection are discussed in the 'HPLC workshop' section of this volume. Secondly, miniaturized versions of the electrodes can be chronically implanted into the brain, so that levels of electroactive compounds in the extracellular fluid (ECF) of the brain can be directly monitored on a continuing basis. This technique has advantages over sampling techniques in speed and frequency of measurement and in the small size of the probe used (resulting in better localization and less trauma). However the countervailing disadvantage is the difficulty in unambiguous interpretation of the voltammetric signals obtained, Initial expectations that the catecholamines and indoleamines and their metabolites, which are among the few species in the ECF which are electroactive at modest potentials, could be readily determined have been qualified. While the contribution of other electroactive species present in large amounts in brain (e.g. ascorbic acid) to the voltammetric signal was recognized in the earliest studies on *in vivo* voltammetry, their resolution from the amine and metabolite signals has proved a difficult problem. *In vivo* voltammetry is now going through a period of consolidation, with the recognition of the implications of the high levels of ascorbic acid and uric acid in the ECF and the investigation of their modulation in relation to neural events. Not only the baseline electrochemical signals, but particularly their changes in response to stimuli must be carefully analysed pharmacologically, neurochemically and electrochemically in order that the contributing species can be clearly identified.

In this volume these problems are fully discussed and examples of the application of *in vivo* voltammetry demonstrated. Dr Marsden and colleagues discuss the combined use of voltammetry and intracerebral dialysis to validate one another and to identify amine receptors involved in the modulation of amine release, while Dr Freed describes voltammetric experiments designed to show the relationship between dopamine release and movement and 5-hydroxytryptamine and blood pressure. Finally, Dr Fillenz presents data supporting a link between changes in extracellular ascorbate and the release of excitatory amino acids. Results obtained with these techniques are further discussed in the report of the '*in vivo* workshop'. The different methods for measuring transmitter release *in vivo* are complementary, as indicated by many of the contributors; greater progress can be made by learning from the differences, as well as the similarities, between the results obtained with each technique.

Three of the editors of this volume organized a meeting on electrochemical detection in pharmacology and neurochemistry in Nottingham in April 1982. The present volume is based upon a second meeting, held in Oxford in September 1984. We thank all our speakers and other invited contributors for agreeing to contribute to this volume, and doing so in such a thorough and interesting way. The session chairmen are also to be thanked for their commentaries based around the presentations in their respective sessions. The meeting was held under the auspices of the Neurochemical Group of the Biochemical Society, London, and thanks are due to the Group Committee and to Ellis Horwood, publishers of the 'Biochemistry in Medicine and Pharmacology' series.

We also thank the staff of the University Laboratory of Physiology and of St Anne's College, University of Oxford, for so successfully implementing the practical arrangements for the meeting. Financial support was provided by the Royal Society, the Wellcome Trust, Beecham Pharmaceuticals, Boots plc, ICI Pharmaceuticals plc, Lilly Research Centre, Merck, Sharp & Dohme Ltd and Reckitt & Colman Ltd. We should also like to thank the companies that supported the trade exhibition associated with the meeting: Anachem Ltd, Applied Chromatography Systems Ltd (now HPLC Technology), Dyson Instruments, Jones Chromatography, Laboratory Data Control, LKB Instruments Ltd, Perkin-Elmer Ltd, Pye Unicam Ltd, Roth Scientific, Severn Analytical and Waters Associates.

Michael H. Joseph
Marianne Fillenz
Ian A. Macdonald
Charles A. Marsden

Part

II

Catecholamine and peptide release in relation to sympathoadrenal function

Measurements of plasma catecholamines by HPLC and the relation of their concentrations to sympathoadrenal activity

Paul Hjemdahl

Department of Pharmacology, Karolinska Institutet,
S-104 01 Stockholm, Sweden

1. INTRODUCTION

Sympathoadrenal activity, i.e. peripheral sympathetic nerve activity and circulating catecholamines, is considered to be of importance for cardiovascular, metabolic and other physiological processes, under normal circumstances, under stressful conditions and in various pathological states. The primary neurotransmitter of the sympathetic nerves is noradrenaline (NA), but a subset of the renal sympathetic nerves may have dopamine(DA) as neurotransmitter (Goldberg and Weber, 1980; Bradley and Hjemdahl, 1984). Furthermore, it has been proposed that adrenaline (ADR), which mainly acts as a circulating hormone secreted from the adrenal medulla (Cryer, 1980), may have a role as a co-transmitter in peripheral sympathetic nerves (Rand and Majewski, 1984). Apart from being the primary neurotransmitter of sympathetic nerves, NA may under some conditions reach concentrations in plasma which are compatible with an additional role as a circulating hormone (Silverberg *et al.*, 1978; Hjemdahl and Linde, 1983). The relative importance of neuronally released transmitter (mainly

NA) and circulating catecholamines (mainly ADR) will, however, not be discussed in this chapter. The focus will be on plasma catecholamine analyses by HPLC with electrochemical detection (ECD) and on physiological problems which should be considered when using plasma catecholamine determinations to monitor sympathoadrenal activity.

Plasma catecholamines are now frequently used to monitor sympatho-adrenal activity in animals and man. This is based on the assumption that circulating NA gives a good reflection of sympathetic nerve activity (see below) and the fact that ADR is a circulating hormone, the plasma concentrations of which are of obvious interest. Furthermore, NA and ADR levels in venous plasma are elevated, more or less in the expected fashion, in connection with various kinds of stress (Cryer, 1980). A prerequisite when using plasma catecholamine determinations to study sympathoadrenal activity is, of course, that the assay used gives correct estimates of the catecholamine concentrations in the sample. Since the basal levels of NA are about $1-2$ nmol/l ($150-300$ pg/ml) and the basal levels of ADR and free (i.e. unconjugated) DA are about $0.1-0.2$ nmol/l ($15-40$ pg/ml) in venous plasma, the analytical challenge is considerable.

2. CATECHOLAMINE MEASUREMENTS BY HPLC–ECD

Many different or more or less modified plasma catecholamine assays have been developed (see, for example, Johnson et al., 1980; Hjemdahl, 1984a, 1984b). This multitude of assays implies that the methods have faults and/or that they are difficult to use. Like any other assay, a plasma catecholamine assay must possess adequate *sensitivity*, as well as good *specificity*. Furthermore, as a sign of accuracy it must also produce reasonably *reproducible* results. It is important not to confuse reproducibility and specificity, since it is quite possible to reproduce both erroneous and correct results. Thus, it is most important to validate an assay to show that it gives correct results. The latter aspect has been rather neglected in this field.

The early fluorimetric assays for catecholamines in plasma have largely been abandoned because of problems with the sensitivity and the specificity of these assays. In the 1970s several radioenzymatic assays for catecholamines in plasma were developed (see Johnson et al., 1980). Later, the development of better detectors, in particular those based on electrochemical oxidation of the catecholamines, has led to a steadily increasing interest in the possibility of using high performance liquid chromatography (HPLC) to measure catecholamines in plasma (see Hjemdahl, 1984a).

2.1 Clean-up procedures

When using an HPLC assay for catecholamines in plasma (and other biological materials) it is important to purify and concentrate the sample before analysis. This increases the specificity of the assay by eliminating or reducing the concentrations of possibly interfering substances and it also increases the sensitivity of the assay. Furthermore, it protects and prolongs the life of the analytical HPLC column. It goes without saying that the sensitivity and reproducibility of an HPLC–ECD assay may be improved by concentrating a larger sample volume in the clean-up step.

The simplest and most common procedure is extraction with alumina, which selectively binds catechols at a high pH (Anton and Sayre, 1962). With this method the catecholamines in a sample containing a suitable internal standard are adsorbed onto activated aluminium oxide at pH 8.6, which requires good protection against oxidation of the catecholamines. Following careful rinsing of the alumina the catecholamines are desorbed into a smaller volume of an acid, e.g. 0.1 M perchloric acid. The recovery through this extraction step is typically about 70–80%. When a cation exchange HPLC column is used, this extraction procedure appears to yield sufficient selectivity for catecholamines in plasma (Hjemdahl, 1984a).

When reverse phase HPLC columns are used in the analytical step further purification of the samples may be required (see below), although it has been claimed that alumina extraction may suffice if the column has a high degree of resolution (e.g. Davis *et al.*, 1981). Other sample clean-up procedures which may be combined with the alumina extraction procedure to enhance the selectivity of reverse phase HPLC assays include purification either on a cation exchange resin (e.g. Davis *et al.*, 1981) or a boric acid gel (Higa *et al.*, 1977) or ion pair extraction with diphenylborate (Smedes *et al.*, 1982).

2.2 Analytical HPLC columns

The second level at which selectivity for catecholamines is gained in an HPLC–ECD assay is the chromatographic separation of the catecholamines from each other and from potentially interfering substances on the HPLC column. Two main approaches have been used: cation exchange HPLC or reverse phase HPLC.

The first described HPLC–ECD assay for catecholamines in plasma (Hallman *et al.*, 1978) utilized a pellicular (i.e. rather large and irregularly shaped) cation exchange resin. To obtain a higher degree of resolution we (Hjemdahl, Daleskog and Kahan, 1979) and others (Allenmark and Hedman, 1979; Watson, 1981) turned to microparticulate cation exchange HPLC. In our experience this has proved to be a reliable approach (Hjemdahl, 1984a, 1984b), provided that a good batch of cation exchange resin is used.

Reverse phase HPLC is the most commonly used approach in bioanalytical assays based on HPLC and this methodology is now also widely used to assay catecholamines in plasma (for references see Hjemdahl, 1984a). Reverse phase columns separate substances mainly on the basis of lipophilicity. They are very versatile, since the chromatographic behaviour of these columns may be varied by changes in the pH and ionic composition of the mobile phase (including the use of ion pairing agents) and by the addition of organic modifiers to the mobile phase. This versatility, however, also entails the risk of variable results when modifications are introduced. Furthermore, the principle of organic extraction appears to be less selective for catecholamines than is cation exchange. For example, one may experience problems in separating NA from uric acid (which is present in appreciable concentrations in plasma samples also after alumina extraction) on a reverse phase HPLC column (Davis *et al.*, 1981). The cation exchange columns used in this context do not retain uric acid, thus eliminating this problem. It is the opinion of the present author that cation exchange HPLC usually offers a better selectivity and better reproducibility than reverse phase HPLC for the assay of catecholamines in plasma (see below).

2.3 Electrochemical detection

The use of ECD is based on the ability to convert catechols into quinones when a potential is applied to the sample. In the process electrons are liberated, resulting in a current which is directly proportional to the amount of sample oxidized. Since catecholamines are more readily oxidized by this principle than many other substances, ECD offers a third level of selectivity (Kissinger, 1977), provided that the oxidation potential is kept low. ECD is adequately sensitive to measure catecholamines in plasma and has the advantages over fluorometric detection of being simpler and sensitive to all the endogenous catecholamines (see Hjemdahl, 1984a). Amperometric (less than complete conversion of the sample) or coulometric (quantitative conversion of the sample) detectors may be used (Kissinger, 1977). Good sensitivity may be achieved with amperometric detection when using either a carbon paste electrode or a good glassy carbon electrode. It is essential to reduce the noise level by using highly purified water and other components constituting the mobile phase and to minimize electrical disturbances by grounding and shielding of the equipment. Although the coulometric principle offers the advantage of a larger signal, owing to complete oxidation of the sample, improvements in the signal-to-noise ratio have yet to be demonstrated (see Hjemdahl, 1984a). Furthermore, adequate validation of assays utilizing ECD based on the coulometric principle is lacking.

2.4 Validation of assays

Most new plasma catecholamine assays are validated by demonstrating a sufficient sensitivity to measure basal plasma catecholamine levels and a good reproducibility. Furthermore, recovery experiments using known amounts of catecholamines added to the sample are usually performed. This, however, does not guarantee that the assay measures the *endogenous* plasma catecholamine concentrations correctly. Ideally, a new technique (or any modification of an old technique) should be validated by comparison with a well established previously used method to show that the new method achieves equally good results in a better (simpler or cheaper) way or that the previously established method gives erroneous results. Few attempts to do this have been published.

Intra-laboratory comparisons of assay results obtained with HPLC–ECD and radioenzymatic methods have been reported from three independent laboratories using microparticulate cation exchange HPLC with amperometric detection (Hjemdahl *et al.,* 1979; Allenmark *et al.,* 1980; Eriksson and Persson, 1982) and one laboratory using reverse phase HPLC with amperometric detection (Goldstein *et al.,* 1981). Fig. 1 shows the excellent agreement which can be obtained when comparing cation exchange HPLC with a radioenzymatic technique (essentially according to Peuler and Johnson, 1977) on an *intra*-laboratory

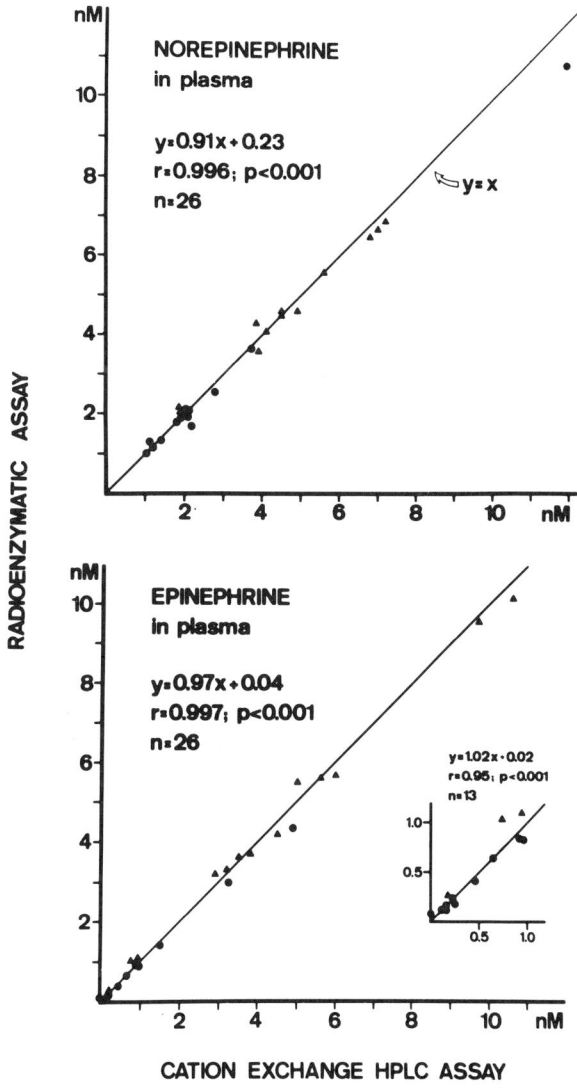

Fig. 1 – An *intra*-laboratory comparison of assay results obtained by cation exchange HPLC–ECD and by slight modification of the single isotope radio-enzymatic technique of Peuler and Johnson (1977). Results from our laboratory (▲) and the laboratory of Eriksson and Persson, AB Hässle, Mölndal, Sweden (●) have been pooled. (Reproduced from Hjemdahl (1984a) with the permission of the American Physiological Society.)

basis. Note the excellent agreement between results obtained with the two techniques even at low, physiologically relevant concentrations of ADR. In our hands, this HPLC technique has been shown to have inter- and intra-assay coefficients of variation in the order 2–3% at catecholamine concentrations above 1–2 nmol/l (i.e. basal NA concentrations) and about 10% at 0.1–0.2 nmol/l (i.e. basal ADR and DA concentrations), which compares favourably with other published data (see Hjemdahl, 1984a).

Recently, an *inter*-laboratory comparison of plasma catecholamine assays using different methods was performed (Hjemdahl, 1984b). In this study 34 laboratories performing altogether 41 assays on four different samples participated. Eight assays were performed by various modifications of reverse phase HPLC–ECD, whereas one laboratory used pellicular and five laboratories used microparticulate cation exchange HPLC–ECD. One laboratory using the latter approach did not achieve sufficient sensitivity to detect basal ADR levels, presumably because of limited experience in the field, and was therefore excluded from the evaluation of ADR results.

Fig. 2 shows that measurements of basal ADR levels in a plasma pool gave quite variable results. The laboratories using reverse phase HPLC reported a tenfold variation between the highest and lowest level measured, whereas four laboratories using microparticulate cation exchange HPLC found the concentrations of ADR to be about 0.2 nmol/l. The recoveries of known amounts of ADR (0.7 or 3.0 nmol/l) added to the basal plasma pool and measurements of higher concentrations of endogenous ADR (about 0.7 nmol/l in an exercise sample) were less variable with the microparticulate cation exchange approach than with reverse phase HPLC (Fig. 2). Duplicate determinations of NA (about 1.7 nmol/l) also showed important inter-laboratory variability and occasional problems with intra-laboratory reproducibility when using reverse phase HPLC, whereas good agreement was found with cation exchange HPLC (Fig. 3). Similarly, greater problems were associated with the use of reverse phase techniques when the

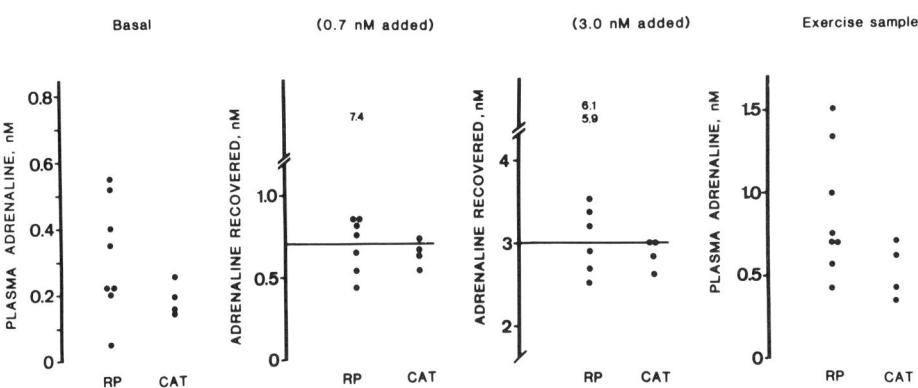

Fig. 2 – *Inter*-laboratory comparison of ADR analyses in plasma by reverse phase HPLC–ECD (RP) in eight different laboratories and microparticulate cation exchange HPLC–ECD (CAT) in four different laboratories. The samples analyzed were (from left to right): a basal human plasma pool, the same pool with 0.7 or 3.0 nmol/l ADR added and a pool obtained from healthy volunteers following exercise. (Modified from Hjemdahl (1984b) and reproduced with the permission of *Acta Physiol. Scand.*)

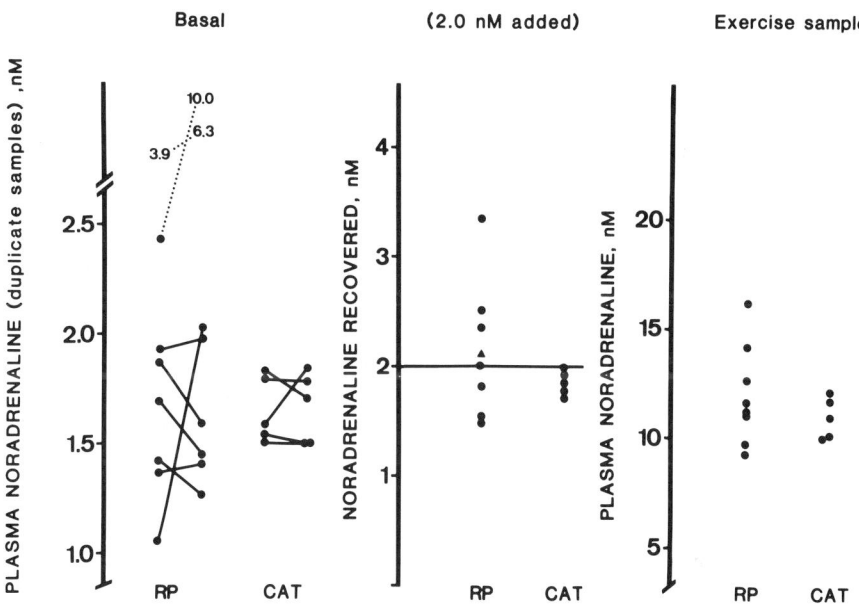

Fig. 3 — *Inter*-laboratory comparison of NA analyses in plasma. Symbols as in Fig. 2. The samples analysed were: duplicate determinations from the basal human plasma pool, the recovery of 2.0 nmol/l NA added to this pool and the exercise pool which was also studied in Fig. 2. The triangle in one of the RP determinations of NA recovery indicates that an obviously erroneous result (10 nmol/l) in one of the duplicate determinations on the basal pool was discarded when calculating the recovery in that assay. (Modified from Hjemdahl (1984b) and reproduced with the permission of *Acta Physiol. Scand.*)

recovery of NA (2.0 nmol/l) from the basal pool or a high concentration of endogenous NA (about 11 nmol/l) in the exercise sample were studied (Fig. 3).

Although some laboratories using reverse phase HPLC performed well, the inter-laboratory comparison clearly demonstrates that reverse phase HPLC is associated with greater variability than microparticulate cation exchange HPLC when assaying NA and ADR in plasma (Hjemdahl, 1984b). It has been argued that the various sample clean-up procedures used in conjunction with these reverse phase HPLC assays may be responsible for the variability observed in the inter-laboratory comparison. This may well be the case, since the laboratory yielding the best overall results with reverse phase HPLC used both alumina and cation exchange extractions in its clean-up procedure. However, the rapid and simple alumina extraction procedure seems to suffice when cation exchange HPLC columns are used.

Reverse phase HPLC thus appears to be less selective for catecholamines in plasma and prone to greater variability than cation exchange HPLC. It should be borne in mind that seemingly clean peaks in a chromatogram *may* contain contaminating substances. Furthermore, more elaborate extraction procedures involving several steps *may* introduce greater variability. Although not discussed here, equally large problems were found when these samples were assayed by various radioenzymatic methods (see Hjemdahl, 1984b, for details). The results of this inter-laboratory study support the contention that all modifications of plasma catecholamine assays should be thoroughly validated, preferably by comparisons with a well documented method, before being accepted for general use (Hjemdahl, 1984b).

3 INTERPRETATIONS OF PLASMA CATECHOLAMINE CONCENTRATIONS

The outflow of NA from an isolated blood perfused tissue, such as skeletal muscle (Kahan *et al.*, 1984), is directly proportional to the number of nerve impulses delivered and is closely related to the vasoconstrictor response. Similarly, we have found that the outflow of both NA and free DA into renal venous plasma is closely related to the frequency of sympathetic nerve stimulation in the canine kidney (Bradley and Hjemdahl, 1984). Thus, the spillover of endogenous NA from sympathetic nerve endings to the venous effluent from a tissue *in vivo* gives a good reflection of the local sympathetic nerve impulse activity. Similarly, the spillover of DA may be used to evaluate the possible existence of a subset of peripheral dopaminergic nerves. When the entire sympathetic outflow is stimulated, such as in the pithed rat, there is also a strictly frequency-dependent increase in circulating NA and a good correlation between increases in plasma NA and increases in blood pressure (Yamaguchi and Kopin, 1979). However, uniform activation of the sympathetic nervous system rarely occurs (Folkow, 1984). Instead, sympathetic nerve activity occurs in a differentiated fashion, the pattern of which varies with the type of physiological stimulus prevailing (Folkow *et al.*, 1983; Folkow, 1984). Therefore, the NA content of a plasma sample obtained from a vein draining one particular organ may be unrepresentative of the activity in sympathetic nerves in other, perhaps more important organs in the body or in the body as a whole.

The catecholamine concentrations in plasma will be determined by their release rates from sympathetic nerves and the adrenal medulla, as well as by the rate at which they are cleared from plasma (Esler, 1982). NA turnover in plasma is rapid. For example, the concentrations of NA in arterial plasma are elevated within 1–2 min during orthostatic stress (Linde and Hjemdahl, 1982). Similarly, NA is rapidly cleared from plasma, with a half-life of about 2 min (Esler, 1982), owing to various uptake mechanisms and metabolism in peripheral tissues. Fortunately, the NA concentrations in plasma correlate well with the calculated appearance rate (i.e. NA spillover from sympathetic nerves), but not with the clearance of NA from plasma, when NA kinetics in plasma have been studied by radiotracer methodology (Esler, 1982; Daleskog *et al.*, 1983; and unpublished work concerning both arterial and venous sampling from our group). Thus, catecholamine concentrations are useful indices of sympathoadrenal activity even if changes in catecholamine clearance from plasma may affect the interpretation of results in some circumstances (Esler, 1982).

The rapid turnover of NA and ADR in plasma may lead to rapid fluctuations of their concentrations in plasma. To minimize this problem when studying basal sympathoadrenal activity it is essential to use indwelling catheters for blood sampling and standardized experimental conditions with regard to rest, posture etc. Furthermore, it may be advisable to average assay results from several resting samples (Åkerstedt *et al.,* 1983) or to use a continuous blood withdrawal system (Dimsdale, 1984) to obtain more reliable measures of the resting plasma catecholamine levels.

3.1 Assessment of local sympathetic nerve activity by the outflow of NA from human tissues

To study local sympathetic activity in a tissue one must measure the blood flow in the tissue and obtain arterial and venous plasma samples and know how much of the venous NA outflow is derived from arterial plasma and how much is derived from the tissue in question.

The removal of NA in a tissue can be assessed by radiotracer methodology (infusions of ^{3}H-NA), and has been found to vary from one tissue to another (Esler *et al.,* 1984). In tissues consisting mainly of skeletal muscle, such as the limbs, about 50% of the arterial content of ^{3}H-NA is removed during one passage through the tissue (Esler *et al.,* 1984; Christensen *et al.,* 1984; Hjemdahl, Frey-schuss, Wallin, *et al.,* to be published) and ADR is removed to a similar extent (Hjemdahl *et al.,* 1984). Thus, if there is no veno-arterial concentration difference for NA over, for example, the forearm, *half* of the NA measured on the venous side is derived from local sympathetic nerve activity, i.e. mainly from

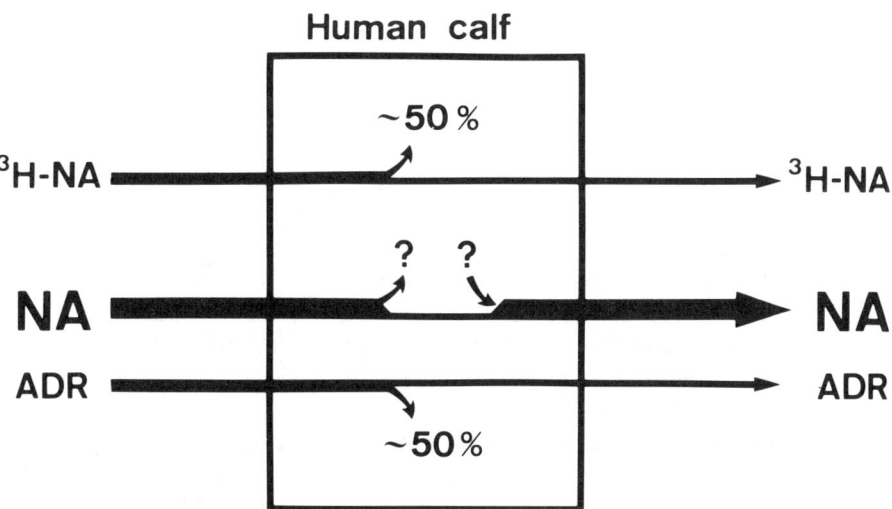

Fig. 4 – A schematic representation of the release and clearance of NA in a tissue consisting mainly of skeletal muscle, the human calf. The clearance of arterial NA in the tissue may be assessed either by calculating the clearance of endogenous ADR or the clearance of infused tracer amounts of ^{3}H-NA, both of which are approximately 50% in this tissue. See text for further discussion.

skeletal muscle nerves. If the venous concentration of NA exceeds that in arterial plasma (as it often does), the local sympathetic nerve activity will contribute even more importantly to the NA determined. Esler *et al.* (1984) have recently published estimates of the local clearances of ^{3}H-NA in various organs and the relative contributions of these organs to circulating NA in man.

The importance of evaluating the arterial contribution to venous NA concentrations is schematically illustrated in Fig. 4. The figure also illustrates that the removal of endogenous ADR in the tissue may be used to assess NA removal from arterial plasma when radiotracer studies with ^{3}H-NA cannot be performed. It is important to realize that the relative contribution of arterial NA to the outflow of NA from a tissue must be determined (preferably by the radiotracer technique) if an accurate estimate of the NA outflow from an organ, i.e. the local sympathetic nerve activity, is to be obtained.

3.2 Relationship between muscle sympathetic nerve activity and peripheral venous plasma NA levels

Plasma samples taken with the intention to assess sympathetic nerve activity in man are usually obtained from an antecubital vein. This has, for example, been the approach used in a very large number of studies of the sympathetic contribution to human essential hypertension (Goldstein, 1983). However, it has not been discussed from which sympathetic nerves this NA is mainly derived. Several lines of evidence suggest that venous plasma NA concentrations are closely related to the activity of skeletal muscle sympathetic nerves. Such a relationship would markedly affect the interpretation of the numerous studies of venous NA levels in hypertension, since there is evidence indicating that the activity of skeletal muscle nerves is not increased in primary hypertension (see Folkow *et al.,* 1983).

It is possible to record the burst activity of sympathetic nerves supplying skeletal muscle in man (Wallin, 1984). The activity level in these nerves varies between individuals but is remarkably constant within individuals. It is subject to dynamic arterial baroreceptor control from blood pressure variations during the cardiac cycle (heart beat to heart beat), but not by the blood pressure level as such. The cardiovascular low pressure (volume) receptors, on the other hand, exert a static influence on the activity of these skeletal muscle nerves. Thus, manoeuvres such as lower body negative pressure (which reduces venous return to the heart) induce a marked and sustained elevation of sympathetic skeletal muscle nerve activity (see Wallin, 1984).

Interestingly, Wallin and coworkers (1981) demonstrated a significant correlation between skeletal muscle sympathetic nerve activity and plasma NA concentrations obtained by the commonly used antecubital venous sampling technique, even though the measurements were performed on different occasions, months apart. Recently, we have performed simultaneous measurements and confirmed this relationship between skeletal muscle sympathetic nerve activity and NA concentrations in venous plasma from the forearm (Daleskog *et al.,* 1983, and manuscript in preparation) or the leg (Hjemdahl, Freyschuss, Wallin *et al.,* in preparation). In agreement with these findings, radiotracer studies have indicated that skeletal muscle is an important source of circulating NA (Esler *et al.*, 1984; Christensen *et al.*, 1984. Hjemdahl *et al.*, in preparation). Thus, plasma NA concentrations are correlated to muscle sympathetic nerve activity in man, especially when peripheral venous blood sampling is performed.

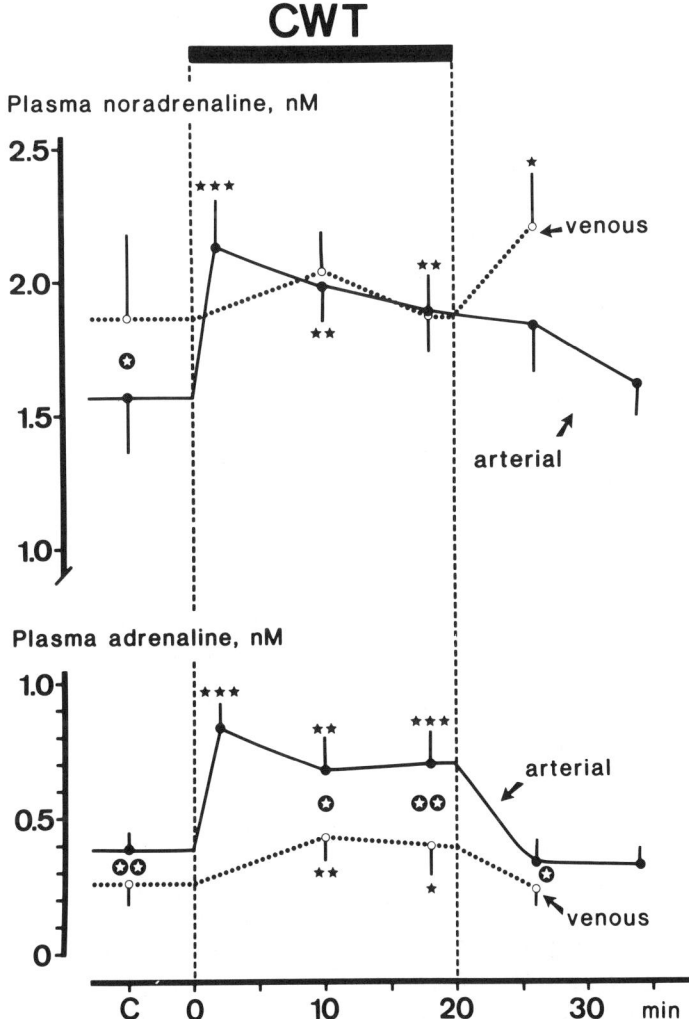

Fig. 5 – Arterial and peripheral venous plasma NA and ADR concentrations at rest and during mental stress induced by Stroop's colour–word conflict test (CWT) in twelve healthy volunteers. The haemodynamic reaction consisted of marked tachycardia and increases in cardiac output and blood pressure, but systemic and calf vasodilation (see Hjemdahl *et al.*, 1984). Note that there is a positive veno-arterial concentration difference for NA at rest and that the arterial but not the venous NA concentrations increase during mental stress. (Reproduced from Hjemdahl *et al.* (1984) with the permission of *Acta Physiol. Scand.*) Stars indicate significant changes from basal values (* $p < 0.05$, ** $p < 0.01$, *** $p < 0.001$) and white stars significant veno-arterial concentration differences. Vertical bars indicate S.E.M.

It is possible to demonstrate marked discrepancies between venous plasma NA responses and haemodynamic responses to various provocations which increase sympathetic nerve activity. A striking example is mental stress, which produces marked increases in heart rate and blood pressure but no change, or only minor changes in venous NA levels (Åkerstedt *et al.*, 1983; Eliasson *et al.*, 1983). In the latter study the subjects were also exposed to an orthostatic test and a cold pressor test, both of which caused clear-cut elevations of NA in venous plasma despite less pronounced haemodynamic responses than those seen during mental stress. The reason for this discrepancy seemed to be that orthostatic stress and the cold pressor test induced peripheral vasoconstriction, whereas mental stress does not (Eliasson *et al.*, 1983). This was verified in a more extensive study of the responses to mental stress which showed marked cardiac stimulation combined with peripheral vasodilatation (Hjemdahl *et al.*, 1984). The NA concentrations rose in arterial plasma, as a sign of increased sympathetic activity in some parts of the body, but remained unchanged in peripheral venous plasma during the mental stress (see Fig. 5 from this investigation). Thus, the sympathetic nerve activity pattern will differ markedly under different circumstances and venous NA levels may give erroneous conclusions concerning systemic sympathetic nerve activity if the peripheral sympathetic nerves (supplying mainly skeletal muscle) are not activated in a representative fashion (see Folkow *et al.* (1983) for further discussion).

3.3 Advantages of arterial sampling to assess sympathoadrenal activity

To obtain a more correct estimate of overall sympathetic nerve activity it is better to measure arterial than venous plasma NA concentrations, because of the disproportionately large influence of local (mainly skeletal muscle) sympathetic nerve activity on NA levels in venous plasma, as discussed in sections 3.1 and 3.2. However, ADR levels may also be monitored more accurately in arterial plasma than in venous plasma, owing to the marked and sometimes variable removal which takes place for this catecholamine too in peripheral tissues. Thus, β-adrenoceptor blockade has been shown to reduce the peripheral extraction of ADR (Best and Halter, 1982) and we have observed that changes in the peripheral extraction of ADR may vary in connection with various provocations causing various blood flow responses. For example, we have seen that lower body negative pressure may increase arterial but not venous plasma ADR concentrations, owing to enhanced extraction of ADR in the vasoconstricted forearm (Hjemdahl, Eklund and Kaijser, 1982, and manuscript in preparation). Thus, arterial ADR levels give a better estimate of ADR release from the adrenal medullae. Furthermore, they give a precise measure of the ADR concentrations to which the body has been exposed, which is important when evaluating the role of the ADR as a circulating hormone.

4 CONCLUSIONS

Plasma catecholamine levels are useful indices of sympathoadrenal activity, provided that a good assay is used and that the physiology of the sympatho-adrenal system is taken into account when interpreting the assay results. Problems with various plasma catecholamines assays have led to the introduction of a very large number of minor or major modifications of these assays. Most of these assays have not been adequately validated. Among HPLC–ECD assays those using cation exchange HPLC have so far been shown to give better results than those using reverse phase HPLC. Plasma NA concentrations reflect sympathetic nerve activity and studies of the regional outflow of NA from an organ will give good estimates of sympathetic nerve activity in that organ, provided that the arterial contribution to the venous outflow of NA is assessed. Peripheral venous NA levels overemphasize the activity in skeletal muscle sympathetic nerves, since this plasma is drained mainly from skeletal muscle. Arterial sampling gives more correct estimates of overall sympathetic nerve activity and circulating ADR levels than does venous sampling and is therefore preferred, when possible.

ACKNOWLEDGEMENTS

The work performed in our laboratory has been financed mainly by grants from the Swedish National Association against Heart and Chest Diseases, the Swedish Medical Research Council (5930) and the Karolinska Institute. The invaluable help of my collaborators and the secretarial assistance of Mrs. Monica Häggbom are gratefully acknowledged.

REFERENCES

Åkerstedt, T., Gillberg, M., Hjemdahl, P., Sigurdson, K., Gustavsson, J., Daleskog, M. and Pollare, T. (1983). Comparison of urinary and plasma catecholamine responses to mental stress. *Acta Physiol. Scand.* 117, 19–26.

Allenmark, S. and Hedman, L. (1979). Cation exchange liquid chromatography with amperometric detection as a method for the analysis of endogenous catecholamine concentrations in plasma or serum. *J. Liquid Chromatogr.* 2, 277–286.

Allenmark, S., Hedman, L. and Söderberg, A. (1980). Microanalysis of catecholamines in human plasma by high-performance liquid chromatography with amperometric detection as compared with a radioenzymatic method. *Microchem. J.*, 25, 567–575.

Anton, A. H. and Sayre, S. F. (1962). A study of the factors affecting the aluminium oxide–trihydroxyindole procedure for the analysis of catecholamines. *J. Pharmacol. Exp. Ther.*, 138, 360–375.

Best, J. D. and Halter, J. B. (1982). Release and clearance rates of epinephrine in man: importance of arterial measurements. *J. Clin. Endocrinol. Metab.*, 55, 263–268.

Bradley, T. and Hjemdahl, P. (1984). Further studies on renal nerve stimulation induced release of noradrenaline and dopamine from the canine kidney in situ. *Acta Physiol. Scand.*, 122, 369–379.

Christensen, N. J., Galbo, H., Gjerris, A., Henriksen, J. H., Hilsted, J., Kjaer, M. and Ring-Larsen, H. (1984). Whole body and regional clearance of noradrenaline and adrenaline in man. *Acta Physiol. Scand.* Suppl., **527**, 17–20.

Cryer, P. E. (1980) Physiology and pathophysiology of the human sympathoadrenal neuroendocrine system. *N. Engl. J. Med.*, **303**, 436–444.

Daleskog, M., Wallin, G., Mörlin, C. and Hjemdahl, P. (1983). Relationship between muscle sympathetic nerve activity, venous plasma noradrenaline levels and noradrenaline plasma kinetics in man. *Progr. Neuro-Psychopharmacol. & Biol. Psychiatry*, Suppl. 2, *Abstr. 96*.

Davis, G. C., Kissinger, P. T. and Shoup, R. E. (1981). Strategies for determination of serum or plasma norepinephrine by reverse-phase liquid chromatography. *Anal. Chem.*, **53**, 156–159.

Dimsdale, J. E. (1984). Techniques for collecting blood samples in the field and in the laboratory. In: *Cardiovascular Instrumentation*, NIH Publication 84-1654, 263–276.

Eliasson, K., Hjemdahl, P. and Kahan, T. (1983). Circulatory and sympathoadrenal responses to stress in borderline and established hypertension. *J. Hypertension*, **1**, 131–139.

Eriksson, B.-M. and Persson, B.-A. (1982). Determination of catecholamines in rat heart tissue and plasma samples by liquid chromatography with electrochemical detection. *J. Chromatogr.*, **228**, 143–154.

Esler, M. (1982). Assessment of sympathetic nervous function in humans from noradrenaline plasma kinetics. *Clin. Sci.*, **62**, 247–254.

Esler, M., Jennings, G., Leonard, P., Sacharias, N., Burke, F., Johns, J. and Blombery, P. (1984). Contribution of individual organs to total noradrenaline release in humans. *Acta Physiol. Scand.* Suppl., **527**, 11–16.

Folkow, B. (1984). Introductory remarks to the Workshop 'Plasma catecholamines as markers of sympatho-adrenal activity in man'. *Acta Physiol. Scand.* Suppl., **527**, 7–9.

Folkow, B., DiBona, G. F., Hjemdahl, P., Thorén, P. H. and Wallin, G. (1983). Measurements of plasma norepinephrine concentrations in human primary hypertension. A word of caution on their applicability for assessing neurogenic contributions. *Hypertension*, **5**, 399–402.

Goldberg, L. I. and Weder, A. B. (1980). Connections between endogenous dopamine receptors, and sodium extraction: evidences and hypotheses. *Rec. Adv. Clin. Pharmacol.*, **3**, 149–166.

Goldstein, D. S. (1983). Plasma catecholamines and essential hypertension. An analytical review. *Hypertension*, **5**, 86–99.

Goldstein, D. S., Feurstein, G., Izzo, J. L., Kopin, I. J. and Keiser, H. R. (1981). Validity and reliability of liquid chromatography with electrochemical detection for measuring plasma levels of norepinephrine and epinephrine in man. *Life Sci.*, **28**, 467–475.

Hallman, H., Farnebo, L.-O., Hamberger, B. and Jonsson, G. (1978). A sensitive method for the determination of plasma catecholamines using liquid chromatography with electrochemical detection. *Life Sci.*, **23**, 1049–1052.

Higa, S., Suzuki, T., Hayashi, A., Tsuge, I. and Yamamura, Y. (1977). Isolation of catecholamines in biological fluids by boric acid gel. *Anal. Biochem.*, **77**, 18–24.

Hjemdahl, P. (1984a). Catecholamine measurements by high-performance liquid chromatography. *Am. J. Physiol.*, **247**, E13–E20.

Hjemdahl, P. (1984b). Inter-laboratory comparison of plasma catecholamine determinations using several different assays. *Acta Physiol. Scand.* Suppl., **527**, 43–54.

Hjemdahl, P. and LInde, B. (1983). Influence of circulating NE and Epi on adipose tissue vascular resistance and lipolysis in humans. *Am. J. Physiol.*, **245**, H447–H452.

Hjemdahl, P., Daleskog, M. and Kahan, T. (1979). Determinations of plasma catecholamines by high performance liquid chromatography with electrochemical detection: comparison with radioenzymatic method. *Life Sci.*, **25**, 131–138.

Hjemdahl, P., Eklund, B. and Kaijser, L. (1982). Catecholamine handling by the human forearm at rest and during isometric exercise and lower body negative pressure. *Br. J. Pharmacol.*, **77**, 324P.

Hjemdahl, P., Freyschuss, U., Juhlin-Dannfelt, A. and Linde, B. (1984). Differentiated sympathetic activation during mental stress evoked by the Stroop test. *Acta Physiol. Scand.* Suppl., **527**, 25–29.

Johnson, G. A., kupiecki, R. M. and Baker, C. A. (1980). Single isotope derivative (radioenzymatic) methods in the measurement of catecholamines. *Metabolism,* **29** (Suppl. 1), 1106–1113.

Kahan, T., Hjemdahl, P. and Dahlöf, C. (1984). Relationship between the overflow of endogenous and radiolabelled noradrenaline from canine blood perfused gracilis muscle. *Acta Physiol. Scand.,* **122**, 571–582.

Kissinger, P. T. (1977). Amperometric and coulometric detectors for high-performance liquid chromatography. *Anal. Chem.,* **49**, 447A–456A.

Linde, B. and Hjemedahl, P. (1982). Effect of tilting on adipose tissue vascular resistance and sympathetic activity in humans. *Am. J. Physiol.,* **242**, H161.

Peuler, J. D. and Johnson, G. A. (1977). Simultaneous single isotope radioenzymatic assay of plasma norepinephrine, epinephrine and dopamine. *Life Sc.,* **21**, 625–636.

Rand, M. J. and Majewski, H. (1984). Adrenaline mediates a positive feedback loop in noradrenergic transmission: its possible role in development of hypertension. *Clin. and Exper. Hyper. – Theory and Practice,* **A6**(1&2), 347–370.

Silverberg, A. B., Shah, S. D., Haymond, M. W. and Cryer, P. E. (1978). Norepinephrine: hormone and neurotransmitter in man. *Am. J. Physiol.,* **234**, 252–256.

Smedes, F., Kraak, J. C. and Poppe, H. (1982). Simple and fast solvent extraction system for selective and quantitative isolation of adrenaline, noradrenaline and dopamine from plasma and urine. *J. Chromatogr.,* **231**, 25–39.

Wallin, G. (1984). Muscle sympathetic activity and plasma concentrations of noradrenaline. *Acta Physiol. Scand.* Suppl., 527, *21–24.*

Wallin, B. G., Sundlöf, G., Eriksson, B.-M., Dominiak, P., Grobecker, H. and Lindblad, L.-E. (1981). Plasma noradrenaline correlates to sympathetic muscle nerve activity in man. *Acta Physiol. Scand.,* 111, 69–73. 237, H305–H310.

Watson, E. (1981). Liquid chromatography with electrochemical detection for plasma norepinephrine and epinephrine. *Life Sci.,* 28. 493–497.

Yamaguchi, I. and Kopin, I. J. (1979). Plasma catecholamines and blood pressure responses to sympathetic stimulation in pithed rats. *Am. J. Physiol.,* 237, H305–310.

2

Assessment of sympathetic nervous activity from measurements of noradrenaline turnover in rats

Lewis Landsberg and **James B. Young**
Harvard Medical School and Beth Israel Hospital, Boston,
Massachusetts, USA

1. INTRODUCTION: DIFFICULTIES INHERENT IN THE ASSESSMENT OF SYMPATHETIC ACTIVITY

The effects of catecholamines on physiological processes are exerted, in the main, by circulating adrenaline secreted from the adrenal medulla and by locally released noradrenaline (NA) derived from sympathetic nerve endings in innervated tissues. Although various physiological conditions are associated with alterations in sensitivity to catecholamines, it is generally recognized that the level of activity of the sympathetic nervous system (SNS) or the adrenal medulla is the prime determinant of the physiological effects exerted by catecholamines. Catecholamines, moreover, affect virtually all physiological processes. For most processes, however, catecholamines are not the sole regulators; they participate in the regulation of the various organ systems along with other hormonal and neuronal systems. The resultant redundancy in physiological regulation, while assuring a significant physiological reserve and conveying the possibility of finely discriminating control, limits the usefulness of physiological measurements in the evaluation of SNS function. Thus, full appreciation of the physiological role played by catecholamines in the regulation of different processes requires the accurate biochemical assessment of sympathoadrenal activity.

Adrenal medullary activity is reasonably assessed by measurement of circulating adrenaline level or urinary adrenaline excretion, although the difficulty in measuring plasma adrenaline accurately at basal levels of secretion is well recognized. Assessment of SNS activity, however, remains a major problem. Although commonly utilized for the purpose, plasma NA concentration and urinary NA excretion are relatively insensitive indices of SNS activity. This insensitivity is a consequence of the fact that NA is, under usual circumstances, a neurotransmitter and not a circulating hormone. The circulating pool of NA is derived from that small portion of released neurotransmitter that escapes both re-uptake at the nerve ending and metabolism at the effector tissue thereby diffusing into the circulation from the area of the synapse. Thus, the circulating level of NA is generally below the threshold for stimulation of adrenergic receptors (Silverberg *et al.*, 1978). Infused NA, moreover, stimulates sympathetically mediated processes only when the level achieved by infusion greatly exceeds the level noted during physiological stimulation of the same process (Silverberg *et al.*, 1978). Furthermore, physiologically significant activation of the SNS has been demonstrated in the absence of a rise in plasma NA concentration (Cryer *et al.*, 1976). Alterations in plasma NA clearance appear to contribute to the low sensitivity of plasma NA measurements since, under some circumstances, increased sympathetic activity is associated with increased plasma NA clearance rate while diminished sympathetic activity is, conversely, associated with diminished clearance (O'Dea *et al.*, 1982). These same considerations limit the usefulness of urinary NA excretion as a measure of sympathetic activity, although the latter does provide a rough measure of the plasma level integrated over time.

In addition to this substantial problem created by lack of sensitivity, plasma and urinary NA levels also lack specificity in two important respects. In the first place, if the adrenal medulla is stimulated, origin of circulating or urinary NA from the SNS cannot be inferred. Although under basal circumstances plasma and urinary NA derive largely from the SNS, when the adrenal medulla is stimulated substantial quantities of NA are derived from the adrenal (Young and Landsberg, 1979b; Landsberg *et al.*, 1980; Rappaport *et al.*, 1982). Since the adrenal medulla may be stimulated when the SNS is suppressed (Young *et al.*, 1984) plasma and urinary NA levels may provide misleading information about the functional state of the SNS. In the second place, specificity is further compromised by the fact that sympathetic outflow is nonhomogeneous. It is well established that sympathetic outflow to various tissues is not uniform but differentiated (Brown *et al.*, 1981; Ninomiya *et al.*, 1971; Nijima 1976; Young *et al.*, 1982; Folkow *et al.*, 1983); consequently, plasma sampling at a single site, usually forearm, reflects disproportionately events within the direct venous drainage of the sampling site, usually the tissues of the arm. Significant alterations in SNS activity in anatomically separate regions may, therefore, be missed. Similar considerations apply to urinary NA excretion which receives a 'nephrogenous' contribution from the sympathetic nerves of the kidney (Morgunov and Baines, 1981).

Because of the serious limitations imposed upon the use of plasma and urinary catecholamines in the assessment of sympathetic activity, we have utilized measurements of NA turnover in sympathetically innervated organs of the rat (and mouse) to define the functional state of the SNS in a variety of different physiological and pathophysiological states. These studies have provided insight into both the regulation of sympathoadrenal activity and into the role played by the sympathoadrenal system in the regulation of physiological processes.

2. NA TURNOVER AS A MEASURE OF SNS ACTIVITY IN TISSUES OF THE RAT

2.1 Relationship between NA turnover and SNS activity

The theoretical basis for utilizing measurements of NA synthesis or turnover rate to assess SNS activity depends upon the fact that both release and biosynthesis of NA are coupled to nerve impulses in postganglionic sympathetic fibres (Kopin, 1977). Increased transmitter release in response to increased impulse traffic is associated with an acceleration in NA biosynthesis and an increased rate of NA turnover. Correspondence between measurements of NA biosynthesis and turnover, and other methods of assessing sympathetic activity, has been amply demonstrated in a variety of situations, particularly cold exposure (see Landsberg and Young, 1983a). Additional evidence in support of the relationship between NA turnover and sympathetic activity is provided by experiments utilizing ganglionic blockade. As shown in the subsequent section physiological states associated with increased sympathetic activity demonstrate an enhanced effect of ganglionic blockade on turnover rate, consistent with increased sympathetic impulse traffic.

2.2 Methods of assessing NA synthesis and turnover *in vivo*

Four of the most commonly used techniques for the *in vivo* assessment of NA turnover or synthesis in experimental animals are summarized in Table 1 along with references that describe the use of these methods. Each of these techniques provides a measure of SNS activity *in vivo*; as indicated in Table 1, however, the various techniques are most suitable for assessment of SNS activity over different time intervals. Synthesis of labelled NA from labelled tyrosine, and the rate of accumulation of DA after inhibition of dopamine beta-hydroxylase, provide a measure of NA turnover over relatively short intervals, in the range of one or two hours. The rate of depletion of endogenous NA after inhibition of tyrosine hydroxylase with alpha-methyl-para-tyrosine provides a measure of NA turnover over an intermediate period of approximately 2 to 6 hours. The rate of disappearance of labelled NA after pulse labelling with tracer ^{3}H-NA (rate of decline of specific activity over time) provides an assessment of NA turnover over a considerably longer period and is most useful over a 12-to 24-hour interval. In general, assessment over longer time intervals is preferable since the NA turnover rate, integrated over longer periods of time, is less likely to be affected by transient alterations in sympathetic activity that result from handling during the experimental procedure.

We have utilized predominantly the tracer ^{3}H-NA technique in defining the level of sympathetic activity in a variety of different states. We have utilized the synthesis inhibition technique in situations associated with very rapid turnover of NA and as a confirmatory technique to exclude the possibility of tracer-induced artifacts (Young *et al.*, 1982; Young and Landsberg, 1983). After intravenous administration of tracer ^{3}H-NA (or inhibition of NA synthesis) the rate of fall of specific activity (or the rate of fall of endogenous NA after synthesis inhibition) in individual sympathetically innervated tissues follows first order kinetics. This monoexponential model permits computation of a slope, which is proportional to the fractional turnover of the neurotransmitter store, and calculation of a turnover rate (product of slope and endogenous NA content), thus enabling convenient statistical comparison of the effect of different experimental conditions on sympathetic activity in different organs. Measurement of the endogenous NA content of the tissue under study provides a measure of pool size; in general the endogenous NA level changes little despite marked changes in NA turnover. The calculated NA turnover rate represents an attempt to correct for variations in endogenous NA concentration. Although theoretical objections to the use of ^{3}H-NA in the measurement of NA turnover, and as an index of sympathetic activity, have been raised (summarized in Young and Landsberg, 1979a), the usefulness of this technique in the assessment of the SNS is generally acknowledged. Specific examples of the application of both the ^{3}H-NA and synthesis inhibition techniques are provided below.

Table 1 — Techniques for assessment of NA turnover (or synthesis)

	Method	Integrated time interval (hours)	References
↑	^{14}C-NE after ^{14}C-Tyr	1	Gordon *et al.*, 1966 Sedvall and Kopin, 1967 Landsberg *et al.*, 1969
↑	DA after DBH inhibition with CHMI	1–2	Fuller *et al.*, 1982
↓	NE after TH inhibition with AMPT	2–6	Brodie *et al.*, 1966 Young *et al.*, 1982
↓	^{3}H-NE after labelling with tracer ^{3}H-NE	12–24	Neff *et al.*, 1968 Young and Landsberg, 1979a

Tyr, tyrosine, DBH, dopamine-beta-hydroxylase; TH, tyrosine hydroxylase; CHMI, 1-cyclohexyl-2-mercapto-imidazole; AMPT, alpha methyl-para-tyrosine.

3. COLD EXPOSURE

Cold exposure markedly stimulates the sympathetic nervous system (Landsberg and Young, 1983a). Sympathetic stimulation during cold exposure is importantly involved in the regulation of both heat production and heat conservation. The effect of acute cold exposure on cardiac NA turnover is shown in Fig. 1. At

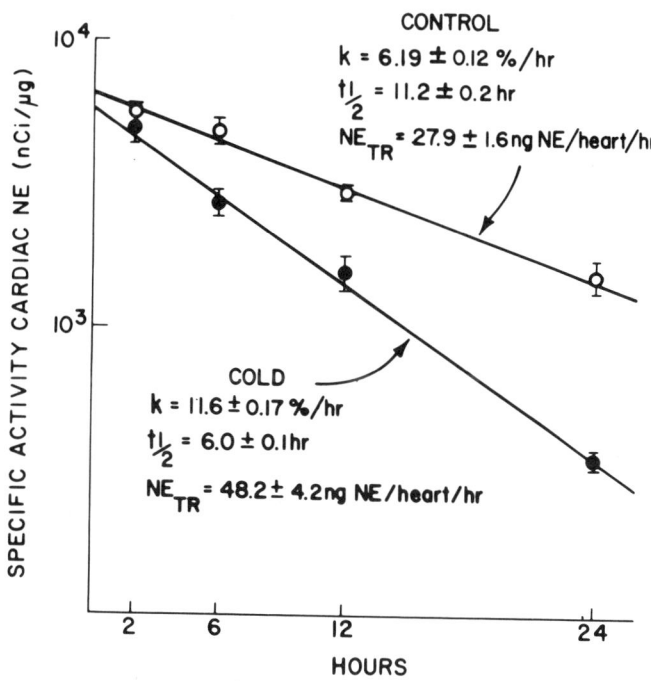

Fig. 1 – Effect of cold exposure on NA (NE) turnover in heart. Tracer ³H-NA was administered at time 0 (see text for details). The specific activity of cardiac NA is plotted semilogarithmically as a function of time. The turnover rate is significantly increased in animals exposed acutely to a cold (4°C) environment. NE$_{TR}$, NA turnover rate. (From Landsberg and Young, *N. Engl. J. of Med.*, **298**: 1295 – 1301, 1978, with permission).

time 0, 40 rats were injected with tracer ³H-*l*-NA. Five minutes after administration of the tracer half the animals were placed in the cold at 4°C while the remainder (controls) were maintained at ambient temperature (22°C). At various preselected times, animals from each group were killed and the hearts removed and analysed for tritiated and endogenous NA. The decline in specific activity obeys first order kinetics as shown by the close adherence of the experimental data to the monoexponential model. Slope t$_{½}$, and calculated NA turnover rate are shown in the figure. A significant increase in NA turnover in heart is shown by the statistically significant increase in the slope from the cold exposed animals.

Data from the same experiment for pancreas and liver are shown in Fig. 2. NA turnover in pancreas is increased in cold exposed rats as it is in heart; in liver, however, the turnover rate is similar in both cold exposed and control animals. This difference is consistent with nonhomogeneous sympathetic outflow to different organs during cold exposure and is consonant with other published data (see Landsberg and Young, 1983a).

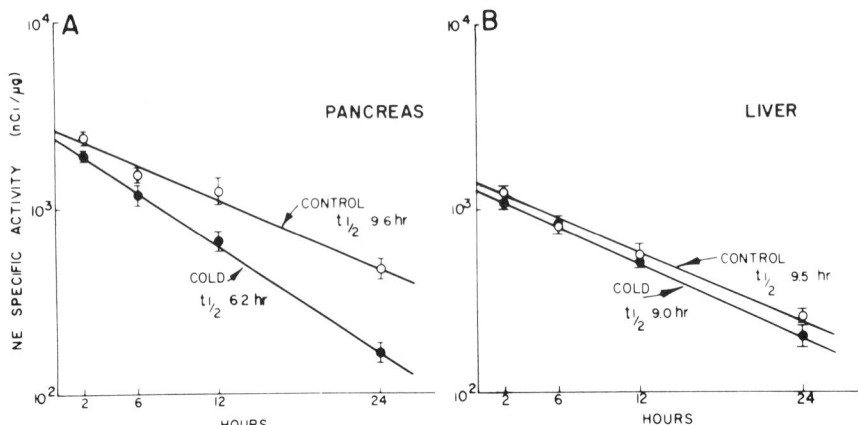

Fig. 2 – Effect of cold exposure on NA (NE) turnover in rat pancreas (A) and liver (B). Data for pancreas and liver from the same experiment shown in Fig. 1 are displayed. NA turnover in pancreas is significantly increased in cold exposed animals while NA turnover in liver is essentially unchanged. (From Young and Landsberg (1979a), with permission).

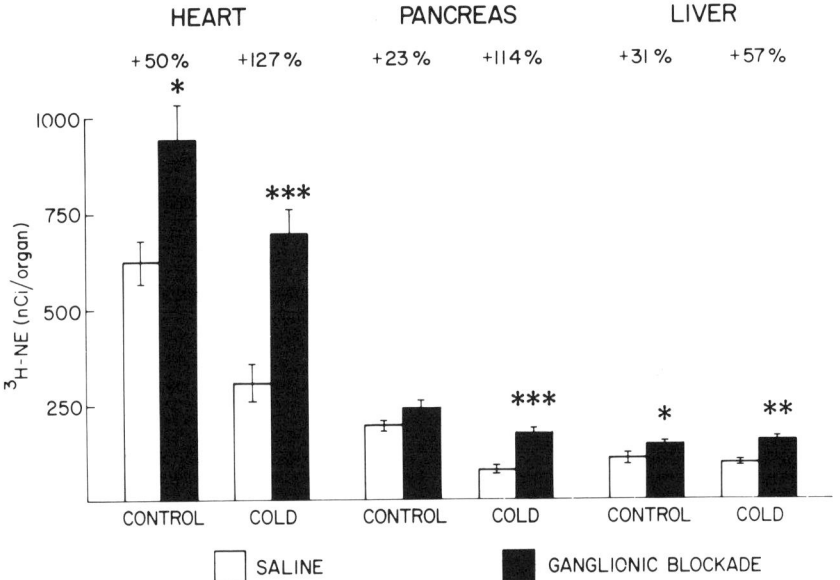

Fig. 3 – Effect of ganglionic blockade on the retention of ^{3}H-NA (NE) during cold exposure in rat heart, pancreas, and liver. After injection of tracer ^{3}H-NA the long-acting ganglionic blocking agent chlorisondamine (or saline) was administered intraperitoneally at 5 min and again at 5 hours. Cold exposed animals were placed at 40°C immediately after the first intraperitoneal injection. Data represent the level of ^{3}H-NA 10 hours after injection of tracer (means ± SEM). The percentage increase in retention induced by ganglionic blockade is shown over the black bar. Asterisk is for statistical comparison with saline treated control (single asterisk $p < 0.05$, two asterisks $p < 0.01$, three asterisks $p < 0.001$). The enhanced effect of ganglionic blockade in cold exposed animals is similar in heart and pancreas; in liver, in contrast, cold exposure did not change the effect of ganglionic blockade. (From Young and Landsberg, 1979a, with permission).

The relationship between these changes in NA turnover and SNS activity is demonstrated by experiments with ganglionic blocking agents. Fig. 3 demonstrates the effect of ganglionic blockade on the retention of ^{3}H-NA, a measure of NA turnover. As shown in the figure, the effect of ganglionic blockade is substantially greater in heart and pancreas from cold-exposed animals as compared with ambient temperature controls; in liver, however, the effect of ganglionic blockade is similar in control and cold exposed animals consistent with the turnover data demonstrated in Fig. 2.

Further evidence on non-homogeneous sympathetic outflow is shown in Fig. 4. In rats exposed to cold, NA turnover rate in interscapular brown adipose tissue (IBAT) is very rapid (Young et al., 1982); as a consequence the ^{3}H-NA technique carried out over a 12- or 24-hour period fits the monoexponential model poorly, making it difficult to quantify changes in SNS activity. Use of the synthesis inhibition technique with alpha-methyl-para-tyrosine does permit reasonable estimation of NA turnover in IBAT as shown in Fig. 4. The changes in NA turnover in IBAT are considerably greater than those occurring in heart, consistent with the known important role of IBAT in the generation of metabolic heat in the rat, and providing further evidence for nonhomogeneous sympathetic outflow during cold exposure.

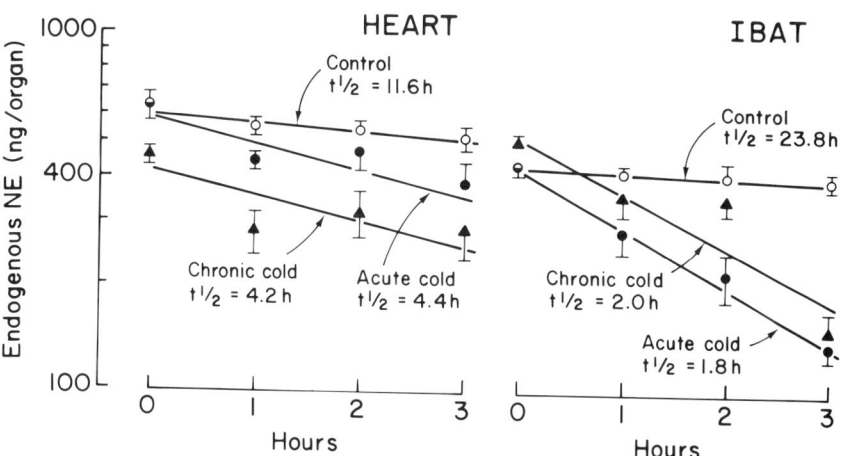

Fig. 4 – Effect of acute and chronic cold exposure on NA (NE) turnover in heart and IBAT. Chronically cold exposed animals were maintained at 4°C for 10 days before and during the experiment. Thirty-two warm and 12 cold exposed animals recieved a single i.p. injection of alpha-methyl-para-tyrosine (AMPT) (250 mg/kg) at time 0. Half of the injected warm animals were placed in the cold (acute cold) and four to six animals from each group were killed at hourly intervals for the next three hours. Eight animals from both warm and chronically cold exposed groups were not injected with AMPT and served as the t_0 reference point for all three groups. Data represent the mean ± S.E.M. for endogenous NA. Open circles represent warm animals, solid circles acutely cold exposed animals, and solid triangles chronically cold exposed animals. Both acute and chronic cold exposure significantly increased NA turnover in IBAT; the increase is of a greater degree than that noted in heart. (From Young et al., 1982, with permission).

4. DIETARY INTAKE

4.1 Fasting

Measurements of NA turnover rate have been particularly useful in the demonstration of suppressed SNS activity, since the latter is particularly difficult to document from measurements of plasma and urinary NA. Thus, utilization of NA turnover techniques permitted the important observation that fasting suppresses sympathetic activity (Young and Landsberg, 1977a). As shown in Fig. 5 fasting suppresses NA turnover in heart; a similar decrease in NA turnover is demonstrable in a variety of other organs (Young and Landsberg, 1979a; Young et al., 1982). Experiments with ganglionic blocking agents demonstrate' less of an effect on NA turnover during fasting (Young and Landsberg, 1977a, 1979a), consistent with a reduction in central symapthetic outflow. Suppression of SNS activity during fasting appears to be mediated by insulin-glucose sensitive neurons related to the ventromedial hypothalamus (Young and Landsberg, 1980).

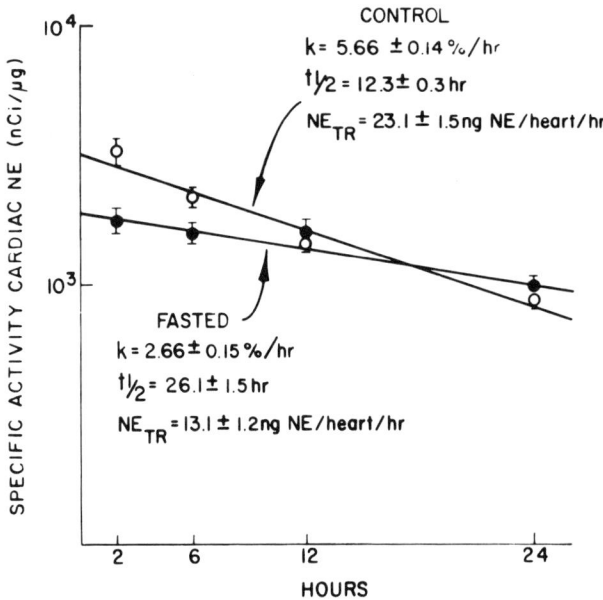

Fig. 5 – Effect of fasting on NA (NE) turnover in rat heart. Animals were fasted for 48 hours prior to and including the day of the turnover study; they were allowed *ad lib* access to 0.045 M NaCl during the fast. NA turnover rate in heart was significantly slowed by fasting as shown by the significant reduction in slope. (From Young and Landsberg (1977a), with the permission of the American Association for the Advancement of Science).

In larger turnover experiments the interaction of two different variables can be studied. Fig. 6 demonstrates the effect of cold exposure in both fed and fasted animals. Fasting diminishes NA turnover in cold exposed animals as well as in those maintained at room temperature (Young and Landsberg, 1981); NA turnover, nonetheless, is faster in cold exposed fasted animals than in those fasted at room temperature. Experiments of this type, employing four experimental groups, require approximately 80 animals.

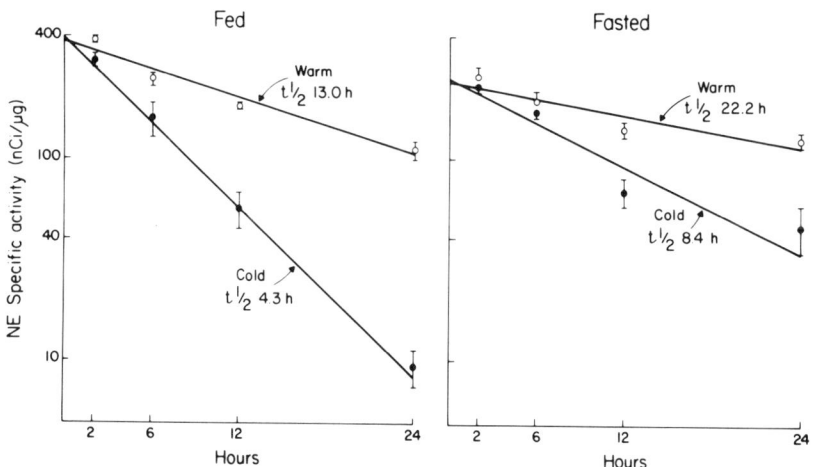

Fig. 6 — Effect on concomitant fasting and cold exposure on NA (NE) turnover in rat heart. Fasted animals had been without food for 48 hours prior to the turnover study and remained fasting for the duration of the experiment. Cold exposure began immediately after injection of tracer. Significant effects of both cold and fasting were demonstrated. Cardiac NA turnover in the fasted warm group was significantly reduced as compared with fasted cold animals. (Modified from Young and Landsberg, 1981).

4.2 Sucrose feeding and other nutrients

Two different experimental conditions may also be compared with control in a single experiment. In Fig. 7 the effect of fasting and sucrose feeding are compared with normally fed animals. As shown in Fig. 7 *ad lib* access to 10% sucrose for three days significantly increased NA turnover in heart as compared with control fed and fasted animals; the fasted animals had significantly slower NA turnover than those fed the control diet. Experiments of this type, with three different treatment groups, require approximately 60 animals. Both sucrose (Young and Landsberg, 1977b; Young and Landsberg, 1979a), and fat (Schwartz *et al.*, 1983) increase sympathetic activity in a variety of organs even when total caloric intake is not increased. Overfeeding a mixed highly palatable diet also increases sympathetic activity in heart and brown adipose tissue (Young *et al.*, 1982). Interestingly, protein appears to have a minimal effect on SNS activity in comparison with the stimulatory effects of sucrose and fat (Kaufman *et al.*, 1984). These dietary effects on SNS activity appear to be related to changes in thermogenesis (Landsberg and Young, 1981, 1983b) and may also have implications for some of the cardiovascular changes that occur during caloric restriction (Einhorn *et al.*, 1982) and caloric excess.

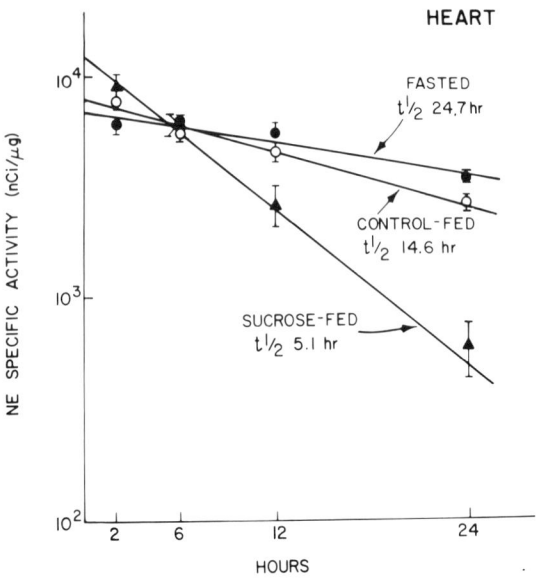

Fig. 7 — Effect of sucrose feeding and fasting on NA (NE) turnover in heart. Sucrose-fed animals had access to 8% sucrose in the drinking water for 72 hours prior to and during the duration of the experiment; fasted animals were without food for 48 hours prior to and remained without food during the experiment although access to 0.045 M NaCl was provided. Cardiac NA turnover in both sucrose-fed and fasted animals differ significantly from the control fed group. (From Young and Landsberg (1979a), with permission).

5. DISSOCIATION OF SNS AND ADRENAL MEDULLARY ACTIVITY

5.1 Hypoglycaemia

Classical studies, performed over 50 years ago in the laboratories of Cannon and Houssay, demonstrated that hypoglycaemia profoundly stimulated the adrenal medulla. Since plasma and urinary NA increase during hypoglycaemia it had been widely assumed that the SNS was stimulated as well, although increases in NA during hypoglycaemia are generally considerably less than the corresponding increases in adrenaline. Utilizing the ^{3}H-NA turnover technique it has been possible to demonstrate, however, that the SNS is actually suppressed in three experimental forms of hypoglycaemia in the rat (Table 2). Thus, when hypoglycaemia is induced by fasting in pregnant rats, or in fasting rats treated with the glycosuric agent phlorizin, sympathetic activity is diminished as shown by reduced NA turnover rate (in comparison with similarly treated fed, normoglycaemic animals), and despite marked concomitant adrenal medullary stimulation (Young and Landsberg, 1979b; Landsberg et al., 1980). Similarly, parenteral administration of 2-deoxy-glucose to freely feeding rats significantly reduces NA turnover as compared with vehicle injected controls, once again in association with marked adrenal medullary stimulation (Rappaport et al., 1982). Suppression of the SNS during hypoglycaemia cannot be attributed to the marked rise

Table 2 — Hypoglycaemia and sympathoadrenal activity

State	SNS activity % decrease NA turnover rate)	Adrenal medullary activity (% increase urinary adrenaline excretion)	References
Fasting pregnancy	−66% (compared with fed pregnant)	+420%	Young and Landsberg, 1979b
Fasting phlorizin	−17% (compared with fed phlorizin)	+1000%	Landsberg et al., 1980
2-DG (fed ad lib)	−25% (compared with vehicle injected controls	+440%	Rappaport et al., 1982

2-DG, 2-deoxyglucose.

in adrenaline secretion since it is demonstrable when adrenal medullary secretion is blocked by splanchnic nerve section or adrenal demedullation. These studies demonstrate the utility of NA turnover measurements in defining the functional state of the SNS in situations in which the adrenal medulla is stimulated. They further emphasize the limitations of urinary and plasma NA measurements as indices of SNS function when adrenal medullary secretion is enhanced.

5.2 Hind-limb ischaemia and hypoxia

Dissociation of SNS and adrenal medullary responses is not unique to hypoglycaemia. In the hind-limb ischaemia model of traumatic injury in mice, and in hypoxic exposure of moderate degree (10% oxygen) in rats, the acute sympathoadrenal response appears to consist of SNS suppression and adrenal medullary stimulation (Young et al., 1983; Johnson et al., 1983), although in both the latter situations SNS suppression is more subtle and more difficult to demonstrate than in hypoglycaemia. The chronic response, furthermore, to both trauma and hypoxic exposure is increased SNS activity (Young et al., 1983, Johnson et al., 1981, Johnson et al., 1983). The physiological significance of suppressed SNS activity in the acute phase of trauma and during the acute phase of hypoxic exposure is uncertain but may be related, as it is in fasting, to suppression of metabolic rate and the conservation of vital resources. Under these situations, circulating catecholamines of adrenal medullary origin may support vital circulatory and metabolic functions at a lower net energy cost, since circulating catecholamines are generally less effective than the SNS in the stimulation of metabolic rate, unless the circulating level achieved is very high.

NA turnover studies, therefore, have suggested a new and potentially important role for the adrenal medulla: in the face of SNS suppression, adrenal medullary catecholamines may defend the blood pressure and mobilize substrates thereby providing for the function of vital organs systems when the integrity of the internal environment is threatened, and when the SNS is suppressed in the interest of energy conservation. In a variety of other situations not yet studied, it seems likely that NA turnover measurements will be useful in describing the SNS response when the integrity of the internal milieu is challenged.

6. SUMMARY AND CONCLUSIONS

The measurement of NA turnover provides a useful approach to the assessment of SNS activity in individual sympathetically innervated organs of the rat and mouse. The major advantages of this technique may be summarized as follows: (1) Nonhomogeneity in sympathetic outflow is frequently reflected in NA turnover measurements, giving a more detailed and complete assessment of SNS activity. Turnover studies have demonstrated that during cold exposure sympathetic activity is unchanged in liver, stimulated in heart and pancreas, and markedly stimulated in IBAT. (2) Turnover studies permit recognition of suppressed SNS activity. These techniques have shown that during fasting, SNS activity is suppressed in many organs of the rat. (3) Turnover measurements reflect the state of the SNS independent of changes in adrenal medullary activity. Turnover experiments have provided evidence of a coordinated dissociation of SNS and adrenal medullary activity in several situations. In hypoglycaemia, for example, SNS suppression coexists with marked adrenal stimulation.

It is important to recognize, however, that changes in NA turnover are most suitable for demonstrating relative differences in SNS activity. Comparison with controls is required in each study, since absolute values are too variable to be compared across different experiments. Turnover series, furthermore, are time consuming, tedious and costly. A single experiment comparing two variables requires approximately 40 animals. When interactions among two factors are being studied as many as 80 animals per experiment may be required. Nonetheless, when properly applied and judiciously interpreted, NA turnover studies would appear to be the best currently available technique for assessing SNS activity in the experimental animal.

ACKNOWLEDGEMENT

This work was supported in part by USPHS grants AM 20378, HL 24084, and AG 00059.

REFERENCES

Brodie, B. B., Costa, E., Dlabac, A., Neff, N. H. and Smookler, H. H. (1966). Application of steady state kinetics to the estimation of synthesis rate and turnover time of tissue catecholamines. *J. Pharmacol. Exp. Ther.*, **154**, 493–498.

Brown, M. J., Jenner, D. A., Allison, D. J. and Dollery, C. T. (1981). Variations in individual organ release of noradrenaline measured by an improved radioenzymatic technique; limitations of peripheral venous measurements in the assessment of sympathetic nervous activity. *Clin. Sci.*, **61**, 585–590.

Cryer, P. E., Haymond, M. W., Santiago, J. V. and Shah, S. D. (1976). Norepinephrine and epinephrine release and adrenergic mediation of smoking-associated hemodynamic and metabolic events. *N. Engl. J. Med.*, **295**, 573–577.

Einhorn, D., Young, J. B. and Landsberg, L. (1982). Hypotensive effect of fasting: possible involvement of the sympathetic nervous system and endogenous opiates. *Science*, **217**, 727–729.

Folkow, B., Di Bona, G. F., Hjemdahl, P., Toren, P. H. and Wallin, B. G. (1983). Measurements of plasma norepinephrine concentrations in human primary hypertension. A word of caution on their applicability for assessing neurogenic contributions. *Hypertension*, **5**, 399–403.

Fuller, R. W., Snoddy, H. D. and Perry, K. W. (1982). Dopamine accumulation after dopamine-beta-hydroxylase inhibition in rat heart as an index of norepinephrine turnover. *Life Sci.*, **31**, 563–570.

Gordon, R., Spector, S., Sjoersdma, A. and Udenfriend, S. (1966). Increased synthesis of norepinephrine and epinephrine in the intact rat during exercise and exposure to cold. *J. Pharmacol. Exp. Ther.* **153**, 440–447.

Johnson, T. S., Young, J. B. and Landsberg, L. (1981). Norepinephrine turnover in lung: effect of cold exposure and chronic hypoxia. *J. Appl. Physiol.*, **51**, 614–620.

Johnson, T. S., Young, J. B. and Landsberg, L. (1983). Sypathoadrenal responses to acute and chronic hypoxia in the rat. *J. Clin. Invest.*, **71**, 1263–1272.

Kaufman, L. N., Young, J. B. and Landsberg, L. (1984). Protein stimulates nervous system (SNS) activity less than carbohydrate: evidence for nutrient-specific SNS responses. *Clin. Res.*, **32**, 478A.

Kopin, I. J. (1977). Catecholamine metabolism (and the biochemical assessment of sympathetic activity). *Clin. Endocrinol. Metab.* **6**, 525–549.

Landsberg, L. and Young, J. B. (1981). Diet-induced changes in sympathoadrenal activity: implications for thermogensis. *Life Sci.*, **28**, 1801–1817.

Landsberg, L. and Young, J. B. (983a). Autonomic regulation of thermogenesis. In: *Mammalian Thermogensis*, Girardier, L. and Stock, M. J. (eds.), Chapman & Hall, London, pp. 99–140.

Landsberg, L. and Young, J. B. (1983b). The role of the sympathetic nervous system and catecholamines in the regulation of energy metabolism. *Am. J. Clin. Nutr.*, **38**, 1018–1024.

Landsberg, L., de Champlain J. and Axelrod, J. (1969). Increased biosynthesis of cardiac norepinephrine after hypophysectomy. *J. Pharmacol. Exp. Ther.*, **165**, 102–107.

Landsberg, L., Greff, L., Gunn, S. and Young, J. B. (1980). Adrenergic mechanisms in the metabolic adaptation to fasting and feeding: effects of phlorizin on diet-induced changes in sympathodrenal activity in the rat. *Metabolism*, **29**, 1128–1137.

Morgunov, N. and Baines, A. D. (1981). Renal nerves and catecholamine excretion. *Am. J. Physiol.*, **240**, F75–F81.

Neff, N. H., Tozer, T. N., Hammer, W., Costa, E. and Brodie, B. B. (1968). Application of a steady-state kinetics to the uptake and decline of ^{3}H-NE in the rat heart. *J. Pharmacol. Exp. Ther.*, **160**, 48–52.

Niijima, A. (1976). Baroreceptor effects on renal and adrenal nerve activity. *Am. J. Physiol.*, **230**, 1733–1736.

Ninomiya, I., Nishimaru, N. and Irisawa, H. (1971). Sympathetic nerve activity to the spleen, kidney, and heart in response to baroceptor input. *Am. J. Physiol.*, **221**, 1346–1351.

O'Dea, K., Esler, M., Leonard, P., Stockigt, J. R. and Nestel, P. (1982). Noradrenaline turnover during under- and over-eating in normal weight subjects. *Metabolism,* **31**, 896–899.

Rappaport, E. B., Young, J. B. and Landsberg, L. (1982). Effects of 2-deoxy-D-glucose on the cardiac sympathetic nerves and the adrenal medulla in the rat: further evidence for a dissociation of sympathetic nervous system and adrenal medullary responses. *Endocrinology,* **110**, 650–656.

Schwartz, J. H., Young, J. B. and Landsberg, L. (1983). Effect of dietary fat on sympathetic nervous system activity in the rat. *J. Clin. Invest.*, **72**, 361–370.

Sedvall, G. C. and Kopin, I. J. (1967). Acceleration of noreprinephrine synthesis in the rat submaxillary gland *in vivo* during sympathetic nerve simulation. *Life Sci.,* **6**, 45–51.

Silverberg, A. B., Shah, S. D., Haymond, M. W. and Cryer, P. E. (1978). Norepinephrine: hormone and neurotransmitter in man. *Am. J. Physiol.* **234**, E252–E256.

Young, J. B. and Landsberg, L. (1977a). Suppression of sympathetic nervous system during fasting. *Science,* **197**, 1473–1475.

Young, J. B., Landsberg, L. (1977b). Stimulation of the sympathetic nervous system during sucrose feeding. *Nature,* **269**, 615–617.

Young, J. B. and Landsberg, L. (1979a). Effect of diet and cold exposure on norepinephrine turnover in pancreas and liver. *Am. J. Physiol.*, **236**, E524–E533.

Young, J. B. and Landsberg, L. (1979b). Sympathoadrenal activity in fasting pregnant rats: dissociation of adrenal medullary and sympathetic nervous system responses. *J. Clin. Invest.*, **64**, 109–116.

Young, J. B. and Landsberg, L. (1980). Impaired suppression of sympathetic activity during fasting in the gold thioglucose-treated mouse. *J. Clin. Invest.*, **65**, 1086–1094.

Young, J. B. and Landsberg, L. (1981). Effect of concomitant fasting and cold exposure on sympathoadrenal activity in rats. *Am. J. Physiol.*, **240**, E314–E319.

Young, J. B. and Landsberg, L. (1983). Diminished sympathetic nervous system activity in the genetically obese mouse. *Am. J. Physiol.*, **245**, E148–E154.

Young, J. B., Saville, E., Rothwell, N. J., Stock, M. J. and Landsberg, L. (1982). Effect of diet and cold exposure on norepinephrine turnover in brown adipose tissue of the rat. *J. Clin. Invest.*, **69**, 1061–1071.

Young, J. B., Rosa, R. M. and Landsberg, L. (1984). Dissociation of sympathetic nervous system and adrenal medullary responses. *Am. J. Physiol.*, **247**, E35–E40.

Young, J. B., Fish, S. and Landsberg, L. (1983). Sympathetic nervous system and adrenal medullary responses to ischemic injury in mice. *Am. J. Physiol.*, **245**, E67–E73.

3

Peptides in the autonomic nervous system with particular reference to neuropeptide Y

J. M. Allen, J. M. Polak and **S. R. Bloom**
Departments of Medicine and Histochemistry, Royal Postgraduate Medical School, Du Cane Road, London W12 0HS, UK

1. INTRODUCTION

In recent years, there has been an increasing awareness of the concept of the peptidergic innervation as part of the autonomic nervous system. These peptides in some cases would appear as candidates for the non-cholinergic, non-adrenergic responses previously described within the autonomic nervous system and are considered as putative neurotransmitters or neuromodulators. Additions to the list of peptides appear at an ever-increasing rate as new methods are employed in their identification and isolation. The chemical approach to peptide identification has yielded within the last 3 years the novel peptides, peptide histidine isoleucine (PHI), peptide YY (PYY) (Tatemoto and Mutt, 1980), neuropeptide Y (NPY) (Tatemoto et al., 1982) and galanin (Tatemoto et al., 1983). The novel technique of molecular biology has identified further peptides flanking the DNAH sequences coding for some of the recognized regulatory peptides. In addition by means of prediction of alternative gene splicing, these new techniques have been applied to predict and subsequently isolate a new peptide, Calcitonin Gene Related Peptide (CGRP) (Amara et al., 1982). The application of these new technologies provides yet further scope to identify new peptides suggesting a hitherto undefined complexity to the control of autonomic function.

Peptides may either be localized within specific p-type neurons or may be co-localized with classic transmitters of the autonomic nervous system such as VIP in cholinergic nerves. Peptidergic innervation within many structures may be derived from extrinsic neurons and may also be found within a population of intrinsic neurons such as that of the myenteric plexus in the gastro-intestinal tract. This is most commonly observed within the gastro-intestinal tract. Similar patterns of innervation have been described within many other 'organ systems'.

2. TECHNIQUES

The most widely used techniques for the measurement and localization of peptides are those of radioimmunoassay and immunocytochemistry. These tools allow the mapping of peptides within structures and exploration of possible co-storage within existing systems, either directly or by manipulation of the autonomic nervous system. By radioimmunoassay, it is also possible to determine whether the peptide is released. It is not intended here to discuss in detail these methods, but reference can be made to two recent publications (Bloom and Long, 1982; Polak and Van Norden 1983). Using these two techniques the distribution of a new regulatory peptide, NPY, has been extensively explored and this is used as an example.

3. NEUROPEPTIDE Y

NPY was isolated using a novel chemical approach, developed by Dr. Tatemoto and Dr. Mutt at the Karolinska Institute, for the identification of peptides possessing C terminal amide residues. The peptide was purified and sequenced from porcine brain (Tatemoto *et al.*, 1982). NPY consists of 36 amino acids and is characterized by a tyrosine residue at its N terminus and a tyrosine amide residue at its C terminus (Tatemoto, 1982). It bears remarkable aminoacid sequence homology with avian pancreatic polypeptide (APP) (Table 1). On the basis of this homology, NPY is regarded as a member of the pancreatic poly-peptide family of peptides. Antisera raised to APP have consistently immuno-stained neuronal structures although this peptide could not be identified within extracts of mammalian tissue. It seems likely that these antisera were cross-reacting with NPY (Adrian *et al.*, 1983) and that NPY represents the true PP-like peptide within the mammalian nervous system (Y. S. Allen *et al.*, 1983).

Table 1 — Comparison of the amino acid sequences of porcine NPY with porcine PYY and pancreatic polypeptides of porcine (PPP) and avian (APP) origin. Homologies with NPY are underlined, (a — amidated C terminus).

	1		5		10		15		20		25		30		35	
NPY	Y P S K P	D N P G E	D A P A E	D L A R Y	Y S A L R	H Y I N L	I T R Q R	Y^a
PYY	Y P A K P	E A P G E	D A S P E	E L S R Y	Y A S L R	H Y L N L	V T R Q R	Y^a
PPP	A P L E P	V Y P G D	D A T P E	Q M A Q Y	A A E L R	R Y I N M	L T R P R	Y^a
APP	G P S Q P	T Y P G D	D A P V E	D L I R F	Y D N L Q	Q Y L N V	V T R H R	Y^a

By means of the new technique of molecular biology, the precursor for human NPY has been identified and its DNA sequence determined (Minth *et al.*, 1984). This has shown that the sequence of NPY is highly conserved in phylogenetic terms since there is only one amino acid substitution between the originally identified porcine sequence and the human form: methionine replaces a leucine residue in the porcine sequence in position 17. The complete DNA sequence consists of 291 bases, suggesting a precursor of 97 amino acids. The deduced amino acid sequence would generate three peptides, a signal peptide consisting of 28 amino acids, NPY (36 amino acids) followed by a C terminal peptide consisting of 30 amino acids.

The development of specific antisera to NPY and their application in radioimmunoassay measurements of tissue extracts and body fluids together with the precise localization of NPY-immunoreactivity by immunocytochemical techniques has allowed the distribution of NPY and its possible physiological role to be explored. Antisera were raised to NPY in rabbits either by direct immunization of the peptide in complete Freund's adjuvant or by conjugation of the peptide to bovine serum albumin by carbodiimide, bisdiazotized benzidine or glutaraldehyde, as described previously. The regional specificity of binding of these antisera has been characterized. For radioimmunoassay, NPY was iodinated by conventional chloramine T oxidation and the product purified by high performance liquid chromatography to provide a tracer for the assay with a specific activity of 70 Bq/fmol. The details of the radioimmunoassay procedures have been described previously (Allen *et al.*, 1984a).

4. DISTRIBUTION OF NPY

4.1 Central nervous system

NPY has been identified in high concentrations in the human (Adrian *et al.*, 1983) and rat brain (Y. S. Allen *et al.*, 1983) with a widespread but discrete distribution. Immunocytochemical techniques have shown NPY is present within neuronal cell bodies and in long, projecting pathways.

The role of NPY in the central nervous system has not yet been determined. The peptide appears very early in the developing rat brain, being present in the brain stem and diencephalon at the fourteenth day post conception (Allen *et al.*, 1984b). Hokfelt and colleagues (1983) have proposed that NPY is co-localized with catecholamines in the medulla oblongata and intraventricular injection of NPY has been reported to result in systemic hypotension and bradycardia (Fuxe *et al.*, 1983). In other regions of the brain, however, particularly in the cerebral cortex, NPY would appear to be independent of the catecholaminergic system, as the majority of NPY-immunoreactivity is localized to neuronal cell bodies (Adrian *et al.*, 1983; Dawbarn *et al.*, 1984). Early work using APP antisera suggested that NPY may be co-localized with somatostatin in the forebrain nuclei (Vincent *et al.*, 1982). However, a recent neuropathological study has demonstrated a specific reduction of somatostatin concentrations in the cortex, with no change in NPY concentrations in Alzheimer-type dementia (Fig. 1; Allen *et al.*, 1984c) indicating that these two peptides occur independently in this region.

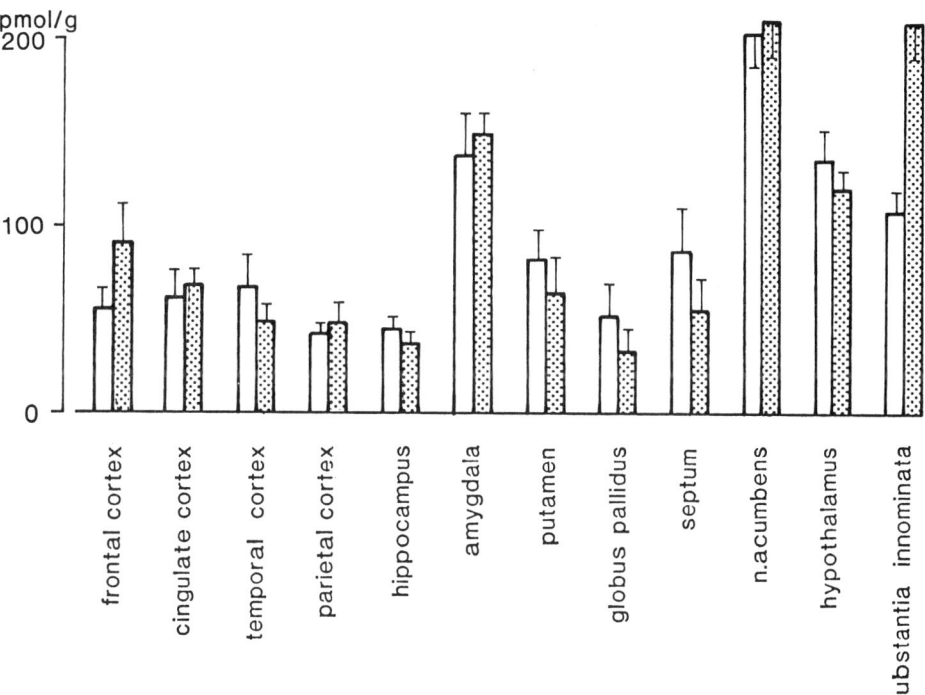

Fig. 1 – Concentrations of NPY within 12 areas of human post mortem brain. For each area, the unshaded value represents the mean concentration in 12 control subjects and the shaded value represents the mean concentration for 13 subjects with histologically confirmed Alzheimer type dementia. Variability shown as S.E.M. (From *J. Neurol. Sci.*, 1984, **64**, 328, with permission).

4.2 Peripheral nervous system

Since its isolation, NPY has been identified within nerves throughout the peripheral autonomic system, frequently in association with sympathetic nerves (Lundberg *et al.*, 1982). The cardiovascular system has been reported to be particularly richly innervated by NPY-containing nerve fibres. The distribution of these nerve fibres paralleled that of noradrenergic fibres as demonstrated by use of antisera directed against the catecholamine synthesizing enzymes, tyrosine hydroxylase and dopamine-B hydroxylase (Gu *et al.*, 1984). Furthermore pretreatment of rats with 6-hydroxydopamine resulted in a reduction in extractable concentrations of NPY from cardiac tissue (J. M. Allen, unpublished). A dense plexus of NPY-immunoreactive nerve fibres was found around the coronary vasculature. Subsequently, NPY has been demonstrated in other vascular tissues, including the major cerebral vessels (Edvinsson *et al.*, 1983; Allen *et al.*, 1984d).

The peptide would, however, appear to exist within two different classes of neurons. Firstly, in many structures, such as the cardiovascular system, NPY is co-localized with sympathetic nerves (Lundberg *et al.*, 1982) as shown by double staining techniques using immunocytochemistry (Varndell *et al.*, 1984) and by depletion of extractable concentrations of NPY following surgical (Allen *et al.*, 1983a) and chemical sympathectomy (J. M. Allen, unpublished).

In contrast, some NPY-containing nerves appear to be independent of the adrenergic nervous system. This is best illustrated within the gastro-intestinal tract where NPY-immunoreactive nerve fibres surrounding the blood vessels are depleted by treatment with 6-hydroxydopamine; however, the majority of immunoreactive nerve fibres constitute intrinsic type neurons of the myenteric plexus, being unaffected by chemical sympathectomy (Furness *et al.*, 1983). A similar pattern of dual innervation is apparent in the urogenital tract.

Within the peripheral autonomic nervous system, this pattern of dual innervation appears to be associated in part with a functional difference in the pharmacological actions of this peptide. NPY has been shown to act directly as a vasoconstrictor in many vascular beds *in vivo* (Lundberg and Tatemoto, 1982; Allen *et al.*, 1983b; Allen *et al.*, 1984d). This vasoconstrictor effect appeared resistant to alpha adrenergic blocking agents and was characterized by its prolonged duration of effect. *In vitro*, this response has been confirmed (Edvinsson *et al.*, 1983. Ekblad *et al.*, 1984). In vascular tissue, NPY has also been reported to enhance the response to exogenous noradrenaline. In contrast, in tissues where NPY appears to be localized in neurons independent of the catecholaminergic nerves, the peptide apparently acts more as a neuromodulator of classic neurotransmitters. Thus, in the female genital tract, Stjernquist and colleagues (1983) have proposed that NPY modulates cholinergic transmission. Similarly, using the mouse vas deferens preparation, NPY has been shown to inhibit the field-stimulated twitch, but had no effect on resting tension (Fig. 2; Allen *et al.*, 1982). This data was interpreted to suggest that NPY may modulate noradrenergic transmission at a presynaptic site and subsequently, Lundberg and Stjarne (1984) have shown NPY *in vitro* reduces the efflux of tritiated noradrenaline from the vas deferens preparation.

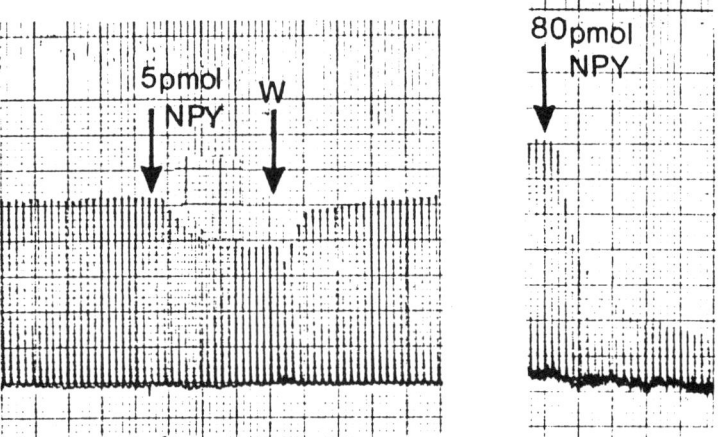

Fig. 2 − Effect of NPY on the field stimulated contraction of the mouse vas deferens preparation. NPY resulted in a dose-dependent inhibition of the neurally mediated contraction. (From *Neuropeptides* 1982, **3**, 71, with permission).

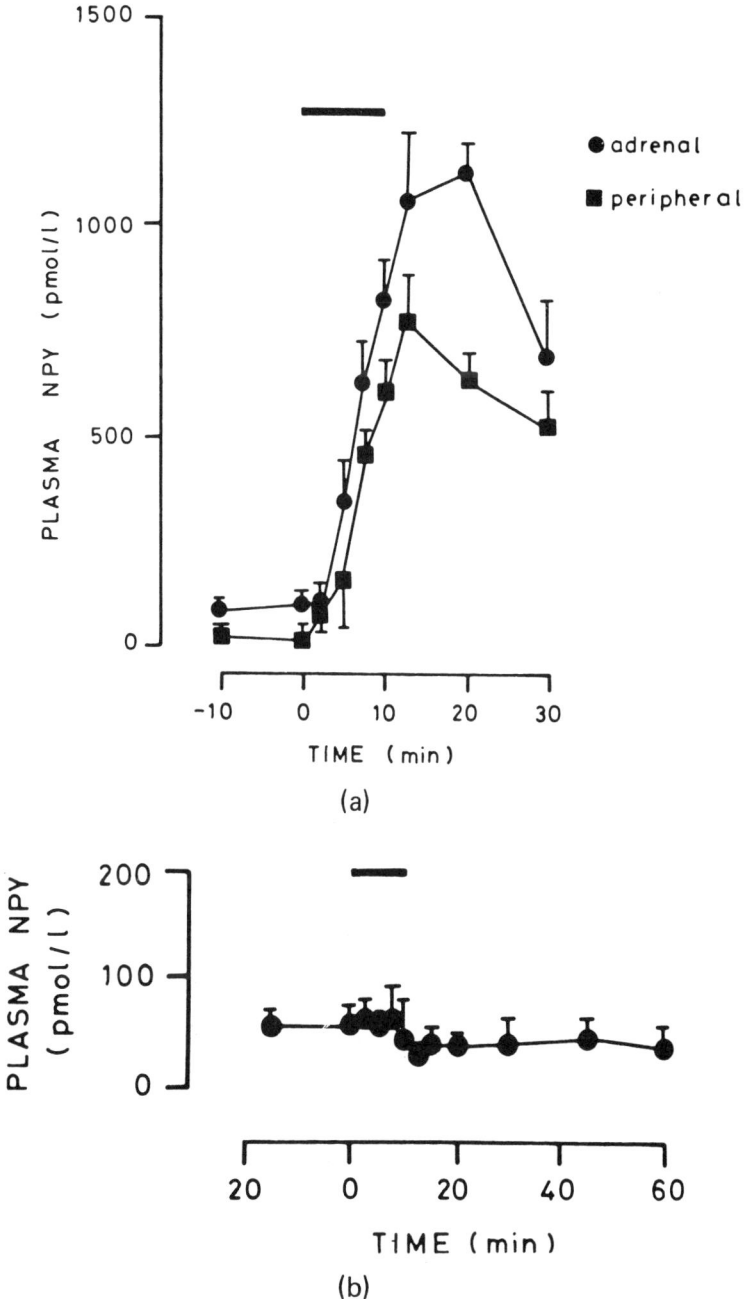

Fig. 3 – Release of NPY during stimulation of the splanchnic nerve. (a) Release of NPY into the adrenal vein [●] and systemic plasma [■] during stimulation of the right splanchnic nerve at 40 Hz in bursts for 1 second in every 10 seconds. Systemic plasma concentrations of NPY during stimulation of both splanchnic nerves at 40 Hz in bursts for 1 second in every 10 seconds in calves pretreated with hexamethonium. (From *J. Physiol.*, 1984, **357**, 401, with permission).

5. RELEASE OF NPY

The presence of NPY in sympathetic nerves has led to investigation of the mechanisms of release of the peptide. Studies in the conscious calf have shown that stimulation of the splanchnic nerves results in a rise in systemic plasma concentrations of NPY (Fig. 3(a); Allen *et al.,* 1984e). This release was dependent on the type of stimulus applied to the nerves, as high frequency bursts (40 Hz delivered for 1 second in every 10 seconds) resulted in much higher plasma concentrations of NPY than stimulation at a low frequency continuously (4 Hz). Using the experimental procedure of the adrenal clamp, it was demonstrated that the adrenal gland contributed by only a small extent to the increase in plasma NPY concentrations. Pretreatment of calves with hexamethonium completely abolished the rise in plasma concentrations of NPY (Fig. 3(b)), suggesting that NPY is released from postganglionic sympathetic nerves.

6. SUMMARY

In summary, NPY is a newly discovered peptide that is isolated using a novel chemical approach for its identification. The two techniques of radioimmunoassay and immunocytochemistry have been used to determine the distribution, localization and release of the peptide.

ACKNOWLEDGEMENTS

JMA is in receipt of a Wellcome Trust Training Fellowship.

REFERENCES

Adrian, T. E., Allen, J. M., Bloom, S. R., Rossor, M. N., Roberts, G. W., Crow, T. J., Tatemoto, K. and Polak, J. M. (1983). Neuropeptide Y in the human brain. *Nature,* **306,** 584–586.

Allen, J. M., Adrian, T. E., Tatemoto, K., Polak, J. M., Hughes, J. and Bloom, S. R. (1982). Two novel related peptides, neuropeptide Y (NPY) and peptide YY (PYY) inhibit the contraction of the electrically field stimulated mouse vas deferens. *Neuropeptides,* **3,** 71–78.

Allen, J. M., McGregor, G. P., Adrian, T. E., Bloom, S. R., Zhang, S. Q., Ennis, K. W. and Unger, W. G. (1983a). Reduction of neuropeptide Y (NPY) in the rabbit iris-ciliary body after chronic sympathectomy. *Exp. Eye Res.,* **37,** 213–215.

Allen, J. M., Bircham, P. M. M., Edwards, A. V., Tatemoto, K. and Bloom, S. R. (1983b). Neuropeptide Y (NPY) reduces myocardial perfusion and inhibits the force of contraction of the isolated perfused rabbit heart. *Regul. Pept.* **6,** 247–254.

Allen, J. M., Yeats, J. C., Adrian, T. E. and Bloom, S. R. (1984a). Radio immunoassay of Neuropeptide Y (NPY). *Regul. Pept.,* **8,** 61–70.

Allen, J. M., McGregor, G. P., Tatemoto, K., Polak, J. M. and Bloom, S. R. (1984b). Ontogeny of a novel peptide, neuropeptide Y (NPY) in rat brain. *Brain Research*, **303**, 197–200.

Allen, J. M., Ferrier, I. N., Roberts, G. W., Cross, A. J., Adrian, T. E., Crow, T. J. and Bloom, S. R. (1984c). Elevation of neuropeptide Y (NPY) in substantia innominata in Alzheimer type dementia. *J. Neurol. Sci.*, **64**, 325–331.

Allen, J. M., Schon, F., Todd, N., Yeats, J. C., Crockard, H. A. and Bloom, S. R. (1984d). Presence of Neuropeptide Y (NPY) in the human circle of Willis and its possible role in cerebral vasospasm. *Lancet* ii, 550–552.

Allen, J. M., Bircham, P. M. M., Bloom, S. R. and Edwards, A. V. (1984e). Release of neuropeptide Y in response to splanchnic nerve stimulation in the conscious calf. *J. Physiol.*, **357**, 401–408.

Allen, Y. S., Adrian, T. E., Allen, J. M., Tatemoto, K., Crow, T. J., Bloom, S. R. and Polak, J. M. (1983). Neuropeptide Y distribution in rat brain. *Science*, **221**, 877–879.

Amara, S. G., Jonas, V., Rosenfeld, M. G., Ong, E. S. and Evans, R. M. (1982). Alternative RNA processing in calcitonin gene expression generates mRNAs encoding different polypeptide products. *Nature*, **298**, 240–298.

Bloom, S. R. and Long, R. G. (eds.) (1982). *Radioimmunoassay of Gut Regulatory Peptides*, W. G. Saunders, Philadelphia.

Dawbarn, D., Hunt, S. P. and Emson, P. C. (1984). Neuropeptide Y: regional distribution, chromatographic characterisation and immunohistochemical demonstration in post mortem human brain. *Brain Res.*, **296**, 168–173.

Edvinsson, L., Emson, P., McCullock, J., Tatemoto, K. and Uddman, R. (1983). Neuropeptide Y: cerebrovascular innervation and vasomotor effects in the rat. *Neurosci Lett.*, **43**, 79–84.

Ekblad, E., Edvinsson, L., Wahlstedt, C., Uddman, R., Hakanson, R. and Sundler, F. (1984). Neuropeptide Y coexists and co-operates with noradrenaline in perivascular nerve fibres. *Regul. Pept.*, **8**, 225–236.

Furness, J. B., Costa, M., Emson, P. C., Hakanson, R., Moghimzadeh, E., Sundler, F., Taylor, I. L. and Chance, T. E. (1983). Distribution, pathways and reactions to drug treatment of nerves with neuropeptide Y- and pancreatic polypeptide-like immunoreactivity in the guinea pig digestive tract. *Cell Tissue Res.*, **234**, 71–92.

Fuxe, K., Agnati, L. F., Harfstrand, A., Zini, I., Tatemoto, K., Pich, E. M., Hokfelt, T., Mutt, V. and Terenius, L. (1983). Central administration of neuropeptide Y induces hypotension, bradypnea and EEG synchronisation in the rat. *Acta Physiol. Scand.*, **118**, 189–192.

Gu, J., Polak, J. M., Allen, J. M., Huang, W. M., Sheppard, M. N., Tatemoto, K. and Bloom, S. R. (1984). High concentrations of a novel peptide neuropeptide Y, in the innervation of mouse and rat heart. *J. Histochem. Cytochem.*, **32**, 467–472.

Hokfelt, T., Lundberg, J. M., Lagercrantz, M., Tatemoto, K., Mutt, V., Lindberg, J., Terenius, L., Everitt, B. J., Fuxe, K., Agnati, L. and Goldstein, M. (1983). Occurrence of neuropeptide Y (NPY) like immunoreactivity in

catecholamine neurons in the human medulla oblongata. *Neurosci. Lett.*,
36, 217–222.

Lundberg, J. M. and Stjarne, L. (1984). Neuropeptide Y (NPY) depresses the
secretion of ^{3}H-noradrenaline and the contractile response evoked by field
stimulation in the rat vas deferens. *Acta Physiol. Scand.*, **120**, 471–474.

Lundberg, J. M. and Tatemoto, K. (1982). Pancreatic polypeptide family (APP,
BPP, NPY and PYY) in relation to sympathetic vasoconstriction resistant
to alpha adrenergic blockade. *Acta Physiol. Scand.*, **116**, 393–402.

Lundberg, J. M., Terenius, L., Hokfelt, T., Martling, C. G., Tatemoto, K., Mutt,
V., Polak, J., Bloom, S. and Goldstein, M. (1982). Neuropeptide Y (NPY)-
like immunoreactivity in peripheral noradrenergic neurons and effects of
NPY on sympathetic function. *Acta Physiol. Scand.*, **116**, 477–480.

Minth, C. D., Bloom, S. R., Polak, J. M. and Dixon, J. E. (1984). Cloning,
characterization and DNA sequence of a human cDNA encoding neuropeptide tyrosine. *Proc. Natl. Acad. Sci.*, **81**, 4577–4581.

Polak, J. M. and Van Norden, S. (eds.) (1983). *Immunocytochemistry: Practical
Applications in Pathology and Biology*. Wright, P. S. G., Bristol.

Stjernquist, M., Emson, P., Owman, Ch., Sjoberg, N.-O., Sundler, F. and Tatemoto, K. (1983). Neuropeptide Y in the female reproductive tract of the
rat. Distribution of nerve fibres and motor effects. *Neurosci. Lett.*, **39**,
279–284.

Tatemoto, K. (1982). Neuropeptide Y – complete amino acid sequence of the
brain peptide. *Proc. Natl. Acad. Sci. (USA)*, **29**, 5485–5489.

Tatemoto, K. and Mutt, V. (1980). Isolation of two novel candidate hormones
using a chemical method for finding naturally occurring polypeptides.
Nature, **285**, 417–418.

Tatemoto, K., Carlquist, M. and Mutt, V. (1982). Neuropeptide Y – a novel
brain peptide with structural similarities to peptide YY and pancreatic
polypeptide. *Nature*, **296**, 659–660.

Tatemoto, K., Rokaeus, A., Jornvall, H., McDonald, T. J. and Mutt, V. (1983).
Galanin – a novel biologically active peptide from porcine intestine. *FEBS
Letts.*, **154**, 124–128.

Vincent, S. R., Skirboll, L., Hokfelt, T., Johansson, O., Lundberg, J. M., Elde,
R. P., Terenius , L. and Kimmel, J. (1982). Coexistence of somatostatin
and avian pancreatic polypeptide (APP)-like immunoreactivity in some
forebrain neurons. *Neurosci.*, **7**, 439–466.

Varndell, I. M., Polak, J. M., Allen, J. M., Terenghi, G. and Bloom, S. R. (1984).
Neuropeptide tyrosine (NPY) immunoreactivity in noradrenaline containing
cells and nerves of the mammalian adrenal gland. *Endocrinology*, **114**,
1460–1452.

4

Disturbances of autonomic function produced by dietary or metabolic alterations

I. A. Macdonald, T. Bennett and **I. W. Fellows**

Department of Physiology and Pharmacology, University of Nottingham
Medical School, Clifton Boulevard, Nottingham NG7 2UH, UK

The autonomic nervous system (ANS) is one of the principal control systems involved in physiological regulation. In many instances this involves the activation of postganglionic neurons which utilize either acetylcholine or noradrenaline (NA) as transmitter substances, although there is growing evidence of the existence of non-adrenergic, non-cholinergic neurotransmission in the ANS of animals and man (Rowell, 1977). In most cases it is not yet clear if such unidentified neurotransmitters are peptides, but the prospects of neuropeptides as neuromodulators looms ever larger.

Against this shifting background it is, nonetheless, apparent that alterations in energy intake can induce changes in sympathetic nervous system (SNS) activity, as judged by the turnover of NA. A major role of the SNS is in the regulation of the cardiovascular system, both with respect to the control of blood pressure and of body temperature, and the purpose of this chapter is to examine the physiological consequences of such diet-induced changes in SNS activity.

1. BIOCHEMICAL ASSESSMENT OF SYMPATHETIC ACTIVITY

1.1 Animal

In experimental animals such as the rat and mouse, SNS activity in peripheral tissues can be assessed from measurements of the turnover of NA, the major neurotransmitter. Using such a technique, it has been demonstrated that starvation reduces, and overfeeding increases, NA turnover in heart and some other tissues (Landsberg and Young, 1978; and Part II, Chapter 2 of this volume). From these studies, it was suggested that starvation suppresses and overfeeding stimulates the SNS, but it is not clear whether these are general effects which are manifest in all sympathetically innervated tissues. It is important to note that the effect of starvation on NA turnover is only apparent when the sodium intake of the animals is maintained by the provision of a hypotonic saline solution to drink. Without this, starved animals show an increase in SNS activity, presumably because of a decrease in circulating fluid volume and body sodium content.

1.2 Human

In man, the rate of appearance of NA in the circulation can be estimated with the technique of constantly infusing radioactively labelled NA and measuring the specific activity of NA in plasma (Esler *et al.*, 1982). This technique cannot, as used routinely, distinguish between NA released from sympathetic neurons and that originating from the adrenal medulla. A further drawback in employing this technique to assess the activity of the SNS is that any NA which is released from the nerve terminal into the extracellular fluid of a tissue, and then metabolized in that tissue, does not affect the specific activity of plasma NA and, thus, is not detected. However, this technique provides a more valid means of assessing SNS activity than measurements of plasma NA levels (Esler *et al.*, 1982).

Using the technique of infusing radioactive NA, Esler and colleagues have shown that when energy intake was decreased for two weeks, this was accompanied by a reduction in the rate of appearance of NA in the plasma, whilst a similar period of overeating caused an increase in this estimate of SNS activity (O'Dea *et al.*, 1982).

In some studies, decreased energy intake, in obese patients, has been found to cause a marked reduction in plasma NA levels (Jung *et al.*, 1979; Sowers *et al.*, 1982) and a fall in the urinary excretion of one of the principal metabolites of NA, namely 4-hydroxy-3-methoxy mandelic acid (Jung *et al.*, 1979). However, De Haven *et al.* (1980) imposed a similar level of food restriction on obese patients and observed no change in plasma NA levels.

Thus, it would appear that decreases and increases in energy intake in man can have similar effects on the noradrenergic component of SNS activity to those observed in experimental animals, but in some individuals these effects do not occur or are not associated with changes in plasma NA levels.

2. EFFECTS OF CHANGES IN ENERGY INTAKE ON BLOOD PRESSURE

2.1 General

The regulation of arterial blood pressure is achieved by alterations in cardiac output and peripheral vascular resistance, which are mediated by neural and endocrine factors (Fig. 1). Whilst rapid responses will be mediated by the SNS, one would expect the other systems to be recruited to regulate blood pressure if there was any impairment of the SNS response. Thus, when changes in blood pressure regulation occur as a consequence of alterations in energy intake, it is unlikely that such changes would only be due to an alteration in SNS activity.

CONTROL OF BLOOD PRESSURE

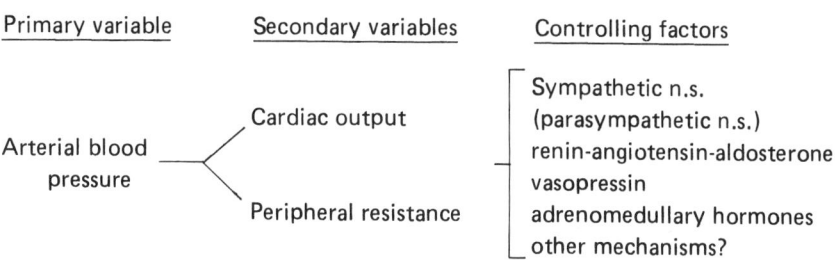

Fig. 1 – Factors involved in the regulation of blood pressure via the control of cardiac output and peripheral resistance.

2.2 Animal

Starvation for 4 days reduced the systolic blood pressure (SBP) of both spontaneously hypertensive (SHR) and normotensive control animals (WKY), although the effect was most marked in the SHR which showed a 19% decrease (Young et al., 1978). Although all animals had access to a saline solution to drink, no measurements were made to determine whether this was effective in maintaining circulating fluid volume and it is possible that some of the reduction in SBP was due to a decreased circulating volume. In a subsequent study it was shown that starvation reduced SNS activity (NA turnover) in cardiac tissue by a similar amount in both the SHR and WKY rats (Einhorn et al., 1982). This was interpreted as indicating that the greater hypotensive effect of starvation in the SHR was not simply due to a suppression of SNS activity. However, it is likely that SNS activity in cardiac tissue does not provide the same index of SNS activity in the peripheral vasculature in the SHR compared to WKY. Other studies have shown that for a given change in heart rate, there is greater change in splanchnic sympathetic nerve firing rate in the SHR than the WKY (Ricksten et al., 1984). The greater hypotensive effect of starvation in the SHR was attributed to a greater release of endogenous opiates (Einhorn et al., 1982) but no consideration was given to the possibility that the opiate antagonist which was used may have had other effects, such as altering ACTH release from the pituitary, which would have influenced corticosteroid production.

SBP was reduced by 10% in the SHR when food intake was reduced to one-half of the normal intake for 4 days, whilst, in the WKY controls, SBP was not affected by such a reduced food intake (Young *et al.*, 1978). Extending the period of underfeeding to 6 weeks had no further effect on SBP in the SHR (Notargiacomo and Freis, 1981).

2.3 Human

When non-obese, male subjects were starved for 2 days, but ingested 80 mmol sodium per day, there were only small changes in resting, supine blood pressure but a marked impairment of orthostatic tolerance (Bennett *et al.*, 1984). In supine subjects, there was a slight increase in systolic, a slight decrease in diastolic, with no change in mean arterial blood pressure after 2 days of starvation. When the subjects stood erect for 10 min there was a 15 mm Hg reduction in SBP and a 25 beats/min increase in heart rate (when the same manouevre was performed in the non-starved state there was no change in SBP and only a 15 beats/min increase in heart rate). Although no formal assessment of baroreflex sensitivity was made in these subjects, one would have expected the fall in SBP during standing in the starved state to be accompanied by a greater increase in heart rate than that which was observed. Thus, there is an indication that the baroreflex control of heart rate is impaired in starvation, but further studies are needed to examine this suggestion. This inability of starved subjects to maintain blood pressure during standing may have been due, in part, to a reduced peripheral vascular resistance and impaired vasoconstrictor responsiveness during starvation; since such changes were observed in the starved subjects when they were exposed to lower body subatmospheric pressure, whilst supine (Bennett *et al.*, 1984). Such alterations (in the peripheral vasculature) are consistent with a reduction in sympathetic vasoconstrictor tone during starvation, but a similar effect might also be produced by a decrease in end-organ sensitivity to neuronally released NA, or by the release of depressor agents such as β-endorphins, during starvation. However, if starvation was only associated with a decrease in end-organ sensitivity to NA, one would expect a compensatory increase in sympathetic neuronal activity which would maintain cardiovascular function. Any such increase in neuronal activity would release more NA from the nerve terminal and should give rise to an elevated plasma NA response to standing. Since the plasma NA levels during standing were similar in the starved and the non-starved states, and since cardiovascular function was not preserved during starvation, it seems unlikely that starvation only affected end-organ sensitivity to sympathetic stimulation (Bennett *et al.*, 1984).

Prolonged starvation (14–28 days) in obese patients is reported to cause small reductions in supine SBP and DBP, compared to the normally fed state (Leiter *et al.*, 1984). However, these patients did not receive sodium supplements during the period of starvation and so may have experienced alterations in SNS activity and cardiovascular control due to a reduction of circulating fluid volume. This suggestion is supported by the observation that after 10 min of standing, in the fasted state, the SBP had fallen by 19 mm Hg and the heart rate had increased by 28 beats/min. Both of these responses were markedly greater than those seen during standing in the fed state.

After two weeks of a reduced food intake, non-obese individuals showed a decrease in SNS activity (as judged by the radiolabelled NA infusion technique) but no change in blood pressure. In contrast, when food intake was increased for a similar period, there was a rise in SNS activity and in SBP (O'Dea *et al.*, 1982).

In the studies by the Jewish Physicians in the Warsaw Ghetto (Winick, 1979), prolonged severe undernutrition was accompanied by a fall in resting blood pressure and heart rate. However, when orthostatic tolerance was assessed using a tilt-table, there was only a slight fall in systolic and a slight rise in diastolic blood pressure, with no change in heart rate. Interestingly, these severely undernourished individuals showed no change in blood pressure during mild exercise, whereas normally nourished subjects increased their blood pressure in these circumstances. A subsequent experimental study of prolonged undernutrition in normal subjects (the Minnesota Study, Keys *et al.*, 1950) showed a fall in systolic and diastolic blood pressures and heart rate at rest after 24 weeks of underfeeding (1500 kcal per day). However, these subjects showed no impairment of their orthostatic reflexes, when these were tested using a tilt-table.

Most other investigations of the effects of underfeeding on the control of blood pressure in man have been performed in obese individuals, but the effects of such underfeeding on SNS activity in obese individuals has not been determined. However, indirect assessments of SNS activity (estimated from changes in plasma NA levels (Jung *et al.*, 1979); Sowers *et al.*, 1982) and from the urinary excretion of catecholamine metabolites (Jung *et al.*, 1979) indicate a suppression of SNS activity in such patients during underfeeding.

Reducing the energy intake of normotensive obese females (to 25% of the intake required to maintain body weight) was associated with a reduction in supine systolic and diastolic blood pressure within three days of commencing the underfeeding (Jung *et al.*, 1979). Systolic blood pressure decreased by approximately 8 mm Hg after 3 days of underfeeding but did not change further as the underfeeding proceeded. In contrast, there appeared to be a progressive decline in DBP over the 11 days of underfeeding, but the decrease observed by the eleventh day was only 8 mm Hg. In association with these changes in blood pressure, there was a decrease of 6 beats/min in resting heart rate and a fall in plasma NA levels of 0.41 nmol/l (from a level of 1.0 nmol/l when normally fed). Further studies with this degree of underfeeding in obese patients also showed reductions in supine blood pressure, heart rate and plasma NA levels, but demonstrated that blood pressure was maintained during 5 min of standing as effectively after underfeeding as it was in the normally fed state (Jung *et al.*, 1982). This orthostatic tolerance after underfeeding was accompanied by a smaller absolute change in plasma NA levels than that observed in the fed state (Jung *et al.*, 1982). However, when the change is calculated relative to the baseline NA levels, similar responses occurred in the normally fed state and after underfeeding.

The reduction in supine blood pressure and heart rate during underfeeding in obese patients is consistent with a decrease in SNS activity. However, if a suppression of SNS efferent activity was the only effect of underfeeding, one would expect other mechanisms to be activated to maintain blood pressure at the normally fed level (section 2.1). The situation is further complicated by the demonstration of unimpaired cardiovascular reflexes (i.e. the maintenance of orthostatic tolerance) in underfed obese patients. Thus it seems that such underfeeding may be associated with a reduction in SNS activity when supine, but SNS activation occurs during standing and this contributes to the maintenance of blood pressure.

More severe underfeeding of obese patients (to 15% of the food intake required to maintain weight) has been found to reduce supine blood pressure, with maintained orthostatic tolerance in one (Sowers *et al.,* 1982), but not another (De Haven *et al.,* 1980), study. Sowers *et al.* (1982) studied normotensive obese patients and obese subjects with moderately elevated blood pressure (bordeline hypertension) and found similar reductions in mean arterial blood pressure (18 mm Hg) and pulse rate (10 beats/min) in both groups after 8 weeks of underfeeding. Although there was also a marked reduction in plasma NA levels in both groups, the pattern of change was different from the pattern of change of blood pressure. After 1 week of underfeeding, the normotensive and borderline hypertensive obese patients showed a fall in mean arterial blood pressure of 10 and 14 mm Hg, respectively, which was more than half of the total decrease in pressure observed after 8 weeks. In contrast, the declines in plasma NA levels in both groups after 1 week were only one-fifth of those recorded after 8 weeks of underfeeding. Orthostatic tolerance during underfeeding was only assessed in the obese patients who initially had borderline hypertension. These patients maintained their supine blood pressure when standing for 10 min on all the test occasions during the underfeeding period. The first test reported was after 1 week of underfeeding, so it is possible there may have been some impairments of orthostatic tolerance during the first few days of the reduced food intake. During the underfeeding period, these patients also showed slight reductions in the absolute changes in plasma NA levels on standing. However, as with the study of Jung *et al.* (1982), when the changes in concentration are expressed relative to the baseline levels, the response to standing is increased during underfeeding compared to the normally fed state.

Although a reduction in SNS activity would appear to contribute to the hypotensive effect of underfeeding, the studies cited above indicate that some other factors may also be involved. The recent suggestion that the amount of calcium consumed in the diet, especially in relation to the intake of sodium, may have a marked effect on arterial blood pressure (McArron *et al.,* 1984) is particularly relevant, as starvation and underfeeding may have differential effects on calcium and sodium balance.

Not all studies have revealed a hypotensive effect of underfeeding in obese patients. De Haven *et al.* (1980) reduced the energy intake in obese patients to 15% of normal for 3 weeks and observed no change in supine blood pressure. However, the experimental design was different from the studies cited above, in that, in this study, the reduced energy intake was provided either entirely from protein, or from a mixture of protein and carbohydrate, whereas Sowers *et al.* (1982) provided a mixture of protein and carbohydrate and Jung *et al.* (1982) provided a mixture of protein and fat. The subjects studied by De Haven *et al.* (1980) showed no change in supine blood pressure during underfeeding, and showed a negative sodium balance on both diets, a significantly more negative sodium balance occurring on the 100% protein diet. It seems very likely that the greater depletion of body sodium on the 100% protein diet was accompanied by a reduction in circulating blood volume, because the patients demonstrated marked orthostatic intolerance when consuming this diet.

In relation to the previous comment that alterations in calcium and sodium intake may occur during underfeeding and affect blood pressure, it is interesting to note that in the studies of Jung *et al.* (1979, 1982) and of Sowers *et al.* (1982), the patients were in sodium balance and their calcium intakes were maintained at a normal level during the period of underfeeding when a reduction in blood pressure was recorded, whereas De Haven *et al.* (1980) did not maintain their patients in sodium balance and also allowed the calcium intake to fall from 25 mmol/day (normally fed) to 1.15 mmol/day during a period of underfeeding in which supine blood pressure did not change.

2.4 Summary

The major conclusion to be drawn from these various studies is that starvation or underfeeding, has effects on blood pressure in man. In some instances the effect is to reduce supine blood pressure without affecting the reflex control of blood pressure during standing (Fig. 2), whereas in other situations there is no change in supine blood pressure but a marked orthostatic intolerance (Fig. 3). It is possible that if the starvation, or underfeeding, was accompanied by a marked reduction in sodium and fluid intake (giving severe depletion of circulating blood volume) then the individuals would have both a reduced supine blood pressure and severe orthostatic intolerance.

LOWERED SUPINE BLOOD PRESSURE BUT MAINTAINED ORTHOSTATIC TOLERANCE

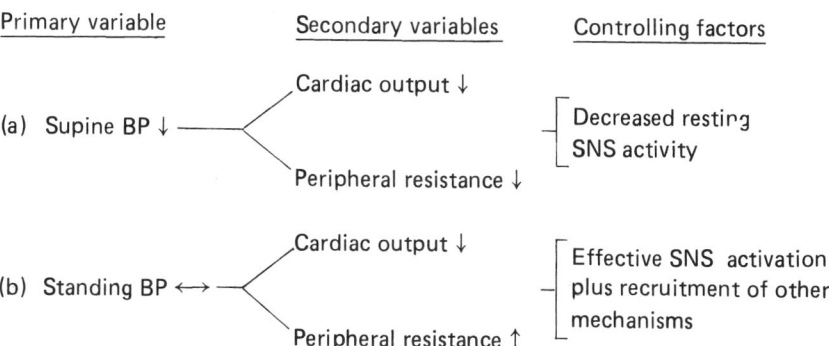

Fig. 2 – Fasting or underfeeding induced decreases in resting sympathetic nervous system (SNS) activity and the effects on blood pressure (BP). For the Supine condition, ↓ indicates the variable is reduced compared to the normally fed state. For standing, ↓, ↑ or ⟷ indicate the variables are decreased, increased or unchanged compared to the underfed Supine posture.

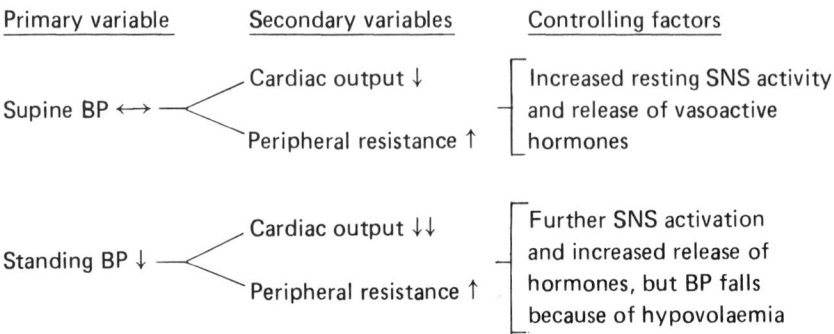

Fig. 3 – Effects of volume, depletion during underfeeding, on SNS activity and BP. For the Supine condition, ↓, ↑ or ⟷ indicate variables decreased, increased or unchanged compared to the normally fed state. For standing, ↓ or ↑ indicate variables decreased or increased compared to the underfed Supine posture, the double arrows, ↓↓, indicates a large decrease.

Some of these effects could be explained by reductions in resting SNS tone, but it seems likely that the other effects of starvation/underfeeding (such as alterations in calcium and sodium balance, changes in adrenoceptor sensitivity, activation of other regulatory mechanisms or release of vasoactive compounds such as β-endorphins) must have contributed to the functional changes described above.

3. EFFECTS OF REDUCTIONS IN ENERGY INTAKE ON BODY TEMPERATURE

3.1 General
The regulation of body temperature is dependent upon maintaining thermal equilibrium by alterations in the rates of heat production and heat loss. The control of heat production and heat loss is mediated by neural and humoral mechanisms (Fig. 4), with the SNS being particularly involved in controlling heat loss in man via the control of peripheral blood flow and sweating.

3.2 Animal
There have been many investigations of the effects of starvation or underfeeding on the resting level of heat production in experimental animals, but very few investigators have examined the thermoregulatory consequences of a reduced food intake. A short period of starvation (18 h) was associated with a decrease in resting heat production in genetically obese mice, but had no effect on lean mice (Macdonald and Stock, 1979). In contrast, starvation had no effect on the

THERMOREGULATION

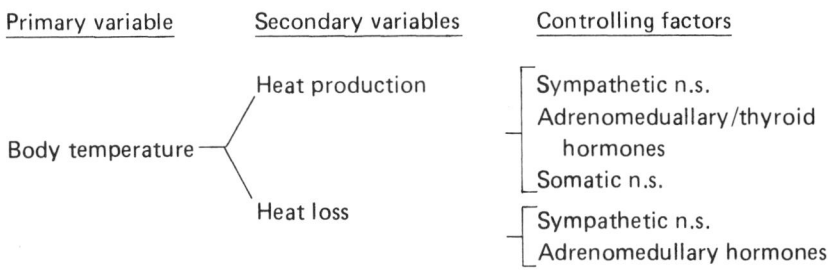

Fig. 4 – Factors involved in the regulation of body temperature via the control of heat production and heat loss.

thermogenic response to exogenous NA in the obese mice, whereas the response of the lean mice was markedly reduced. This reduction in sensitivity to NA is of interest as thermoregulation in rodents is mediated by the SNS (stimulating heat production and reducing heat loss).

Prolonged, severe undernutrition has marked effects on resting heat production and thermoregulation in the pig (McCance and Mount, 1960). When newborn pigs were underfed to the extent that at 12 months of age they were the same body weight as at weaning, this undernutrition was associated with a marked reduction in core temperature in a thermoneutral environment. During the first four months of undernutrition, the reduced core temperature was accompanied by a significant depression of resting heat production in a thermoneutral environment, but the animals were able to increase their heat production 2- to 3-fold and defended their core temperature during short periods of exposure to a cold environment. However, after 12 months undernutrition, although the pigs had a higher resting heat production in the thermoneutral environment, they failed to respond to cold exposure and, thus, were unable to maintain their core temperature. It seems most probable that this effect on thermoregulation was due to the effects of undernutrition on the mass of metabolically active tissues and/or the availability of substrate with which to raise the heat production, but no evidence is available on the responsiveness of the animals to exogenously administered thermogenic agents, such as NA. However, it was apparent that the undernourished pigs were capable of increasing their insulation (presumably, in part, by sympathetically mediated vasoconstriction) as effectively as the normally nourished controls.

3.3 Human
Short periods of starvation in non-obese subjects are associated with impairments of thermoregulation, both in response to cold exposure (Macdonald et al., 1984) and to heat exposure (Luck and Unwin, 1983). Macdonald et al. (1984) showed that, after 48 h of starvation, core temperature fell during

cooling, where core temperature did not change during cooling after an overnight fast. The falls in core temperature during cooling after 48 h of starvation were greatest in those subjects with the lowest body fat contents. Interestingly, this lack of insulation was not detrimental to the thermoregulation of these individuals during cooling after an overnight fast. Although the reflex, sympathetically mediated vasoconstriction in the hand was similar during cooling after an overnight fast and after 48 h of starvation, the blood flow to the forearm was higher at all stages during cooling after 48 h of starvation (compared to after an overnight fast). Thus, the impairment of thermoregulation during starvation could not be explained by a generalized suppression of SNS activity to all vascular beds. An increased forearm blood flow was also observed in a study of the effects of acute starvation on blood pressure regulation (Bennett et al., 1984), and the results of that study, together with the thermoregulatory study cited above, indicate that the forearm hyperaemia occurs in the vasculature of both skin and muscle. It remains to be established whether this hyperaemia is due to a direct effect of starvation on the SNS, or whether some other effect of starvation has an influence on the peripheral vasculature.

Luck and Unwin (1983) observed impaired sweating responses to heat exposure in subjects who had starved for 48 h. This provides evidence of an effect of starvation on a non-adrenergic aspect of sympathetic function, since thermoregulatory sweating is controlled by sympathetic neurons which are cholinergic at the neuroeffector junction.

There have been no experimental studies of the effects of prolonged undernutrition on thermoregulation. This is somewhat surprising, as Keys et al. (1950) demonstrated that core temperature was reduced by approximately 0.7°C after 12 weeks of underfeeding and stated that some subjects had a poor tolerance of cold, but provided no objective measurements of the latter.

The only information concerning the effects of undernutrition on thermoregulation arises from studies in clinically undernourished patients. In babies (Brooke et al., 1973), and in elderly women (Fellows et al., 1984), undernutrition is associated with a failure to increase heat production during cold exposure. It is noteworthy that, in both these studies, it appeared the heat conservation (i.e. reflex vasoconstrictor) responses to cold exposure were not diminished in the undernourished subjects, thus indicating that this aspect of the SNS response to cold exposure was intact. It is still not established whether the increase in heat production which occurs in man on cold exposure is due entirely to shivering thermogenesis (controlled by the somatic nervous system), or if the activation of non-shivering thermogenesis contributes. If the latter is involved in the thermoregulatory responses to cold exposure, it is likely to be controlled, in part, by the SNS. Thus, it may be that the failure of undernourished babies and elderly women to increase their heat production during cold exposure is a manifestation of a specific reduction in SNS activity influencing non-shivering thermogenesis. Alternatively, the failure to increase heat production during cold exposure may be due simply to a reduction in the mass of metabolically active tissue and a failure or inability to mobilize metabolic substrate in the undernourished.

4. CONCLUDING REMARKS

The purpose of this review was to examine the functional consequences of alterations in food intake. The majority of the information presented in this review demonstrates that the control of blood pressure and the control of body temperature, processes which both rely to a large extent upon alterations in SNS activity, are affected by reductions in food intake. Much less information is available regarding the effects on these variables of increasing food intake. Although it appears that fasting and underfeeding do induce functional disturbances in systems which are controlled, in part, by the SNS, there is very little evidence to support the suggestion that fasting and underfeeding induce a generalized suppression of SNS activity. It seems more likely that the SNS efferent control of some peripheral tissues is reduced in fasting and underfeeding, and in addition there may be other effects of fasting and underfeeding which contribute to the functional disturbances described above.

REFERENCES

Bennett, T., Macdonald, I. A. and Sainsbury, R. (1984). The influence of acute starvation on the cardiovascular responses to lower body subatmospheric pressure or to standing in man. *Clin. Sci.,* **66**, 141–146.

Brooke, O. G., Harris, M. and Salvosa, C. B. (1973). The response of malnourished babies to cold. *J. Physiol.,* **233**, 75–91.

De Haven, J., Sherwin, R., Hendler, R. and Felig, P. (1980). Nitrogen and sodium balance and sympathetic nervous system activity in obese subjects treated with a low-calorie protein or mixed diet. *New Engl. J. Med.,* **302**, 477–482.

Einhorn, D., Young, J. B. and Landsberg, L. (1982). Hypotensive effect of fasting; possible involvement of the sympathetic nervous system and endogenous opiates. *Science,* **217**, 727–729.

Esler, M., Leonard, P., O'Dea, K., Jackman, G., Jennings, G. and Korner, P. (1982). Biochemical quantification of sympathetic nervous activity in humans using radiotracer methodology: fallibility of plasma noradrenaline measurements. *J. Cardiovasc. Pharmacol.,* **4**, S152–S157.

Fellows, I. W., Rawlings, J., Bennett, T., Macdonald, I. A. and Allison, S. P. (1984). Failure of thermoregulation in nutritional depletion. (Presented to 6th Congress of the European Society of Enteral and Parenteral Nutrition) *Clinical Nutrition,* **in press**.

Jessen, K. (1980). An assessment of human regulatory non-shivering thermogenesis. *Acta anaesth. scand.,* **24**, 138–143.

Jung, R. T., Shetty, P. S., Barrand, M., Callingham, B. A. and James, W. P. T. (1979). Role of catecholamines in hypotensive response to dieting. *Br. Med. J.,* **1**, 12–13.

Jung, R. T., Shetty, P. S., James, W. P. T., Barrand, M. A. and Callingham, B. A. (1982). Plasma catecholamines and autonomic responsiveness in obesity. *Int. J. Obesity,* **6**, 131–141.

Keys, A., Brozek, J., Henschel, A., Mickelsen, O. and Taylor, H. O. (1950). *The Biology of Human Starvation.* University of Minnesota Press, Minneapolis.

Landsberg, L. and Young, J. B. (1978). Fasting, feeding and regulation of the sympathetic nervous system. *New Engl. J. Med.,* **298**, 1295–1301.

Leiter, L. A., Grose, M., Yale, J.-F. and Marliss, E. B. (1984). Catecholamine responses to hypocaloric diets and fasting in obese human subjects. *Amer. J. Physiol.,* **247**, E190–E197.

Luck, P. and Unwin, A. (1983). Influence of a 48-hour fast on thermoregulatory sweating in man. *J. Physiol.,* **340**, 38–39P.

McArron, D. A., Morris, C. D., Henry, H. J. and Stanton, J. L. (1984). Blood pressure and nutrient intake in the United States. *Science,* **224**, 1392–1398.

McCance, R. A. and Mount, L. E. (1960). Severe undernutrition in growing and adult animals. 5. Metabolic rate and body temperature in the pig. *Br. J. Nutr.,* **14**, 509–518.

Macdonald, I. A. and Stock, M. J. (1979). Influence of norepinephrine and fasting on the oxygen consumption of genetically obese mice. *Nutr. Metab.,* **23**, 250–255.

Macdonald, I. A., Bennett, T. and Sainsbury, R. (1984). The effect of a 48 h fast on the thermoregulatory responses to graded cooling in man. *Clin. Sci.,* **67**, 445–452.

Notargiacomo, A. V. and Freis, E. D. (1981). Effect of weight-reducing diet on the blood pressure of spontaneously hypertensive rats. *Proc. Soc. Exp. Biol. Med.,* **167**, 612–615.

O'Dea, K., Esler, M., Leonard, P., Stockigt, J. R. and Nestel, P. (1982). Noradrenaline turnover during under- and over-eating in normal weight subjects. *Metabolism,* **31**, 896–899.

Ricksten, S.-E., Lundin, S. and Thoren, P. (1984). Spontaneous variations in arterial blood pressure, heart rate and sympathetic nerve activity in conscious normotensive and spontaneously hypertensive rats. *Acta Physiol. Scand.,* **120**, 595–600.

Rowell, L. B. (1977). Reflex control of the cutaneous vasculature. *J. Invest. Dermatol.,* **69**, 154–166.

Sowers, J. R., Whitfield, L. A., Catania, R. A., Stern, N., Tuck, M. L., Dornfeld, L. and Maxwell, M. (1982). Role of the sympathetic nervous system in blood pressure maintenance in obesity. *J. Clin. Endocrinol. Metab.,* **54**, 1181–1186.

Winick, M. (1979). *Hunger disease. Studies by the Jewish Physicians in the Warsaw Ghetto,* Winick, M. (ed.) John Wiley, New York.

Young, J. B., Mullen, D. and Landsberg, L. (1978). Caloric restriction lowers blood pressure in the spontaneously hypertensive rat. *Metabolism,* **27**, 1771–1714.

5

Commentary

T. Bennett

Department of Physiology and Pharmacology, Medical School, Queen's
Medical Centre, Clifton Boulevard, Nottingham NG7 2UH, UK

Most of the discussion in this session was concerned with clarification of the
material presented and does not need to be restated as the speakers' contributions to this book cover their presentations. However, the following points are
worthy of comment.

Dr. Hjemdahl (Chapter 1) illustrated the problems associated with measurement of plasma catecholamines by different techniques, and demonstrated
convincingly the need for careful validation of assay procedures. Assuming one
has a sensitive, reproducible and valid assay, there are still problems associated
with the use of measurements of venous plasma catecholamine levels as indices
of sympathoadrenal activity. For example, the usual procedure of obtaining
blood samples from an antecubital vein may produce values for plasma noradrenaline that are influenced more by forearm efferent noradrenergic activity
than by other sources of noradrenaline. The picture may be even more complicated if systemic arterial plasma noradrenaline levels are changing at the same
time as alterations in release and re-uptake are occurring across the forearm
vascular bed. A proper analysis of dynamics of these sorts of processes is still
some way off, but progress is being made.

Dr. Landsberg (Chapter 2) described two techniques for estimating sympathoadrenal activity in experimental animals. One method involves measurement of the rate of depletion of endogenous catecholamines following inhibition of synthesis with α-methylparatyrosine. Dr. Landsberg pointed out that this drug causes a more marked depletion of central than peripheral catecholamines, and the former effect might influence the level of sympathoadrenal activity. However, the use of appropriate controls goes some way towards meeting this difficulty, as does the finding that similar results are obtained with techniques not requiring inhibition of catecholamine synthesis. The assertion that different rates of catecholamine turnover are due to different levels of sympathoadrenal activity is supported by the finding that such variations are largely abolished by antagonism of nicotinic ganglionic receptors. Interestingly, under these conditions there may be residual numerical differences in the rates of catecholamine turnover. If these are real (rarher than methodological 'noise'), they may be due to one, or several, factors. One possibility is that complete nicotinic receptor blockade is not achieved. Another possibility is that muscarinic receptors are involved in ganglionic transmission. A third, more intriguing, possibility is that circulating hormones can influence catecholamine turnover rate in the absence of efferent impulses. From other types of experiment there is evidence that, following administration of ganglion-blocking drugs, the renin-angiotensin system is activated and vasopressin is released from the pituitary. Both these factors might influence sympathoadrenal activity − as might the multitude of recently discovered neuropeptides.

Dr. Allen (Chapter 3) pointed out that neuropeptide Y (NPY) may function independently as a vasoactive agent since its effects are not inhibited by competitive α-adrenoceptor antagonism. However, such experiments have yet to be carried out in the presence of non-competitive, unselective α-adrenoceptor antagonists. While the normal role of NPY (and that of many other 'newer' neuropeptides) in sympathoadrenal function has yet to be defined, studies are already under way to investigate the possible involvement of neuropeptides in various pathophysiological conditions. At this point it is salutary to remember that vasopressin (one of the 'oldest' neuropeptides on the books) has long been denied any important effect besides that on renal function. This situation came about because many investigators demonstrated that vasopressin only exerted overt extra-renal effects when plasma levels were supraphysiological. However, it is now clear that vasopressin has profound influences on many central nervous mechanisms and, in the periphery, it may be that the control of many visceral processes depends on the synergistic and interactive influences of the autonomic nervous system, the renin-angiotensin system and vasopressin. If we accept the proposition that the functional expression of any given level of sympatho-adrenal activity may be modified in the way and by the sorts of factors alluded to above, then it is clear that these must be taken into account when we are assessing sympathoadrenal activity.

Part

III

Monitoring brain transmitter release and metabolism during behaviour

1

Identification of neurotransmitter autoreceptors using measurement of release *in vivo*

N. T. Maidment, C. Routledge, K. F. Martin, M. P. Brazell[†] and C. A. Marsden

Department of Physiology and Pharmacology, Medical School, Queen's Medical Centre, Clifton Boulevard, Nottingham NG7 2UH, UK

1. INTRODUCTION

The majority of studies concerned with the identification of neurotransmitter receptors and their subtypes have been made using *in vitro* techniques – principally ligand binding methods. An essential requirement however, for the identification of a receptor is that there should be a correlation between the ligand binding data and an *ex vivo* or *in vivo* functional response. This can prove difficult especially with regard to receptors in the CNS. For example, only rarely can behavioural responses be attributed to a single neurotransmitter or receptor system. The demonstration that neurotransmitter release is regulated by an action of the transmitter on autoreceptors offers an alternative approach to the identification of CNS receptors. Transmitter release in response to administration of selective agonists and antagonists of the receptors can be measured. This has been made more attractive by recent improvements in and development of methods that can monitor *endogenous* neurotransmitter release and metabolism from selected brain regions.

†Present address: Department of Chemistry, University of Kansas, Lawrence, Kansas 66045, USA

In this chapter we will briefly describe two approaches to the measurement of transmitter release and metabolism and their use for investigating the *in vivo* pharmacology of dopamine and 5-hydroxytryptamine (5HT) receptors associated with specific neuronal pathways. Preliminary results on the release of noradrenaline and adrenaline from the hypothalmus will also be described. The first and most commonly used approach involves intracerebral perfusion in which brain perfusate samples are collected and assayed for their transmitter and metabolite content using specific and highly sensitive analytical techniques. An example of this approach, and the one used in the present study, is intracerebral dialysis (Zetterström *et al.*, 1983; Ungerstedt, 1984. and Sharp *et al.*, Part III, Chapter 2 of this volume). The advantage of this approach is the positive analytical identification of the substances within the perfusates. Disadvantages include the relatively large size of the probe (approx. 600 μm) which limits the method to the study of larger brain areas, and the long collection time (10–20 min) between each sample. The second category of method attempts to overcome these problems by using a microelectrochemical electrode to continuously monitor changes in amine release and metabolism. *In vivo* electrochemistry differs from intracerebral dialysis in that the assay is performed *in situ* without any collection of perfusate and subsequent separation and assay of amines and metabolites. This allows rapid and frequent sampling but without positive identification of the substances being oxidized.

1.1 Intracerebral dialysis

This method, which has been described in detail elsewhere (Ungerstedt, 1984; and Sharp *et al.*, Part III, Chapter 2 of this volume), involves the stereotaxic implantation of a small diameter (250 μm) dialysis tube folded into a loop and supported by two steel cannulae into the brain area of interest. The tube is then perfused with physiological saline (0.7 ml/min) and fractions collected into a small inverted tube placed on the outlet cannula. The fractions are then assayed by high performance liquid chromatography with electrochemical detection (LCEC) for dopamine, noradrenaline, adrenaline, 5HT, dihydroxyphenylacetic acid (DOPAC), homovanillic acid (HVA), 3-methoxy-4-hydroxyphenylglycol (MHPG) and 5-hydroxyindoleacetic acid (5HIAA) using either reverse phase chromatography (Spherisorb 5 ODS 2 column; mobile phase 0.1 M acetate– citrate pH 4.6 containing 10% methanol) for DOPAC, 5HT, 5HIAA and HVA or ion pair reverse phase (mobile phase 0.1 M NaH_2PO_4 pH 3.6, 0.1 mM EDTA, 0.1 mM sodium octanyl sulphonic acid and 9% methanol) for MHPG, noradrenaline, DOPAC, 5HIAA and dopamine.

Recovery of the amines through the cellulose membrane *in vitro* is inversely related to the rate of perfusion with recovery for 5HIAA of 15.5% at 0.7 μl/min and 5.75% at 2 μl/min for 20 min. However, a more physiological situation is to test recovery using a mixture of the compounds of interest (e.g. a mixture of noradrenaline, dopamine, adrenaline, MHPG and DOPAC). In this case at a flow rate of 2 μl/min the recovery of 5HIAA is only 3.7%. It is not clear to what extent recovery determined *in vitro* reflects the recovery of the amines from the brain environment and there is an obvious need for an *in vivo* method for determining recovery.

Comparison of the estimated *in vivo* extracellular levels of 5HT and its metabolite 5HIAA in the rat striatum and frontal cortex (Table 1) demonstrates two important features. Firstly the higher concentrations of the metabolite compared to the amine and secondly the somewhat higher concentrations of both in the extracellular space of the freely moving rat compared to the anaesthetized (chloral hydrate) rat (Table 1; Marsden and Routledge, 1984).

Table 1 — Estimated extracellular concentrations of 5HT, 5HIAA and DOPAC in the frontal cortex of the anaesthetized and freely moving rat.

	Anaesthetized	Freely moving
5HT	6.2×10^{-8} M	10.2×10^{-8} M
5HIAA	4.3×10^{-7} M	6.1×10^{-7} M
DOPAC	5.0×10^{-8} M	6.7×10^{-8} M

Values determined from 50 μl intracerebral dialysis samples. $n = 6$ (anaesthetized) or 4 (freely moving).

1.2 *In vivo* voltammetry

This approach depends on the ease with which catechol and indoleamines can be oxidized at the surface of a graphite working electrode. The principles of the technique have been discussed in detail elsewhere as have the practical aspects (see Adams and Marsden, 1982; Marsden, 1984). The present discussion will concentrate on the use of carbon fibre working electrodes combined with differential pulse voltammetry (DPV) to monitor the metabolites of dopamine and 5HT, DOPAC and 5HIAA.

The ease of which compounds are oxidized depends on the presence of certain oxidizable groups (e.g. OH or NH in the case of indoleamines) and the potential at which oxidation occurs depends on how readily these groups are oxidized. Generally, compounds with similar chemical structures (i.e. dopamine and DOPAC or 5HT and 5HIAA) oxidize at similar potentials. This is the major limitation of *in vivo* electrochemistry and the emphasis at present is on the production of electrodes with increased selectivity. Fortunately, there are relatively few compounds found in adequate amounts in the extracellular space which are electroactive, particularly within the potential range that can be applied to working electrodes implanted in the brain (about -0.2 to $+0.7$ V).

Electrochemical signals recorded *in vivo* are in the nanoamp range so that working electrodes need to be made of material with very low residual current. This in effect has limited electrode construction to either powdered carbon mixed with a hydrophobic component (i.e. wax, silicon or paraffin oil) or pyrolytic carbon fibres. Once suitable materials have been found the major problem is to produce electrodes that are able to distinguish between the electroactive compounds with similar oxidation potentials found in the extracellular fluid. The most important example is the problem caused by the very high levels of ascorbic acid in brain (Mefford *et al.*, 1981) which oxidizes at a similar potential to dopamine and DOPAC at the surface of untreated carbon paste electrodes (Brazell and Marsden, 1982; Adams and Marsden 1982; Wightman and Dayton, 1982). Another example is the similar oxidation potentials of the indoleamines and uric acid especially as it is now known that the latter is found in high concentrations in the brain (Zetterström *et al.*, 1983). The ascorbic acid problem has been largely overcome using electrically pre-treated carbon fibre electrodes similar to those used in the present studies (Gonon *et al.*, 1980, 1981, 1984; for details of construction and pretreatment, see also Sharp *et al.*, 1984; Maidment and Marsden, 1985; and Fig. 1).

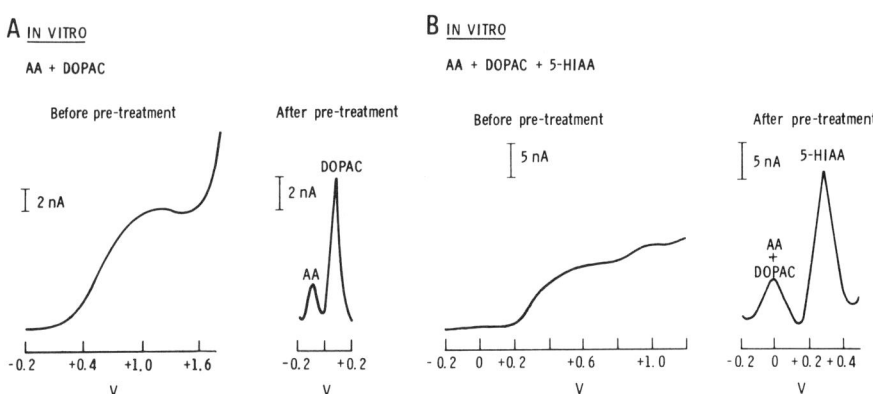

Fig. 1 – Effect of electrical pretreatment of carbon fibre electrodes on the separation of A. ascorbic acid (5×10^{-4}) and DOPAC (5×10^{-5}) and B. ascorbic acid (5×10^{-4}M), DOPAC (5×10^{-5}M) and 5HIAA (5×10^{-5}M) *in vitro* at pH 7.4 using differential pulse voltammetry. Note the absence of separation without electrical pretreatment. *Electrical pretreatments:* A. Triangular waveform 0 to $+3$ V, 70 Hz for 20 s; then held at $+1.5$ V DC for 5 s, -0.9 V DC for 3 s and finally $+1.5$ V DC for 5 s. B. Triangular waveform 0 to $+3$ V, 70 Hz for 20 s, then 0 to $+2$ V, 70 Hz for 20 s and finally 0 to $+1$ V, 70 Hz for 20 s (see Gonon *et al.* (1984) and Sharp *et al.* (1984) for details).

Evidence that the carbon fibre electrodes are able to monitor changes in DOPAC (Peak 2) and 5HIAA (Peak 3) has come from two types of experiment. Firstly pharmacological manipulation of the peaks recorded (see Gonon *et al.*, 1984; Cepuglio *et al.*, 1984; Marsden, 1985; for review – summarised in Table 2) and secondly direct comparison of the effects of drugs on changes in the metabolites monitored simultaneously by intracerebral dialysis and *in vivo* voltammetry (Sharp *et al.*, 1984). In the direct comparison studies it has been shown that haloperidol, which increases dopamine turnover and release, produces a similar and parallel increase in DOPAC measured by dialysis and the

Table 2 – Summary of the effects of pharmacological manipulation of Peak 2 (DOPAC) and Peak 3 (5HIAA) observed with electrically pretreated carbon fibre electrodes.

Treatment	Peak 2	Peak 3
A. *Catecholamine*		
6-hydroxydopamine	↓	
α-methyl-*p*-tyrosine	↓	
DOPA/5HTP decarboxylase inhibitors	↓	↓
MAO inhibitors	↓	↓
d-amphetamine	↓	
Neuroleptics	↑	
Reserpine	↑	↑
L-DOPA	↑	
B. *Indoleamine*		
5,7-dihydroxytryptamine		↓
p-chlorophenylalanine		↓
Stimulation of the raphe nuc.		↑
L-tryptophan		↑
5HTP		↑
C. *Other compounds*		
Probenecid		↑
Uric acid		↑
Uricase		↓

Data from Cespuglio *et al.* (1984), Crespi *et al.* (1984), Gonon *et al.* (1984) and references contained therein.

presumed DOPAC voltammetric oxidation peak (Peak 2). Similarly amphetamine reduces DOPAC levels in the dialysis samples and the height of Peak (Peak 2) (Fig. 2). In general, the evidence that Peak 2 is solely due to the oxidation of DOPAC is convincing; however, with regard to the 5HIAA peak (Peak 3) there is a problem regarding the contribution of uric acid to this peak. The decrease in Peak 3 in the striatum after 5,7-dihydroxytryptamine lesions, monoamine oxidase inhibition and 5HTP decarboxylase inhibition is usually about 20% less than the decrease in tissue 5HIAA (Cespuglio *et al.*, 1984). Conversely the increase in Peak 3 after 5HTP (25 mg/kg) was considerably less than the increase in tissue 5HIAA (Cespuglio *et al.*, 1981) while there was no significant increase in Peak 3 following L-tryptophan (100 mg/kg) (Cespuglio *et al.*, 1981) although striatal 5HIAA levels increase (Knott and Curzon, 1974).

The difference between the change in Peak 3 and the biochemical data might suggest some other compound contributes to the oxidation peak. Another explanation is that while the voltammetric electrodes measure extracellular

5HIAA the tissue measurements include intra- and extracellular metabolite and that the drugs have a greater effect on intra- than extracellular metabolite levels. This latter view is supported by the finding that when intracerebral dialysis and voltammetry were performed simultaneously in the striatum of the same rat

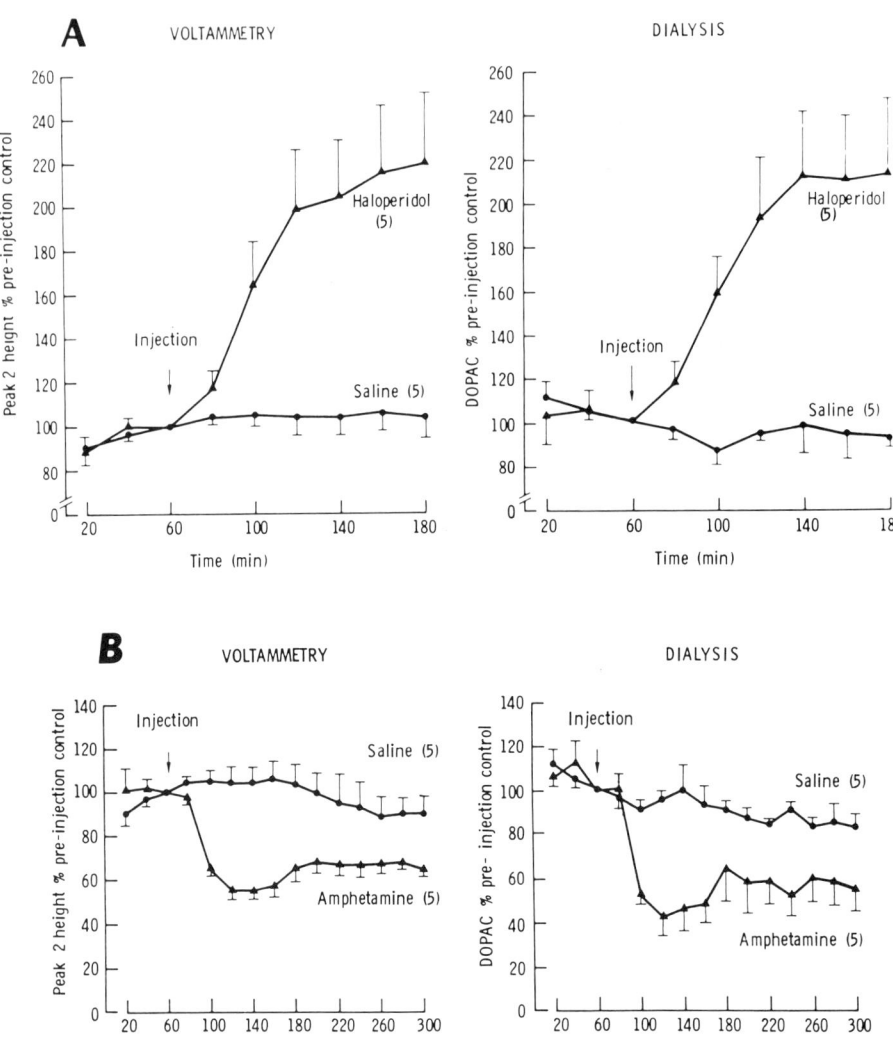

Fig. 2 – Comparison of the changes in striatal extracellular DOPAC, measured in intracerebral dialysis samples and Peak 2 recorded using differential pulse voltammetry following A. haloperidol and B. d-amphetamine. The dialysis probe was placed into one striatum and the voltammetric electrode into the other. Haloperidol (0.5 mg/kg s.c.) or d-amphetamine (2 mg/kg s.c.) were administered 60 min after the start of the experiment. Results are given as percentage of the pre-injection (60 min) value ±S.E.M. Figures in brackets refer to the number of experiments.

there was a very close correlation between the change in Peak 3 and the decrease in 5HIAA in the perfusates after tranylcypromine (10 mg/kg) with maximal decreases of 58% and 54% respectively (Sharp *et al.*, 1984). In contrast, however, are the results obtained following 5HTP (25 mg/kg) administration. In this case although both Peak 3 and 5HIAA in the perfusates increased there was a large difference in the maximal response (+97% in Peak 3 and +447% 5HIAA) (Sharp *et al.*, 1984).

The failure of Peak 3 to keep pace with the increased 5HIAA levels may in part relate to the sensitivity of the electrodes to such high concentrations of 5HIAA as the electrodes only show a linear response over a concentration range of 5–100 μM and above this the response flattens. Alternatively, the pool of 5HIAA sampled by dialysis may differ from that sampled by voltammetry with damaged tissue pools making a significant contribution to the former. However, there still remains the possibility that some other compound contributes to Peak 3 and the main candidate is uric acid which is found in high concentrations in the brain extracellular space (Zetterström *et al.*, 1983). Recently it has been shown (Crespi *et al.*, 1983) that uric acid and 5HIAA have similar oxidation potentials and that uricase, which converts uric acid to the electroactively inert allantoin, abolishes the uric acid oxidation peak *in vitro*. Intrastriatal injection of uric acid (10 μg) increases the height of the striatal Peak 3 while injection of uricase decreased Peak 3 by about 30% and when this was followed by injection of the MAO inhibitor pargyline (75 mg/kg) the Peak was abolished within the subsequent 3 h. These results suggest that uric acid contributes about 30% to Peak 3 recorded with electrochemically pretreated fibre electrodes implanted in the striatum and so this needs to be considered when interpreting changes in this peak.

The following sections describe the application of intracerebral dialysis and *in vivo* voltammetry to the study of the receptor mediated control of dopamine and 5HT release.

2. IDENTIFICATION OF MESOLIMBIC DOPAMINE AUTORECEPTORS

Malfunctions of dopamine neurotransmission have been implicated in two major CNS disorders. Schizophrenia has been linked with an overactivity of dopamine neurons in the limbic lobe whereas Parkinsonism is associated with degeneration of nigrostriatal dopamine neurons. A major problem encountered in the treatment of schizophrenia with neuroleptics is the production of extrapyramidal side-effects as a result of dopamine receptor blockade in the striatum. Furthermore, long-term treatment with these drugs often results in the development of an irreversible syndrome – tardive dyskinesia – possibly associated with production of dopamine receptor supersensitivity on the basal ganglia. A greater understanding of the mechanisms controlling the activity of dopamine neurons in the limbic system and basal ganglia should enable drugs capable of a selective action on each of the two systems to be developed.

Electrophysiological evidence suggests the presence of dopamine autoreceptors on the call bodies and dendrites of midbrain dopamine neurons which serve to modulate the firing rate of these cells. Iontophoretic application of dopamine receptor agonists into the substantia nigra or ventral tegmental area (VTA) causes a reduction in the firing rate of the ascending dopamine neurons (Aghajanian and Bunney, 1977). Conversely, local application of neuroleptics increases neuronal activity, presumably by blocking the effects of dendritically released dopamine (Cheramy et al., 1981). Furthermore, low doses of peripherally administered apomorphine are known to produce hypolocomotion in rodents and have been reported to be beneficial in the treatment of schizophrenia. It is possible that such effects result from an action on somatodendritic autoreceptors in the midbrain since these have been shown to be more sensitive than postsynaptic dopamine receptors (Skirboll et al., 1974).

We have investigated the role of mesolimbic somatodendritic autoreceptors in controlling the turnover of dopamine in the terminal region in vivo. Using differential pulse voltammetry with carbon fibre electrodes implanted in the necleus accumbens of chloral hydrate anaesthetized rats, it was possible to monitor changes in extracellular DOPAC levels following infusion of dopamine or haloperidol into the ipsilateral VTA via 31 gauge steel cannulae (Maidment and Marsden, 1985). Fig. 3 is a typical series of voltammograms recorded in the nucleus accumbens showing clear separation of the ascorbic acid (Peak 1) and DOPAC (Peak 2) signals and the increase in the DOPAC peak following haloperidol (2.5 μg) infusion into the VTA. Voltammograms were recorded every 4 mins and the increase in DOPAC was apparent immediately following infusion reaching maximum levels (145%±8 S.E.M., $n=6$) 56 min post-infusion (Fig. 4(A)). The effect of dopamine (100 μg) infusion into the VTA on DOPAC levels in the nucleus accumbens was more variable. In four animals a 38% decrease in the DOPAC signal 20 min post-infusion was followed by a slow increase above baseline levels of up to 76% 1 h after infusion. In a further three animals a

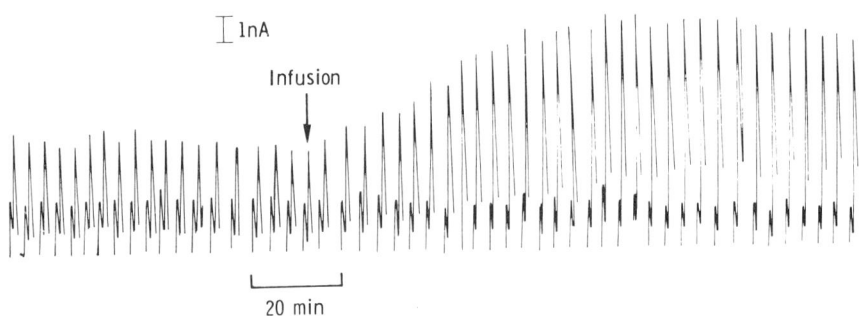

Fig. 3 – An example of a recording from the nucleus accumbens made using differential pulse voltammetry with carbon fibre electrodes. Sweeps 95 mV/s, −0.2 V to +0.15 V) were made every 4 min and at the point marked infusion haloperidol (2.5 μg/0.5 μl) was put into the ipsilateral tegmental area. The rat was anaesthetized with chloral hydrate. The stable baseline response with a small ascorbic acid and larger DOPAC peak and the increase after haloperidol are clearly demonstrated.

transient decrease of approximately 15% was followed by a rapid rise of 108–208% 40 min post-drug.

The increase in extracellular DOPAC levels in the nucleus accumbens following haloperidol infusion into the ipsilateral VTA is in accordance with the increased nuronal activity observed in electrophysiological studies and suggests

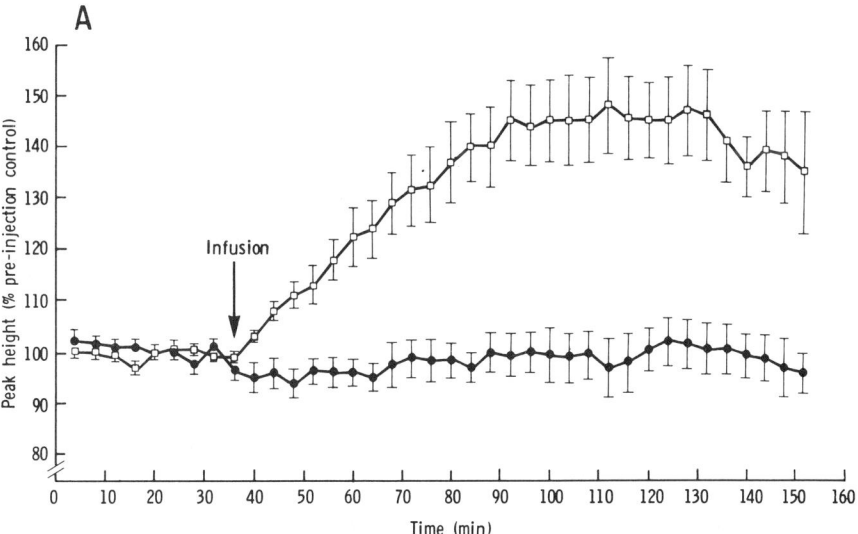

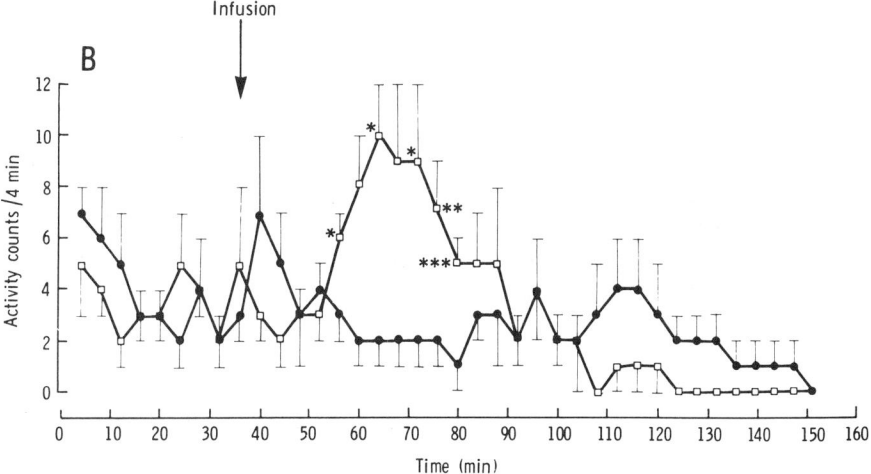

Fig. 4 – Comparison of the effects of haloperidol (2.5 μg) injected directly into the ventral tegmental area (VTA) on the DOPAC voltammetric peak in the nucleus accumbens (top graph) and locomotor behaviour (bottom graph). Note the prolonged rise in DOPAC but the short-lasting increase in locomotor behaviour indicating that changes in extracellular DOPAC do not only reflect dopamine release.

that dendritic release of dopamine exerts a tonic inhibitory effect on the meso-limbic dopamine neurons. Similarly, the decreases in DOPAC levels following dopamine infusion into the VTA are predicted from electrophysiological data. The transient nature of the DOPAC decrease is predictable since the dopamine would be rapidly removed from the synapses by uptake mechanisms but the secondary increase was not expected. A possible explanation is that the infused dopamine (or its metabolite) was diffusing from the site of injection to the nucleus accumbens where it would be detected by the electrodes. Whilst the results of radiolabelled diffusion studies showed only a small amount of radio-activity beyond the midbrain, this possibility cannot be ruled out (Maidment and Marsden, 1985). Alternatively, it is possible that suppression of neuronal firing, whilst reducing dopamine release, may also cause an increase in intra-neuronal DA turnover resulting in increased extracellular DOPAC levels. Simi-larly it is possible that the increased DOPAC levels in the nucleus accumbens following haloperidol infusion into the VTA reflects an increase in DA turnover alone, not necessarily involving DA release. This possibility was investigated using the well-established behavioural model of hyperlocomotion which results from DA release in the nucleus accumbens. Bilateral infusion of haloperidol into the VTA of freely moving rats produced a short period of hyperlocomotion as measured by doppler shift radar peaking 28–36 min post-infusion, normal activity returning at approximately 48 mins (Fig. 4(B)). Since the voltammetric data comes from anaesthetized animals the two experiments are not directly comparable. It is nonetheless interesting to note that extracellular DOPAC levels followed a different time-course, rising gradually to reach a plateau of 56 min and remaining high after 116 min. This could be interpreted as suggesting that increased DA release is transient while the associated increase in DA turnover continues for longer periods. An alternative explanation is that dopamine may in fact, remain elevated whilst the behavioural consequences are prevented by compensatory mechanisms distal to the post-synaptic DA receptor.

Which of the above explanations is correct remains unclear. However, the voltammetric and behavioural data taken together provide clear *in vivo* evidence for the presence of somatodendritic autoreceptors in the VTA which mediate changes in dopamine release and metabolism in the nucleus accumbens. Studies carried out using push–pull techniques in cats have provided similar evidence for somatodendritic autoreceptor control of dopamine release in the nigro-striatal system. The possibility that these two dopamine systems may be differ-entially affected by novel 'atypical' neuroleptics has provided the impetus for our current research effort.

A small number of antipsychotics have been termed atypical on the basis of their apparent lack of extrapyramidial side-effects in the clinic. Recent electrophysiological studies have suggested that this may be due to a selective action on mesolimbic dopamine neurons (Creese, 1983). Acute peripheral administration of classical neuroleptics produces an increase in the firing rate of both A9 and A10 dopamine neurons as a result of somatodendritic auto-receptor blockade and possibly activation of positive feedback loops due to postsynaptic DA receptor blockade. However, the atypical drugs clozapine and thioridazine have been reported to selectively activate A10 dopamine neurons (White and Wang, 1983) after acute administration although a second group observed no such selectivity (Chiodo and Bunney, 1983). However, chronic treatment with neuroleptics produces a reduction in the firing of dopamine neurons – a phenomenon known as depolarization inactivation. In this instance, both groups report a selective action of atypical neuroleptics on A10 neurons (White and Wang, 1983; Chiodo and Bunney, 1983). Thus it is suggested that the lack of extrapyramidal side-effects after treatment with clozapine and thioridazine may be explained by these drugs causing depolarization inactivation in the mesolimbic system whilst having no effect in the basal ganglia.

We have used *in vivo* voltammetry to investigate the possibility that these drugs may have selective actions on dopamine turnover in the two terminal regions. Carbon fibre electrodes were placed in the nucleus accumbens and the contralateral anterior striatum of halothane N_2O anaesthetized Sprague Dawley rates. Thioridazine (20 mg/kg s.c.) produced a 44% increase in the DOPAC signal in the nucleus accumbens and a simultaneous 54% increase in the striatum ($n = 5$). Similarly, clozapine (50 mg/kg s.c.) increased DOPAC by 60% and 86% in the nucleus accumbens and striatum respectively. The effect of chronic treatment with these drugs is currently being investigated.

3. IDENTIFICATION OF 5HT RECEPTORS IN THE FRONTAL CORTEX AND SUPRACHIASMATIC NUCLEUS

3.1 Frontal cortex

Binding, electrophysiological and adenylate cyclase studies have suggested the existence of multiple 5HT receptors, which have been further subdivided $5HT_{1A}$, $5HT_{1B}$ and $5HT_2$ receptors. There is now considerable interest in linking the 5HT sub-receptor types to specific 5HT induced physiological/pharmacological responses. Recently, two putative $5HT_1$ receptor agonists have been developed, 5-methoxy-3(1,2,3,6-tetrahydro-4-pyridinyl)-H-indole (RU 24969) (Hunt and Oberlander, 1981) and 8-hydroxy-2-(di-*n*-propylamine)tetralin (8-OHDPAT) (Arvidsson *et al.*, 1981). Previous studies have suggested that RU 24969 is a potent and selective $5HT_1$ agonist (Hunt and Oberlander, 1981). In rat brain *in vivo* RU 24969 decreased total brain 5HIAA levels indicating decreased 5HT turnover (Euvard and Boissier, 1980) suggesting that the $5HT_1$ receptor is the 5HT autoreceptor, located pre-junctionally and regulating 5HT release and/or metabolism. Based on ligand binding studies, 8-OHDPAT also appears to selectively act on $5HT_{1A}$ (Arvidsson *et al.*, 1981; Middlemiss and Fozard, 1983; Hamon *et al.*, 1984).

The techniques of brain dialysis and differential pulse voltammetry using carbon fibre electrodes were used simultaneously to examine the effect of stimulation and blockade of the 5HT autoreceptors in the pre-fontal cortex. Dialysis loops were implanted into the right pre-frontal cortex and used to monitor 5HIAA and 5HT levels before and after the administration of the putative $5HT_1$ receptor agonists RU 24969 and 8-OHDPAT. A carbon fibre working electrode implanted into the contralateral brain region monitored 5HIAA levels before and after injections of RU 24969.

A marked decrease in extracellular 5HIAA levels was seen after administration of RU 24969 (10 mg/kg i.p.) as measured by simultaneous voltammetry and dialysis. The decrease followed approximately the same time course with both techniques (Fig. 5). Extracellular 5HIAA decreased to 33% ($n=5$) (dialysis)

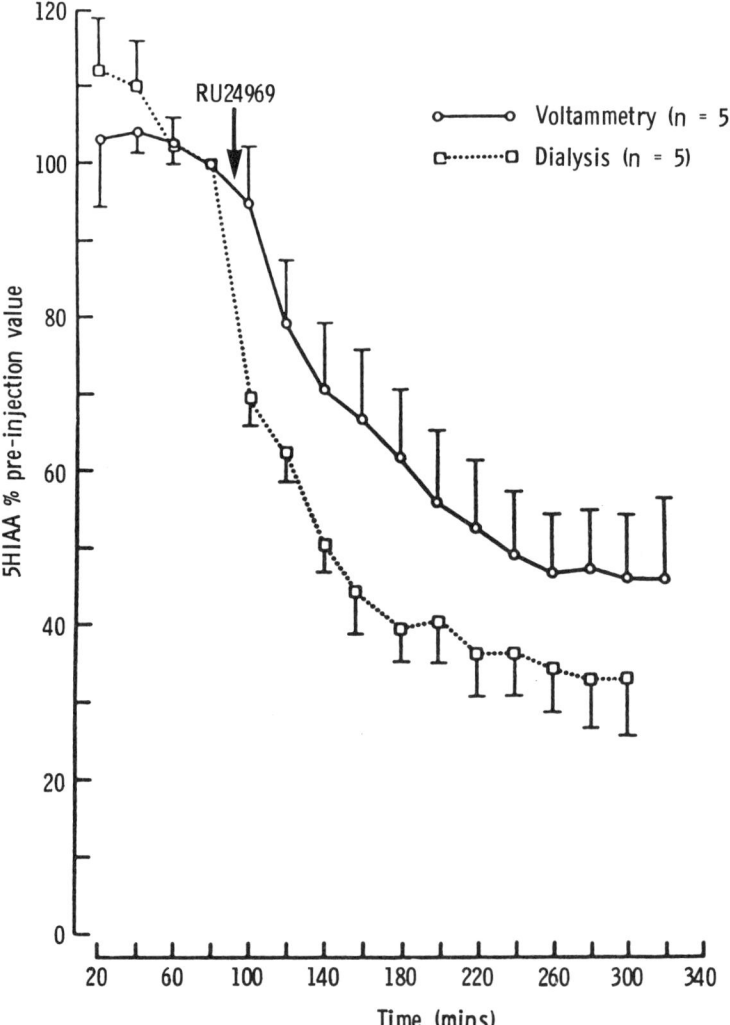

Fig. 5 – Comparison of the effect of the 5HT$_1$ receptor agonist RU 24969 (10 mg/kg i.p.) on extracellular 5HIAA in the rat frontal cortex measured in 20 min intracerebral dialysis samples and Peak 3 recorded using differential pulse voltammetry. The dialysis probe was placed in the frontal cortex on one-side and the voltammetric electrode on the other side. Results are given as percentage of the pre-injection value (±S.E.M. Figures in brackets refer to the number of experiments. Note the similar decrease in 5HIAA measured by dialysis and the decrease in Peak 3 which is thought to be due principally to 5HIAA oxidation. The rats were anaesthetized during the experiment.

and to 47% ($n=5$) (voltammetry) of pre-injection control values 240 minutes post-drug. 5HT levels (dialysis) also decreased following RU 24969 administration to 45% ($n=6$) of pre-injection control values, there was, however, a 20-minute delay in response to drug injection as compared to that of 5HIAA (Fig. 6). The fact that levels of extracellular 5HIAA decreased approximately 20 min before 5HT implies that extracellular 5HIAA is not an index of 5HT release, only 5HT turnover. However, this time lag could be explained if RU 24969 had effects, in addition to inhibiting 5HT release via a $5HT_1$ agonist action on the 5HT autoreceptor. The agonist could (a) decrease 5HIAA turnover and (b) inhibit 5HT uptake and/or metabolism, both these could decrease extracellular 5HIAA before a decrease in extracellular 5HT was observed. This is supported by reports that RU 24969 does have inhibitory effects in addition to a $5HT_1$ agonist action (Euvard and Boissier, 1980). RU 24969 also reduced 5HT release in freely moving animals; however, the effect of the drug was more pronounced (Fig. 7) suggesting that the anaesthetic is also decreasing 5HT release.

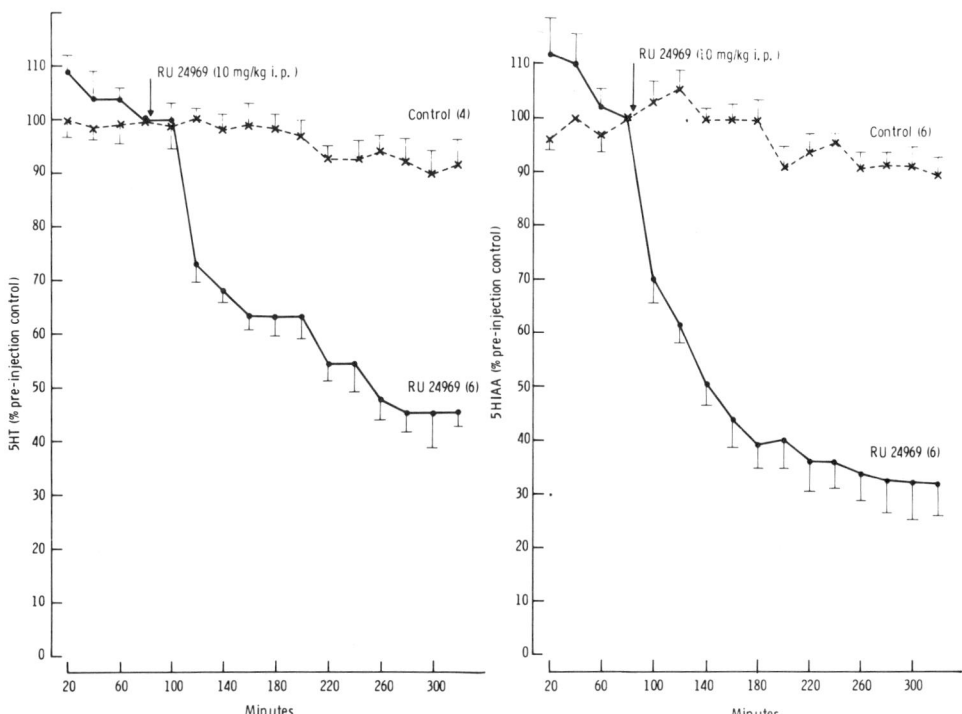

Fig. 6 – Graphs showing the effect of $5HT_1$ receptor agonist RU 24969 (10 mg/kg i.p.) on rat frontal cortex extracellular 5HT and 5HIAA measured in 20 min intracerebral dialysis samples. Results are given as percentage of the pre-injection value ±S.E.M. Figures in brackets refer to the number of experiments. The animals were anaesthetized with chloral hydrate throughout the experiment.

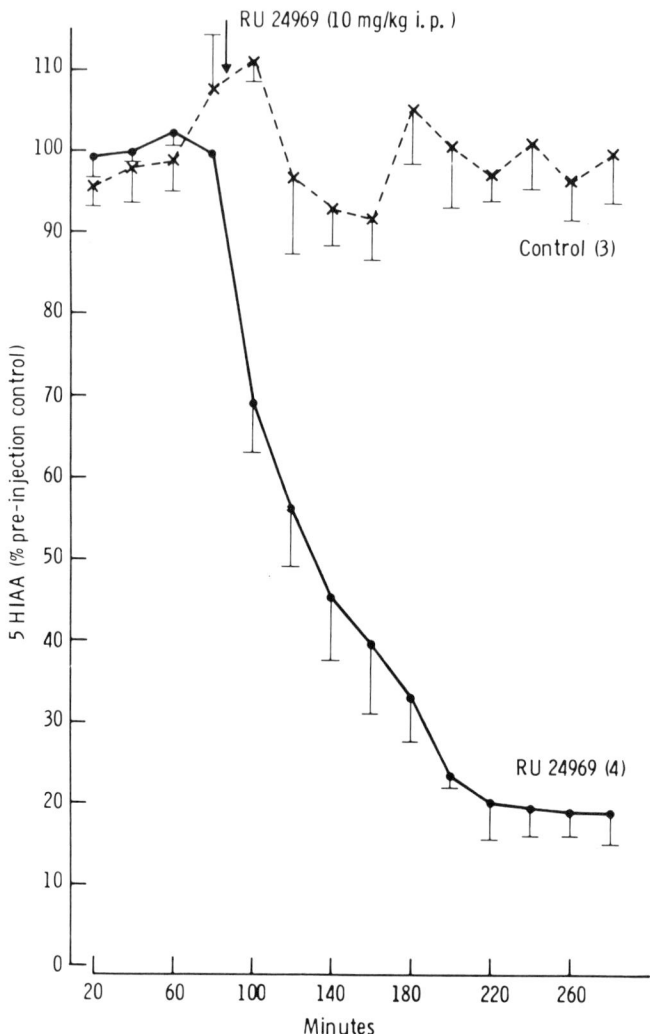

Fig. 7 – Effect of 5HT$_1$ receptor agonist RU 24969 (10 mg/kg i.p) on rat frontal cortex extracellular 5HIAA measured in 20 min intracerebral dialysis samples obtained from freely moving (unanaesthetized) animals. Results are given as percentage of the pre-injection value $\pm$ S.E.M. Figures in brackets refer to the number of experiments.

The decrease in extracellular 5HIAA following RU 24969 was blocked by pre-treatment with a non-selective 5HT antagonist metergoline (2 mg/kg i.p.). The antagonist on its own produced in a small ($\sim$ 10%) increase in signal.

Administration of 8-OHDPAT (0.32 mg/kg s.c.) also decreased extracellular 5HIAA and 5HT levels by 75% ($n=4$) and 60% ($n=3$) respectively (dialysis) of pre-injection control values (Fig. 8). However, the response was delayed compared to that after administration of RU 24969.

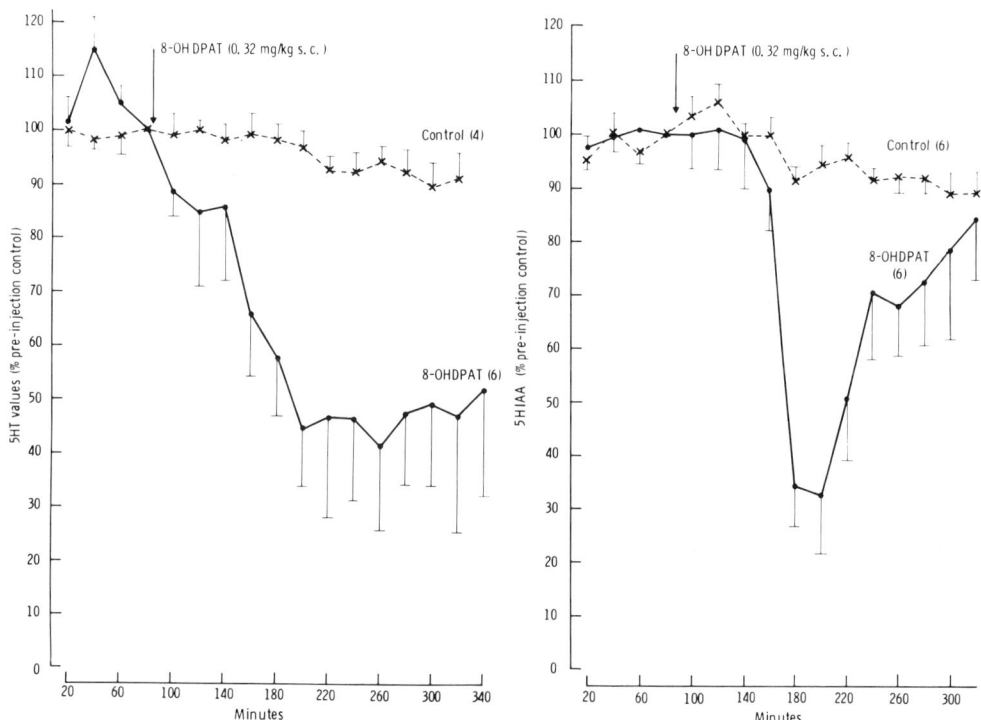

Fig. 8 — Effect of $5HT_{1A}$ receptor agonist 8-OHDPAT (0.32 mg/kg s.c) on rat frontal cortex extracellular 5HIAA measured in 20 min intracerebral dialysis samples. Results are given as percentage of the pre-injection value ±S.E.M. Figures in brackets refer to the number of experiments.

The fall in extracellular 5HIAA and 5HT *in vivo* following RU 24969 and the blockade of the response by pre-treatment with the 5HT antagonist metergoline support the view from *in vitro* studies (Middlemiss, 1984a; Brazell *et al.*, 1985) that $5HT_1$ receptors are involved in the autoregulation of 5HT release and metabolism. The situation with regard to 8-OHDPAT is more ambiguous as while it has been shown to reduce depolarization-induced [³H] 5HT release from rat cortical slices (Gozlan *et al.*, 1983) another study has failed to confirm this (Middlemiss, 1984b; Tricklebank *et al.*, 1984). The present study demonstrates that 8-OHDPAT reduces 5HT metabolism and release *in vivo* in the frontal cortex. It needs to be determined, however, whether this reduction is a primary effect via the 5HT autoreceptor or secondary to an effect on a post-synaptic 5HT receptor on another neuron.

3.2 Suprachiasmatic nucleus (SCN)

Of the clinical features of the effective disorders, perhaps the most striking and consistent, is the failure of dexamethasone to suppress plasma cortisol levels for the 24 hours following administration. For example, Carroll and co-workers (1976) reported that 88% of bipolar depressives and 50% of unipolar depressives exhibited early escape from overnight dexamethasone suppression. It was postulated by Wehr *et al.* (1980) that a phase advance in the circadian rhythms observed in depressed patients might explain the early escape from dexamethasone suppression observed by Carroll *et al.* (1976). The suggestion being then, that there has been a resetting of the 'biological clock'.

It is now widely accepted that control over circadian rhythms is exerted by a system within the central nervous system (CNS) and that the suprachiasmatic nuclei (SCN) of the hypothalmus play a major part in this system (for review see Moore, 1983). However, at the moment, little evidence is available to suggest the mechanisms involved within the SCN by which control is exerted. Evidence in the literature suggested that 5-hydroxytryptamine (5HT) may play a key role in both depressive illness (e.g. Green and Costain, 1982) and rhythm control (Wirz-Justice *et al.*, 1982). However, there is little information about the circadian regulation of 5HT release and metabolism *in vivo*.

In order to try and elucidate the role of the indoleamine innervation of the SCN in the control of circadian rhythm generation we have implanted carbon fibre microelectrodes into the SCN and studied the effects of pharmacological agents on the size of the indole peak recorded. Carbon fibre microelectrodes are ideally suited to this purpose since they have extremely small dimensions, the diameter being in the region of $20~\mu$m.

The size of the oxidation peak recorded at $+0.3$ V ('Peak 3') increases as the electrode is lowered towards the SCN but decreases upon entry. Similar results have been obtained by Faradji *et al.* (1983). We have used this phenomenon to establish electrode localization prior ro histological verification.

When the 5HT receptor agonist RU 24969 was administered i.p., we observed a transient rise in the size of Peak 3 followed by a prolonged and marked decrease to a 60% of control values (Fig. 9). This effect lasted for up to six hours and is similar to results obtained with a working electrode implanted in the frontal cortex (see previous section, Fig. 5). As has previously been suggested, the decrease in the size of Peak 3 was probably due to a decrease in the amount of 5HT released and metabolized to 5HIAA following stimulation of the pre-junctional $5HT_1$ receptor. It has been postulated that this receptor regulates 5HT release and/or metabolism (Middlemiss, 1984b). These results, therefore, suggested that 5HT release in the SCN may be regulated by $5HT_1$ receptors located pre-junctionally.

We have also administered methiothepin, a mixed $5HT_1$ and $5HT_2$ receptor antagonist. Its effects were relatively short-lasting and consisted of a 25% rise in the size of Peak 3 which returned to control levels within three hours post-drug administration. It seems likely that the ability of methiothepin to block $5HT_1$ receptors was the cause of the rise in Peak 3, the blockade of pre-junctional $5HT_1$ receptors leading to an increase in 5HT release and subsequent metabolism to 5HIAA. Similar observations have been reported by Baumann and Waldmeier (1984) when recording from the ventromedial hypothalamus. Administration of methiothepin half-an-hour prior to RU 24969 blocked the normal response to RU 24969, suggesting that the effects of methiothepin when given alone are indeed the result of blockade of the 5HT autoreceptor.

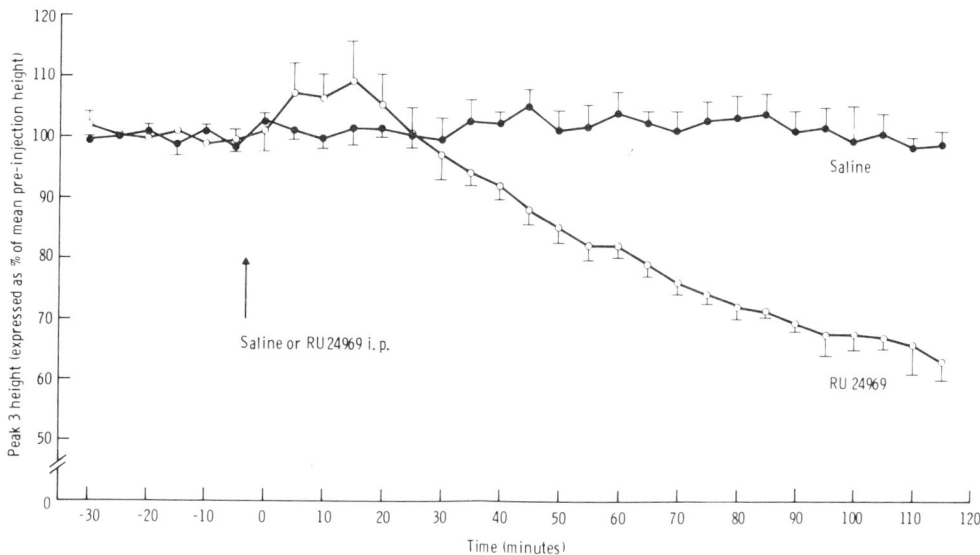

Fig. 9 – Effect of RU 24969 (10 mg/kg i.p.) on the height of Peak 3 (5HIAA peak) recorded in the rat suprachiasmatic nucleus. Results are given as percentage of the pre-injection height ± S.E.M. $n = 5$ for both saline and RU 24969.

It is well-established that changes in the size of Peak 3 reflect changes in the level of 5HIAA in the extracellular fluid (Cespuglio *et al.*, 1984; Crespi *et al.*, 1983, see above). In addition, Sharp *et al.* (Part III, Chapter 2 of this volume) suggest that these changes are the result of changes in the amount of 5HT released though this needs to be fully established. It is therefore tempting to speculate that the diurnal variation in Peak 3 height recorded in the SCN by Faradji *et al.* (1983) is the result of diurnal variation in 5HT release. Thus, by utilizing the information gained from administration of drugs such as RU 24969 it should be possible to examine the role of the indoleaminergic innervation of the SCN in the control of circadian rhythms.

4. CATECHOLAMINES IN THE HYPOTHALAMUS

Modification and refinement of the dialysis technique has allowed measurement of neurotransmitter release from discrete regions of the brain such as the hypothalamus. However, the hypothalamus presents certain problems for *in vivo* measurement of neurotransmitter levels in that there is a very localized distribution of monoamines, and thus selective regional measurements need to be made. It is possible, however, to monitor relative levels of extracellular monoamines in different hypothalamic regions using intracranial dialysis.

Dialysis loops were implanted into the anterior and posterior hypothalamus and extracellular levels of monoamines and their metabolites were measured.

Preliminary studies have shown regional differences within the hypothalamus in extracellular levels of adrenaline, noradrenaline, dopamine, MHPG, DOPAC, 5HT and 5HIAA. The hypothalamus is innervated by the A_1 and C_1 cell bodies in the ventrolateral medulla in the brain stem and preliminary studies have shown that electrical stimulation of the ventrolateral medulla alter levels of catecholamines in the hypothalamus.

5. CONCLUSIONS

The results described demonstrate the application of intracerebral dialysis and *in vivo* voltammetry for monitoring autoreceptor mediated changes in transmitter release and metabolism. The dialysis method provides information about both release and metabolism but is restricted in use to larger brain regions while voltammetry monitors only metabolism but these measurements can be made frequently and in specific brain nuclei. The precise relationship however, between measurement of metabolites and release remains to be determined.

ACKNOWLEDGEMENTS

We thank the Medical Research Council and The Wellcome Trust for financial support. C. A. Marsden is a Wellcome Trust Senior Lecturer and Carol Routledge an SERC CASE student in collaboration with ICI plc.

REFERENCES

Adams, R. N. and Marsden, C. A. (1982). Electrochemical detection methods for monoamine measurements *in vitro* and *in vivo*. In' *Handbook of Psychopharmacology*, vol. 15, L. L. Iversen, Iversen and S. H. Snyder (eds.), Plenum Press, New York, pp. 1–74.

Aghajanian, G. K. and Bunney, B. S. (1977). Dopamine autoreceptors: pharmacological characterisation by microiontophoretic single cell recording studies. *Naunyn-Schmiedeb. Arch. Pharmacol.*, **297**, 1–7.

Arvidsson, L. E., Hacksell, U., Nilsson, J. L. G., Hjorth, S., Carlsson, A., Lindberg, F., Sanchez, D. and Wikstrom, H. (1981). 8-Hydroxy-2-(di-n-propylamino)tetralin, a new centrally acting 5-hydroxytryptamine receptor agonist. *J. Med. Chem.*, **24**, 921–927.

Baumann, P. A. and Waldmeier, P. C. (1984). Negative feedback control of serotonin release *in vivo*: comparison of 5-hydroxyindoleacetic acid levels measured by voltammetry in conscious rats and by biochemical techniques. *Neurosci.*, **11**, 195–204.

Brazell, M. P. and Marsden, C. A. (1982). Intracerebral injection of ascorbate oxidase – effect on *in vivo* electrochemical recordings. *Brain Res.*, **249**, 167–172.

Brazell, M. P., Marsden, C. A., Nisbet, A. P. and Routledge, C. (1985). The 5HT$_I$ receptor against RU-24969 decreases 5-hydroxytryptamine (5-HT) release and metabolism in the rat frontal cortex *in vitro* and *in vivo*. *Br. J. Pharmacol.*, **86**, 209–216.

Carroll, B. J., Curtis, G. C. and Mendels, J. (1976). Neuroendocrine regulation in depression. II. Discrimination of depressed from non-depressed patients. *Arch. Gen. Psychiat.,* **33,** 1951–1958.

Cespuglio, R., Faradji, H., Poncon, J. L., Buda, M., Riou, F., Gonon, F., Pujol, J.-F., and Jouvet, M. (1981). Differential pulse voltammetry in brain tissue. 1. Detection of 5-hydroxyindoles in the rat striatum. *Brain Res.,* **223,** 287–298.

Cespuglio, R., Faradji, H., Hahn, Z. and Jouvet, M. (1984). Voltammetric detection of brain 5-hydroxyindoleamines by means of electrochemically treated carbon fibre electrodes. Chronic recordings for up to one month with moveable cerebral electrodes in the sleeping or waking rat. In: *Measurement of Neurotransmitter Release in vivo,* C. A. Marsden (ed.), John Wiley, Chichester, pp. 173–191.

Cheramy, A., Leviel, V. and Glowinski, J. (1981). Dendritic release of dopamine in the substantia nigra. *Nature,* **289,** 537–542.

Chiodo, L. A. and Bunney, B. S. (1983). Typical and atypical neuroleptics: differential effects of chronic administration on the activity of A9 and A10 midbrain dopaminergic neurones. *J. Neuroscience,* **3,** 1607–1619.

Creese, I. (1983). Classical and atypical antipsychotic drugs: new insights. *T.I.N.S.,* **6,** 479–481.

Crespi, F., Sharp, T., Maidment, N. and Marsden, C. A. (1983). Differential pulse voltammetry *in vivo* – evidence that uric acid contributes to the indole oxidation peak. *Neurosci. Letters,* **43,** 203–207.

Euvard, C. and Boissier, J. R. (1980). Biochemical assessment of the central 5HT agonist activity of RU 24969 (a piperidinyl indole). *Eur. J. Pharmacol.,* **63,** 65–72.

Faradji, H., Cespuglio, R. and Jouvet, M. (1983). Voltammetric measurements of 5-hydroxyindole compounds in the suprachiasmatic nuclei circadian fluctuations. *Brain Res.,* **279,** 111–119.

Gonon, F., Buda, M., Cespuglio, R., Jouvet, M. and Pujol, J.-F. (1980). *In vivo* electrochemical detection of catechols in the neostriatum of anaesthetised rats: dopamine or DOPAC? *Nature (Lond.),* **286,** 902–904.

Gonon, F., Fombarlet, C. M., Buda, M. J. and Pujol, J.-F. (1981). Electrochemical treatment of pyrolytic carbon fibre electrodes. *Anal. Chem.,* **53,** 1386–1389.

Gonon, F., Buda, M. and Pujol, J.-F. (1984). Treated carbon fibre electrodes for measuring catechols and ascorbic acid. In: *Measurement of Neurotransmitter Release in vivo,* C. A. Marsden (ed.), John Wiley, Chichester, pp. 153–172.

Green, A. R. and Costain, D. W. (1982). *Pharmacology and Biochemistry of Psychiatric Disorders.* John Wiley, Chichester.

Groves, P. M., Wilson, C. J., Young, S. J. and Rebec, G. V. (1975). Self-inhibition by dopaminergic neurones. An alternative to the neuronal feedback loop hypothesis for the mode of action of certain psychotropic drugs. *Science,* **190,** 522–529.

Hamon, M., Bourgoin, S., Gozlan, H., Hall, M. D., Goetz, C., Artaud, F. and Horn, A. S. (1984). Biochemical evidence for the 5HT agonist properties of PAT in the rat brain. *Eur. J. Pharmacol.,* **100**, 263–276.

Hunt, P. F. and Oberlander, C. (1981). The interaction of indole derivatives with the serotonin receptor and non-dopaminergic circling behaviour. In: *Serotonin—Current Aspects of Neurochemistry and Function,* B. Haber (ed.), Plenum Press, New York, p. 547.

Knott, P. J. and Curzon, G. (1974). Effect of increased rat brain tryptophan on 5-hydroxytryptamine and 5-hydroxyindoleacetic acid in the hypothalamus and other brain regions. *J. Neurochem.,* **22**, 1065–1071.

Maidment, N. T. and Marsden, C. A. (1985). *In vivo* voltammetric and behavioural evidence of somatodendritic autoreceptor control of mesolimbic dopamine neurones. *Brain Res.,* **338**, 317–324.

Marsden, C. A. ed.) (1984). *Measurement of Neurotransmitter Release in vivo.* John Wiley, Chichester.

Marsden, C. A. (1985). *In vivo* monitoring of pharmacological and physiological changes in endogenous serotonin release and metabolism. In: *Neuropharmacology of Serotonin,* A. R. Green (ed.), Oxford University Press, London, pp. 218–252.

Marsden, C. A. and Routledge, C. (1984). *In vivo* measurements of DOPAC, 5HIAA and 5HT in specific brain regions by intracerebral dialysis. *Br. J. Pharmac.,* **82**, p. 268.

Mefford, I. N., Oke, A. F. and Adams, R. N. (1981). Regional distribution of ascorbate in human brain. *Brain Res.,* **212**, 223.

Middlemiss, D. N. (1984a). 8-Hydroxy-2-(di-n-propylamino)tetralin is devoid of activity at the 5-hydroxytryptamine autoreceptor in rat brain. Implications for the proposed link between the autoreceptor and the ^{3}H-5HT recognition site. *Naunyn-Schmied. Arch. Pharmacol.,* **327**, 18–22.

Middlemiss, D. N. (1984b). RU 24969 inhibited K^+-evoked release of [^{3}H]-5HT from rat frontal cortex slices by stimulation of the 5-HT autoreceptor. 14th C.I.N.P. Congress, p. 657.

Middlemiss, D. N. and Fozard, J. R. (1983) 8-Hydroxy-2-(di-n-propylamino)-tetralin discriminates between subtypes of the 5HT$_1$ recognition site. *Eur. J. Pharmacol.,* **90**, 151–153.

Moore, R. Y. (1983). Organisation and function of a central nervous system circadian oscillator: the suprachiasmatic hypothalmic nuclei. *Fed. Proc.,* **42**, 2783–2789.

Sharp, T., Maidment, N. T., Brazell, M. P., Zetterström, T., Ungerstedt, U., Bennet, G. W. and Marsden, C. A. (1984). Changes in monamine metabolites measured by simultaneous *in vivo* differential pulse voltammetry and intracerebral dialysis. *Neuroscience,* **12**, 1213–1221.

Skirboll, L. R., Grace, A. A. and Bunney, B. S. (1974). Dopamine auto- and postsynaptic receptors. Electrophysiological evidence for differential sensitivity to dopamine agonists. *Science,* **206**, 80–82.

Tricklebank, M. D., Middlemiss, D. N. and Fozard, J. R. (1984). 8-OHDPAT: an enigmatic centrally active 5HT agonist. *Trends in Pharmacol. Sci.,* **5**, 415–416.

Ungerstedt, U. (1984). Measurement of neurotransmitter release by intracranial dialysis. In: *Measurement of Neurotransmitter Reease in vivo.* C. A. Marsden (ed.), John Wiley, Chichester, pp. 81–106.

Wehr, T. A., Sack, D., Rosenthal, N., Duncan, W. and Gillin, J. C. (1983). Circadian rhythm disturbances in manic-depressive illness. *Fed. Proc.*, **42**, 2809–2814.

White, F. J. and Wang, R. Y. (1983). Differential effects of classical and atypical antipsychotic drugs on A9 and A10 dopamine neurones. *Science*, **221**, 1054–1057.

Wightman, R. M. and Dayton, M. A. (1982). Voltammetric techniques for the analysis of biogenic amines. In: *Analysis of Biogenic Amines,* R. T. Coutts and C. G. Baker (eds.), Elsevier, New York.

Wirz-Justice, A., Groos, G. A. and Wehr, T. A. (1982). The neuropharmacology of circadian timekeeping in mammals. In: *Vertebrate Circadian Systems, Structure and Physiology,* J. Aschoff, S. Daan and G. A. Groos (eds.), Springer-Verlag, Berlin, pp. 183–193.

Zetterström, T., Sharp, T., Marsden, C. A. and Ungerstedt, U. (1983). *In vivo* measurement of dopamine and its metabolites by intracerebral dialysis: changes after d-amphetamine. *J. Neurochem.*, **41**, 1769–1773.

2

Intracerebral dialysis – a technique for studying dopamine release in the rat brain in relation to behaviour

T. Sharp, T. Zetterström, M. Herrera-Marschitz, T. Ljungberg and **U. Ungerstedt**
Department of Pharmacology, Karolinska Institute, P.O. Box 604 00, S-104 01, Stockholm, Sweden

Abbreviations used:

DOPAC	– dihydroxyphenylacetic acid
HVA	– homovanillic acid
5HIAA	– 5-hydroxyindoleacetic acid
HPLC-ED	– high performance liquid chromatography with electrochemical detection.

1. INTRODUCTION

Dopaminergic neurotransmission in the mammalian central nervous system is thought to play a major role in the control of motor function. This idea is based on the behavioural changes in animals and man following pharmacological manipulation of the central dopaminergic system (for review see Costall and Naylor (1979) and Ungerstedt (1979)). However, in order to further establish the link between dopaminergic neurotransmission and motor behaviour it is necessary to directly demonstrate the occurrence of a particular functional change in response to local increased release of the neurotransmitter. This necessitates *in vivo* monitoring of dopamine release in the brain.

Measurement of release of endogenous dopamine in the brain *in vivo* is difficult owing to the low extracellular levels of the neurotransmitter (McLennan, 1964). This problem can be overcome by following the efflux of preloaded, radiolabelled dopamine into perfusates collected from the brain using for example 'push–pull' cannulae (Glowinski *et al.*, 1979). An alternative approach is to monitor brain levels of dopamine metabolites, which can be detected in ventricular samples (Sarna *et al.*, 1983) or monitored in brain regions by *in vivo* voltammetry (see Sharp *et al.*, 1984). However, a drawback of these procedures, particularly with regard to behaviour/release studies, is that neither the labelled pool of dopamine nor dopamine metabolite levels may truly reflect changes in release of the endogenous neurotransmitter.

Recently, we described a novel intracerebral dialysis technique which, in combination with sensitive HPLC-ED assays, allows the continuous measurement of extracellular levels of endogenous dopamine and its metabolites in rat brain (Ungerstedt *et al.*, 1982; Zetterström *et al.*, 1983; Ungerstedt, 1984). This technique was based on the earlier ideas of Delgado *et al.* (1972) and Ungerstedt and Pycock (1974). In essence this method involves the perfusion of a piece of small diameter dialysis tubing implanted into the brain, and the collection and analysis of the perfusates. In the present study we have used the dialysis method in an attempt to correlate regional brain dopamine release with drug-induced motor behaviour. These experiments are based on the known behavioural and biochemical effects of *d*-amphetamine.

d-Amphetamine causes a pronounced behavioural syndrome in animals, which includes an increase in locomotion and the onset of a stereotyped pattern of movements, and this has been associated with an enhanced release of catecholamines in the brain (see Randrup and Munkvad, 1975). Further, a current theory based on pharmacological and regional lesion studies, is that amphetamine-induced stereotypy is due to increased dopamine release in striatum while amphetamine-enhanced locomotor activity is mediated via dopamine release in n. accumbens (for review see Costall and Naylor (1979) and Kelly and Roberts (1983)). In this study we have tested this hypothesis by directly comparing amphetamine-induced behaviours with dopamine release in striatum or n. accumbens of awake rats. Particular emphasis is given to the methodology of the dialysis technique. A more detailed discussion of the data is given elsewhere (Sharp *et al.*, 1985).

2. EXPERIMENTAL PROCEDURES

2.1 Preparation of the dialysis loop

Dialysis loops were prepared by glueing a short length of dialysis tubing (DOW 50 cellulose, 5000 m.w. cut off, 300 μm diameter) inside two stainless steel cannulae (0.4 mm o.d.) to expose a 3 mm length of tubing between the cannulae (see Fig. 1). A fine nylon thread was positioned within the tube lumen to provide internal support. One cannula was connected to a microinfusion system (physiological ringer solution was perfused at 2 μl/min), then the exposed tubing was folded into a tight loop and the cannulae were clamped in a stereotaxic

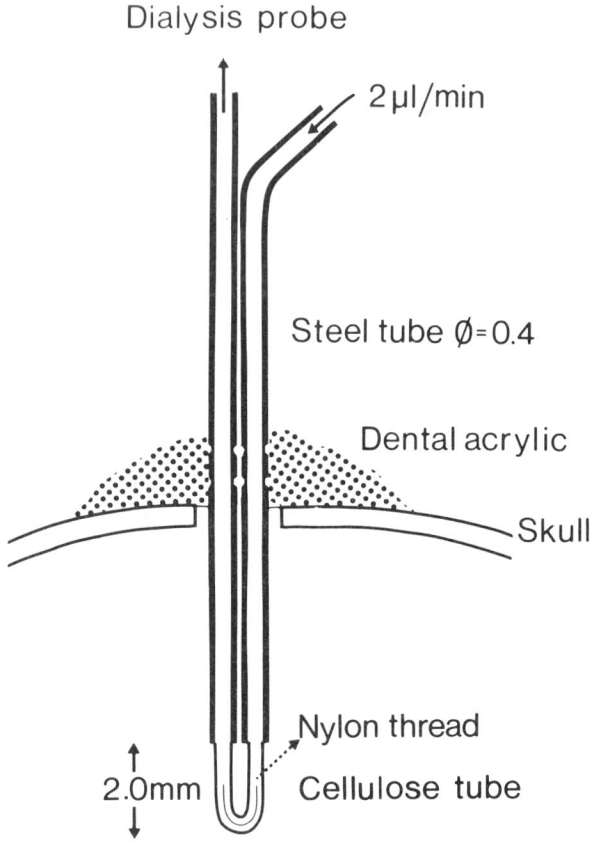

Fig. 1 – Diagrammatic scheme of the brain dialysis probe. See text for details of construction.

holder. A fine tungsten wire was temporarily inserted into the outlet cannula and used to extend the loop to a point during implantation. Previous *in vitro* studies have shown that the amount of monoamine recovered through the dialysis membrane was linearly related to the amount of monoamine in the outside medium. The percentage recovery of monoamine using this short loop ranged from 10% to 12% (Zetterström *et al.*, 1984).

2.2 Implantation of the dialysis loop
Male Sprague Dawley rats (280–300 g) were anaesthetized with halothane and dialysis loops were implanted unilaterally into either the striatum (R + 2.5 mm, L + 2.5 mm, V − 6.5 mm from bregma according to Pellegrino and Cushman, 1967) or n. accumbens (R + 3.2, L + 1.25, V − 7.6). The cannulae were secured using skull screws and dental cement, which also served to seal the opened skin. Following surgery (approximately 30 mins) the ends of the loop were temporarily sealed and animals were returned to their cage with free access to food and water.

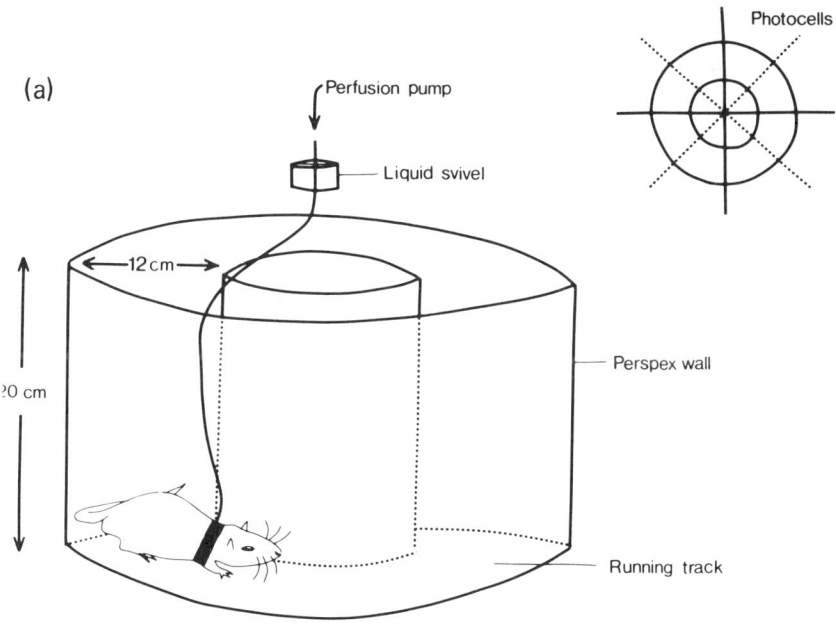

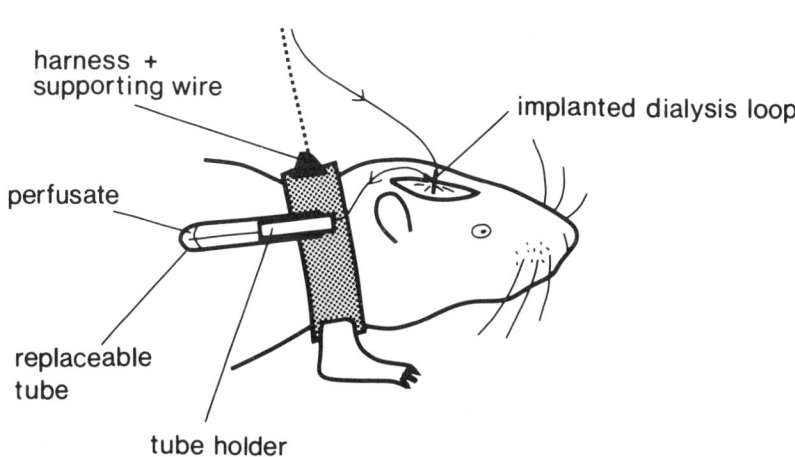

Fig. 2 - Diagrammatic scheme of the apparatus used for the combined behaviour/ dopamine release experiments. Animals previously implanted with a dialysis loop were placed on a circular running track (a) enclosed within a soundproof, air-conditioned chamber (not shown). A system of four pairs of photocell detectors (see insert) allowed continuous activity measurement. General activity counts were registered each time a light beam was broken. Locomotor counts were registered only when two beams set at 90° were consecutively broken. Animals were secured in a harness (b) which also served as a holder for replaceable perfusate collecting tubes.

2.3 Behaviour/release experiments

On the day following surgery animals were placed on a circular running track contained within a soundproof, air-conditioned chamber. The dialysis loops were connected to a microinfusion pump (Carnegie Medicine, Sweden) and perfused with ringer solution (2 μl/min) via a liquid swivel held above the track (see Fig. 2(a)). Animals were secured in a harness connected by a wire to the swivel. The harness also served as a holder for replaceable perfusate collecting tubes (Fig. 2(b)). Perfusates were collected in 10 μl 1 M perchloric acid to prevent oxidation of the monoamines. All animals were familiarized with the experimental conditions on at least 4 occasions prior to surgery.

'Locomotor' and 'general activity' counts were recorded using a system of photocells (see Fig. 2) linked to a digital readout counter. The intensity of two types of behaviour, sniffing and stereotyped head and forepaw movements, were scored by direct observation according to a 0–3 graded scale (for details see Sharp *et al.*, 1985). Behavioural measurements were recorded every 20 min at the time of perfusate collection. Usually 4–5 control samples were taken before administration of *d*-amphetamine (2 mg/kg s.c.) and then measurements were continued for 3 hours. The relationship between dopamine release and behaviour was assessed by correlating the peak increase in dopamine release with the behavioural score accumulated over the 3-hour post-drug period.

2.4 Perfusate analysis

20-min perfusate samples (40 μl + 10 μl perchloric acid) were directly assayed for dopamine, DOPAC, HVA and 5HIAA in a single run by HPLC-ED. No sample preparation was necessary. The monamines were separated on a Spherisorb 50DS 5 μm column (250 $\times$ 4.6 mm) using 0.15 M sodium phosphate (pH 3.8) mobile phase containing 0.5 mM sodium octane sulphonate, 0.1 mM EDTA and 12% methanol, and detected by either a carbon paste or glassy carbon working electrode set at +0.65 V. Using 1.2 ml/min flow rate samples were analysed within 20 minutes and no storage was necessary.

3. RESULTS AND CONCLUSIONS

The present paper describes a method which allows the continuous measurement of extracellular levels of dopamine, and its major metabolites DOPAC and HVA, in brain regions of the awake rat. The technique incorporates three main features: (1) a novel brain perfusion method which involves no direct contact between the perfusing medium and the brain tissue, (2) a rapid, sensitive and specific HPLC-ED system for assay of monoamines and (3) a specially designed experimental chamber which allows constant behavioural assessment with continuous brain perfusion and sample collection.

Basal levels of dopamine in perfusates of striatum and n. accumbens were about 200 times less than its metabolites (Table 1). The low extracellular levels of dopamine probably reflect the rapid re-uptake of dopamine into the nerve terminal and it is unlikely that they indicate actual levels of dopamine in the synapse. However, we assume that these levels represent a spillover from the

Table 1 — Basal monoamine levels in striatum and n.accumbens of the awake rate (pmoles/40 μl)

	Dopamine	DOPAC	HVA	5HIAA
striatum	0.180 ± 0.026 (11)	38.56 ± 6.16 (11)	27.06 ± 4.12 (11)	10.39 ± 1.73 (11)
n. accumbens	0.132 ± 0.018 (12)	30.39 ± 3.81 (12)	14.96 ± 1.31 (12)	9.38 ± 1.17 (12)

synapse which reflects changes in release, especially as we are able to decrease dopamine release with low doses of the dopamine agonist apomorphine (Zetter-ström and Ungerstedt, 1984). The basal monoamine levels 18–24 hours following loop implantation (Table 1) compare well with those obtained in awake acutely operated rats but the amount of monamine recovered declines significantly 48 hours post-surgery, and 5 days after implantation dopamine responds poorly to drug stimulation (Zetterström et al., unpublished observations). This latter finding is probably due to an increased gliosis around the dialysis probe which prevents molecular diffusion through the dialysis membrane.

d-Amphetamine (2 mg/kg s.c.) caused a marked increase in dopamine release in both striatum and n. accumbens (Fig. 3). This effect was maximal 40 min post-drug (striatum +1629%, N=7, n. accumbens +1265%, N=7) and reduced to baseline values within 3 hours. The time course change in dopamine release was closely followed by an increase in general activity (Figs. 3). The relationship between amphetamine-induced dopamine release in the two brain regions and behaviour was examined in more detail by plotting the peak increase in release for each animal against the amount of particular behaviour displayed.

The peak increase in striatal dopamine release was significantly correlated with the amount of stereotyped behaviour but not locomotor activity or sniffing (Fig. 4). This finding is in good agreement with studies showing that certain stereotyped behaviours can be produced by intrastriatal application of dopamine agonists (see Randrup and Munkvad, 1975), and that amphetamine-induced stereotypy is prevented by specific lesions of the striatal dopamine nerve terminals (Kelly et al., 1975). These data, thus, strongly support the idea that the nigrostriatal dopamine pathway has an important role in the mediation of stereotyped movements.

Dopamine release in n. accumbens, was not significantly correlated with any behaviour measured although locomotion was better correlated with dopamine release in n. accumbens (r = 0.44, N = 7) than striatum (r = 0.19, N = 7). Thus, while the data indicated a tendency for locomotor activity to be associated with dopamine release in n. accumbens no direct link could be demonstrated. This result contrasts with studies showing that lesion of the dopamine nerve terminals in n. accumbens prevents amphetamine-enhanced locomotor activity (see Kelly and Roberts, 1983) and that local injection of dopamine or its agonists into the n. accumbens increases locomotor activity (see Pijnenburg *et al.*, 1976; Costall and Naylor, 1979). However, our data showed a tendency for the amount of stereotypy to be inversely related to locomotor activity ($r = -0.437, p <$ 0.1) indicating that stereotyped movements are displayed at the expense of locomotor behaviour. The behavioural dominance of stereotypy might explain the poor correlation between dopamine release in n. accumbens and locomotion. The relationship between dopamine release and locomotion may become clearer if the study was extended to include a wider dose range for amphetamine. Additionally, it is thought that noradrenaline plays a role in the locomotor effects of amphetamine (see Ögren *et al.*, 1983), and increased release of dopamine alone may not underlie this behavioural response to amphetamine treatment.

The dopamine metabolites, DOPAC and HVA, in perfusates from both striatum and n. accumbens were markedly reduced after *d*-amphetamine (Fig. 5), confirming our previous observation (Zetterström *et al.*, 1983). The reason for the reduction in dopamine metabolism is unclear since amphetamine has a complex neurochemical action (it releases dopamine from nerve terminal and

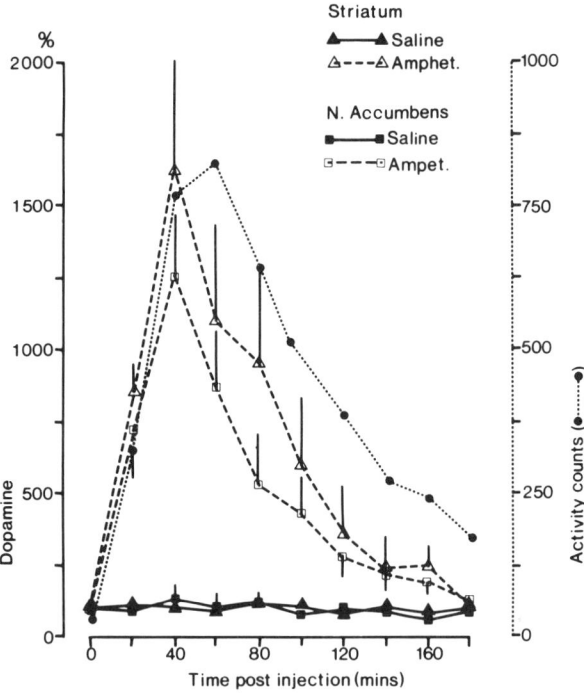

Fig. 3 – The time course change in dopamine release in striatum and n. accumbens in comparison to general behavioural activity following *d*-amphetamine (2 mg/kg s.c.). The release data was obtained from groups of 7 (amphetamine) or 5 (controls) animals and mean values ± S.E.M. are indicated. The behavioural data represents pooled measurements from the striatum and n. accumbens drug-treated groups, and median values are shown.

STRIATUM

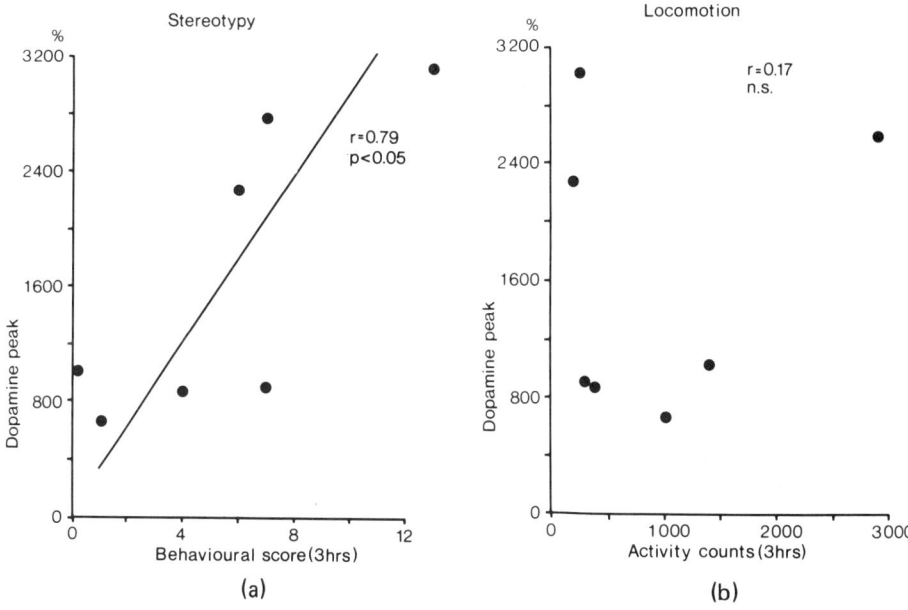

Fig. 4. –Correlation of behaviour ((a) stereotypy; (b) locomotion) with dopamine release in striatum following *d*-amphetamine (2 mg/kg s.c.). Release measurements are peak increase values obtained 40 minutes post-drug. Behavioural data represents measurements accumulated over the 3-hour post-drug period.

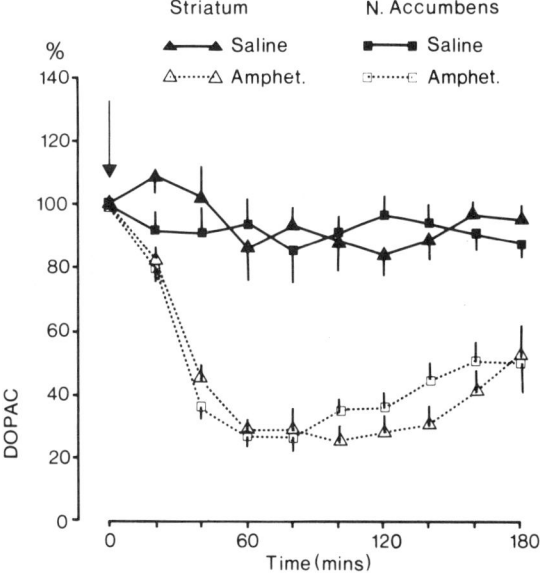

Fig. 5 – Time course.change in dopamine metabolites in striatum and n. accumbens following *d*-amphetamine (2 mg/kg s.c.). These values were obtained from the animals in which the behaviour/release comparisons were made (see Fig. 3).

dendrites, blocks dopamine uptake, inhibits MAO). However, this result emphasizes the need to be able to monitor dopamine release as well as metabolism when studying the relationship between drug-induced behaviour and dopamine release *in vivo*. This point is further emphasized by evidence from our recent study showing that changes in dopamine release correlate poorly with alterations in dopamine metabolism after neuroleptic drugs (Zetterström *et al.*, 1984).

The present data well complements our previous study using long dialysis loops in acutely operated rats, in which striatal dopamine release was closely related to amphetamine-induced circling in rats unilaterally lesioned in the nigrostriatal pathway (Fig. 6; Zetterström *et al.*, 1985). This latter study further emphasizes the close relationship between dopamine release in striatum and motor behaviour. Together, these two investigations indicate that the dialysis method should be a powerful tool for future studies on the relationship between dopamine release in the CNS and functional changes.

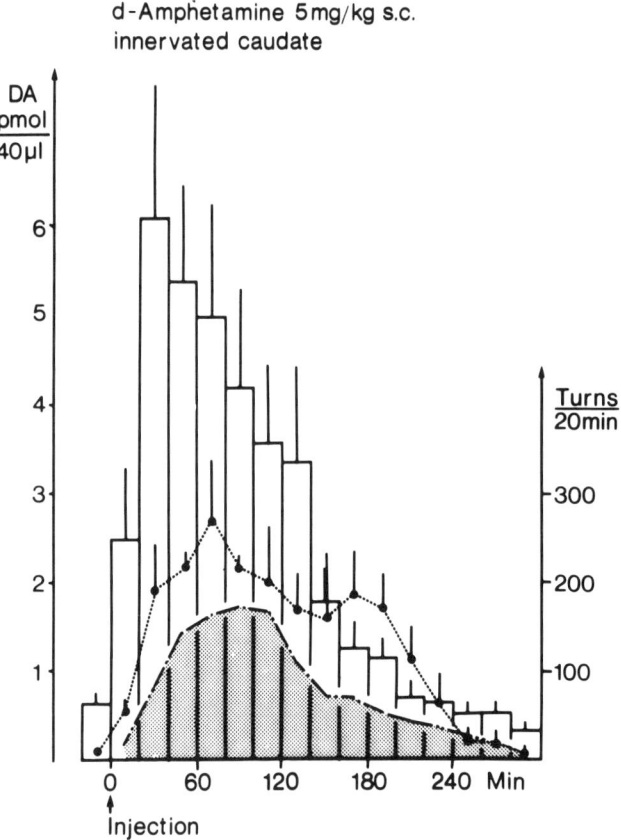

Fig. 6 — Time course change in dopamine release (bars) in the innervated striatum of a unilaterally 6-OHDA lesioned rat in comparison to the number of ipsilateral turns (dotted line) after *d*-amphetamine (5 mg/kg s.c.). The shaded area represents the response of rats without an implanted dialysis loop (taken from Zetterström *et al.*, 1985).

ACKNOWLEDGEMENTS

We wish to thank Anna Karin Collin for her excellent technical assistance and Monica Karlsson for her expert typing of the manuscript. We are grateful to the Karolinska Institute for financial support. Trevor Sharp is in receipt of a Karolinska Institute postdoctoral fellowship.

REFERENCES

Costall, B. and Naylor, R. J. (1979). Behavioural aspects of dopamine agonists and antagonists. In: *The Neurobiology of dopamine,* A. S. Horn, J. Korf and B. H. C. Westerink (eds.), Academic Press, London, pp. 555–576.

Delgado, J. M. R., De Feudis, F. V., Roth, R. H., Ryugo, D. K. and Mitruka, B. M. (1972). Dialytrode for long-term intracerebral perfusion in awake monkeys, *Arch. Int. Pharmacodyn. Ther.,* **198**, 9.

Glowinski, J., Cheramy, A. and Giorgineff, M. S. (1979). *In vivo* and *in vitro* release of dopamine. In: *The Neurobiology of Dopamine,* A. S. Horn, J. Korf and B. H. C. Westerink (eds.), Academic Press, London, 199–216.

Kelly, P. H. and Roberts, D. C. S. (1983). Effects of amphetamine and apomorphine on locomotor activity after 6-OHDA and electrolytic lesions of the nucleus accumbens septi. *Pharm. Biochem. Behav.,* **19**, 137–143.

McLennan, H. (1964). The release of acetylcholine and 3-hydroxytyramine from the caudate nucleus. *J. Physiol.,* **174**, 152–161.

Ögren, S. O., Archer, T. and Johansson, C. (1983). Evidence for a selective brain noradrenergic involvement in the locomotor stimulant effects of amphetamine in the rat. *Neurosci. Letts.,* **43**, 327–331.

Pellegrino, L. J. and Cushman, A. J. (1967). *A Stereotaxic Atlas of the Rat Brain,* Appleton–Century–Crofts, New York.

Pijnenburg, A. J. J., Honig, W. M. M., Van Der Heyden, J. A. M. and Van Rossum, J. M. (1976). Effects of chemical stimulation of the mesolimbic dopamine system upon locomotor activity. *Eur. J. Pharmacol.,* **35**, 45–58.

Randrup, H. and Munkvad, I. (1975). Pharmacology and physiology of stereotyped behaviour. In: *Catecholamines and Schizophrenia,* S. W. Matthysse and S. S. Kety (eds.), Pergamon Press, Oxford, pp. 1–10.

Sarna, G. S., Hutson, P. H., Tricklebank, M. D. and Curzon, G. (1983). Determination of brain 5-hydroxytryptamine turnover in freely moving rats using repeated sampling of cerebrospinal fluid. *J. Neurochem.,* **40**, 383–388.

Sharp, T., Maidment, N. T., Brazell, M. P. and others (1984). Changes in monoamine metabolites measured by simultaneous *in vivo* differential pulse voltammetry and intracerebral dialysis. *Neuroscience,* **12**, 1213–1221.

Sharp, T., Zetterström, T., Ljungberg, T. and Ungerstedt, U. (1985). A direct comparison of amphetamine-induced dopamine release and behaviour in the rat using intracerebral dialysis. *Brain Res.* (submitted).

Ungerstedt, U. (1979). Central dopamine mechanisms and unconditioned behaviour. In: *The Neurobiology of Dopamine.* A. S. Horn, J. Korf and B. H. C. Westerink (eds.). Academic Press, London, pp. 577–596.

Ungerstedt, U. (1984). Measurement of neurotransmitter release by intracranial dialysis. In: *Measurement of Neurotransmitter Release in vivo*, C. A. Marsden (ed.), John Wiley, Chichester, pp. 81–105.

Ungerstedt, U. and Pycock, C. (1974). Functional correlates of dopamine neurotransmission. *Bull. Schweiz, Akad. Med. Wiss.*, **1278**, 1.

Ungerstedt, U., Herrera–Marschitz, M., Jungnelius, U., Ståhle, L., Tossman, U. and Zetterström, T. (1982). Dopamine synaptic mechanisms reflected in studies combining behavioural recordings and brain dialysis. In: *Advances in the Biosciences*, Vol. 37, *Advances in Dopamine Research*, M. Kohsaka *et al.* (eds.), Pergamon Press, Oxford, pp. 219–231.

Zetterström, T. and Ungerstedt, U. (1984). Effects of apomorphine on the *in vivo* release of dopamine and its metabolites studied by brain dialysis. *Eur. J. Pharmacol.*, **97**, 20–36.

Zetterström, T., Sharp, T., Marsden, C. A. and Ungerstedt, U. (1983). *In vivo* measurement of dopamine and its metabolites by intracerebral dialysis: changes after *d*-amphetamine, *J. Neurochem.*, **41**, 1769–1773.

Zetterström, T., Sharp, T. and Ungerstedt, U. (1984). Effects of neuroleptic drugs on striatal dopamine release and metabolism in the awake rat studied by intracerebral dialysis. *Eur. J. Pharmacol.*, **106**, 27–37.

Zetterström, T., Herrera-Marschitz, M. and Ungerstedt, U. (1985). Simultaneous measurements of dopamine release and rotational behaviour in 6OHDA-denervated rats using intracerebral dialysis. *Brain Res.* (in press).

3

In vivo electrochemistry and the trained circling rat

**Curt R. Freed, Bryan K. Yamamoto, Michael E. Morgan,
Hirotoshi Echizen** and **Barbara A. Bennett**
Division of Clinical Pharmacology and Toxicology, Box C-237,
University of Colorado Health Sciences Center, 4200 East
Ninth Avenue, Denver, Colorado 80262, USA

1. INTRODUCTION

The new technique of *in vivo* electrochemistry has made it possible to continuously monitor the release of selected catecholamines, indoleamines and their metabolites with a moderate degree of certainty about the identity of the chemical species being measured (Lane *et al.*, 1978; Gonon *et al.*, 1980; Echizen and Freed, 1983). This new technology offers a way to study neurotransmitters in the behaving animal and so presents the opportunity to discover new brain phenomena. Since the initial discovery by Hornykiewicz that Parkinson's disease was associated with a dopamine deficiency in the basal ganglia (Ehringer and Hornykiewicz, 1960), dopamine has been known to be important for movement. The recognition by Barbeau *et al.* (1962) and Cotzias *et al.* (1967) that L-dopa could substantially restore movement to Parkinsonian patients showed that greater availability of dopamine could lead to improved motor function. Nonetheless, even this clinical finding did not answer the question of whether a burst of dopamine was released for each movement or whether simply a certain level of dopamine was needed for normal motor activity.

We therefore decided to pursue the question of whether dopamine was dynamically regulated during movement. *In vivo* electrochemistry appeared to offer a solution to the problem of studying neurotransmitter release in an awake, freely moving animal. A second problem was to show that neurotransmitter utilization was specifically related to motor behaviour and not to other neurophysiological phenomena such as attention or thirst or appetite. We decided to create a motor task which had a randomly assigned direction so that we could relate the direction of movement to the side of brain in which neurotransmitter release increased. Ungerstedt had shown that animals with unilateral substantia nigra lesions would run in circles after being given amphetamine, presumably because of asymmetric release of dopamine (Ungerstedt, 1971). We reasoned that if dopamine were used during circling behaviour, normal animals trained to run in circles would show unilateral release of dopamine from the caudate.

Another technical problem had to be solved before beginning the behavioural studies. In order to measure dopamine release in both sides of the brain, we needed to implant two electrochemical electrodes. Because individual electrochemical electrodes do not have the same sensitivity and since we wanted to have precise comparisons of the extracellular fluid dopamine concentrations in the two sides of brain, we devised a method for standardizing electrodes *in situ*. By injecting acetaminophen (paracetamol) into animals and comparing the size of the electrochemical peaks generated on each side of brain, we could precisely determine the sensitivity of electrodes.

2. METHODS

Male Sprague Dawley rats 250–350 g were used in all experiments. *In vivo* electrochemical electrodes were made from carbon paste (Ultra F carbon: mineral oil, 1.5 g: 1.0 ml packed into electrode wells made from teflon covered 250 micrometre stainless steel wire (Leico Industries) as previously described (Kissinger *et al.,* 1973). For acute experiments with acetaminophen animals were anaesthetized with urethane 1.5 g/kg. For chronic behavioural experiments, electrodes were implanted under chloral hydrate-ketamine-atropine anaesthesia and dual carbon paste electrodes were placed in anterodorsal caudate with coordinates 1.0 mm anterior to bregma, 2.0 lateral and 5.0 below dura. The electrodes used in the behavioural experiments had stearic acid incorporated into the carbon paste in a ratio of 100 mg stearic acid/1.5 g Ultra F carbon/1.0 ml mineral oil. A stainless steel auxiliary and an Ag/AgCl reference electrode were also implanted and the electrodes were all held in place with dental cement.

In acute experiments, doses of acetaminophen from 25 to 100 mg/kg were given i.p. and plasma and caudate tissue levels of the drug were followed in addition to the electrochemical signal. *d*-Amphetamine 5.0 mg/kg was given to release dopamine from caudate.

In the behavioural experiments, animals were water deprived for 1–2 days and then were randomly assigned to be trained to circle either to the right or to the left using traditional conditioning techniques. Initially, small movements in the assigned direction were rewarded with a drop of water. Once full turns were mastered, a drop was given only for a full turn. The animals remained on an FR 1 schedule. All animals learned to circle in the assigned direction. They circled at an average of 2 rpm during 100 turns on the first day of training and over 7 days increased their speed to 11 rpm (Yamamoto and Freed, 1982). Electrodes were placed following training and signals recorded alternately every 5 minutes using linear sweep voltammetry with voltage ramps from -0.2 to $+0.6$ V at 10 mV/s. Voltammetry output was processed by semidifferentiation. To confirm that changes had occurred in dopamine metabolism during trained circling, animals were sacrificed and caudate removed and assayed for dopamine and DOPAC by HPLC with electrochemical detection (Asmus and Freed, 1979).

3. RESULTS

Acetaminophen standardization data are shown in Fig. 1. The time course of the electrochemical peak in caudate is identical to the time course of the acetaminophen concentration in caudate as measured by sacrificing animals at intervals

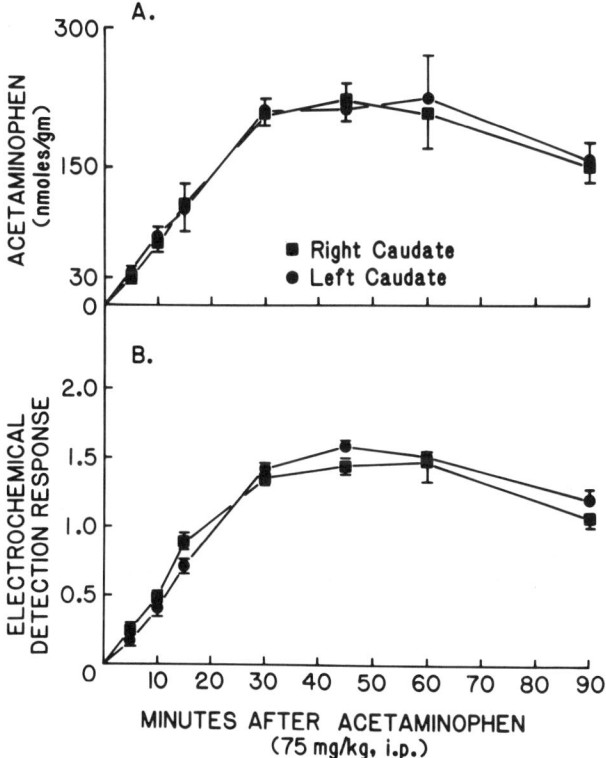

Fig. 1 – Tissue acetaminophen concentrations and electrochemical responses after 75 mg/kg acetaminophen i.p. Panel A shows concentrations of acetaminophen measured in rat caudate after sacrifice of animals at times shown ($n=5$, each time point). Panel B shows the electrochemical signal measured in the caudate nucleus after the same time course ($n=6$). The electrochemical responses have been normalized around the mean response for each animal. Reproduced from Morgan and Freed (1981) by permission.

after the drug dose (Morgan and Freed, 1981). Fig. 2 shows how this technique was applied to standardizing the response to amphetamine on the two sides of brain. Although the amphetamine response from the left side of the brain is over twice as large as the right side, the acetaminophen response is also greater on the left. When the amphetamine response is corrected by the acetaminophen response, the amphetamine response is the same on the two sides of the brain. In a group of seven animals, the left/right ratio of amphetamine responses was 0.90 ± 0.05, not significantly different from 1.0. This result shows that on average, amphetamine releases the same amount of dopamine from each side of brain.

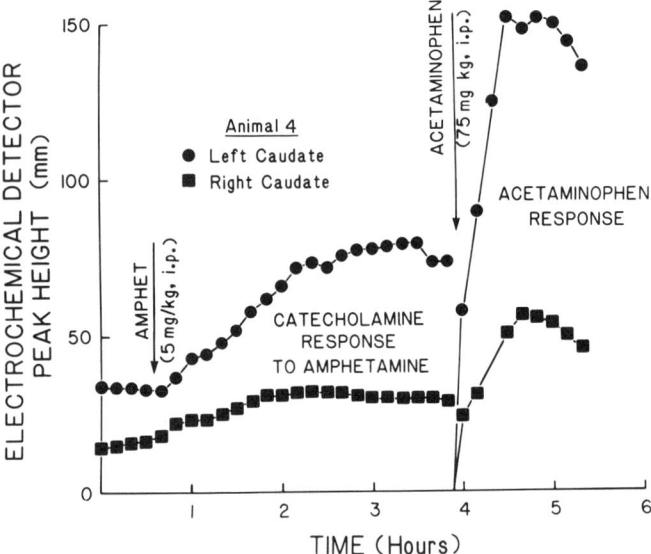

Fig. 2 – Standardization of amphetamine response by acetaminiophen injection. Recordings were made from left and right caudate with two carbon paste electrodes before and after amphetamine 5 mg/kg i.p. The electrochemical response of the left caudate appears to be greater than the right caudate. However, the responses to injected acetaminophen show that the left caudate electrode is simply more sensitive than the right electrode. Reproduced from Morgan and Freed (1981) by permission.

Fig. 3 shows dopamine release during circling in the trained circling rat. Release was the same from both sides of brain before circling. Within 5 minutes of the onset of circling, there was a significant increase in the signal from contralateral caudate compared to the ipsilateral side. The electrochemical signal increased for about 30 min and then fell, over several hours, back to baseline levels. The ipsilateral side showed no significant change during behaviour (Yamamoto *et al.*, 1982). The apparent increase in dopamine release was supported by changes in dopamine and DOPAC concentrations during circling. There was

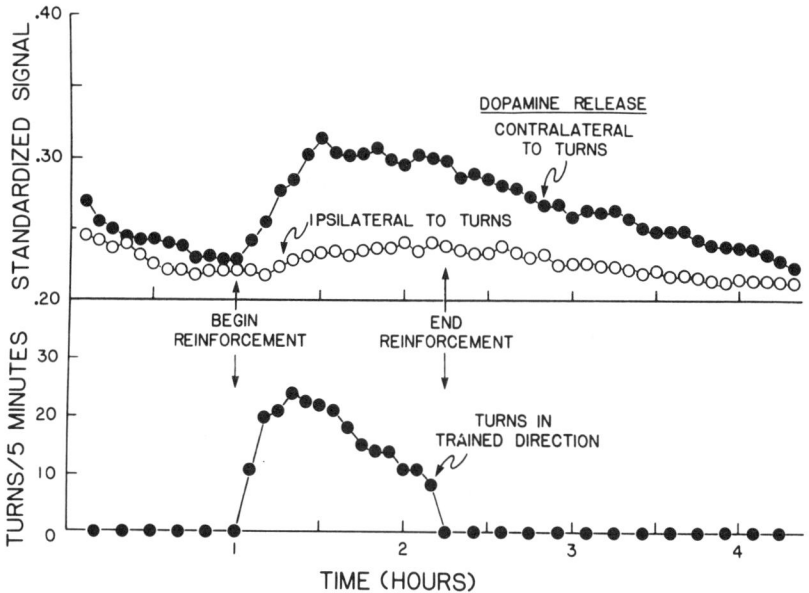

Fig. 3 – Caudate dopamine release in trained circling rats. The lower panel shows the circling behaviour and the upper panel shows the acetaminophen-standardized electrochemical signals recorded bilaterally from caudate of six rats. Before circling apparent dopamine release is the same from both sides of brain. With the onset of circling there is an increase in dopamine release from caudate contralateral to the circling direction. Reproduced from Yamamoto *et al* (1982) by permission.

a 76% increase in dopamine and a corresponding increase in DOPAC in contralateral caudate and no changes in concentration on the ipsilateral side (Yamamoto and Freed, 1982). A further finding with this model was that tyrosine hydroxylase was activated on the contralateral side within 3 minutes of the onset of circling (Morgan *et al.*, 1984). These data represent the first evidence that a neurotransmitter and its synthetic enzyme are activated during normal motor behaviour.

We are concerned about one result of the circling data. The apparent release of dopamine during movement had a rapid onset but then plateaued and remained elevated long after circling had stopped. There has been considerable controversy about the chemical species being measured with electrochemistry (Gonon *et al.*, 1980; Gonon *et al.*, 1981; Ewing *et al.*, 1981; Blaha and Lane, 1983; Gerhardt *et al.*, 1984). We have characterized the carbon paste electrode with pharmacological agents and have found that the signal was not changed by pargyline 75 mg/kg but was reduced by alpha-methyl-*p*-tyrosine and increased with haloperidol. We have also found that ascorbic acid amplifies the apparent dopamine signal although ascorbic acid itself is not seen at an electrode potential of 0.15 to 0.20 V (Freed and Echizen, 1983).

We have seen a similar prolonged time course of apparent dopamine release after amphetamine administration while Zetterström *et al* (1983) have seen a much more abbreviated peak of dopamine release measured by the technique of *in vivo* dialysis. Fig. 4 shows their dialysis data and our electrochemistry data after a dose of 5 mg/kg amphetamine. These apparently very different data can be reconciled by a mathematical model. If we assume that the electrochemical electrode lies in a relatively large and slowly cleared pool of extracellular fluid, then the electrode may measure the accumulation of dopamine released from neighbouring neurons over a prolonged period. By contrast, the dialysis catheter is clearing the extracellular fluid space of dopamine by its perfusion fluid. Assuming that the electrochemical electrode measures integrated dopamine release and that the dialysis catheter measures dopamine release itself, we fit both sets of data to a function. The function we selected to model the integral was the product of two rising exponentials. The rationale for two exponentials comes from the fact that we needed to model both the rise in amphetamine concentration and the increase in dopamine concentration asociated with the amphetamine. Since dialysis removed dopamine as it was released, the dialysis

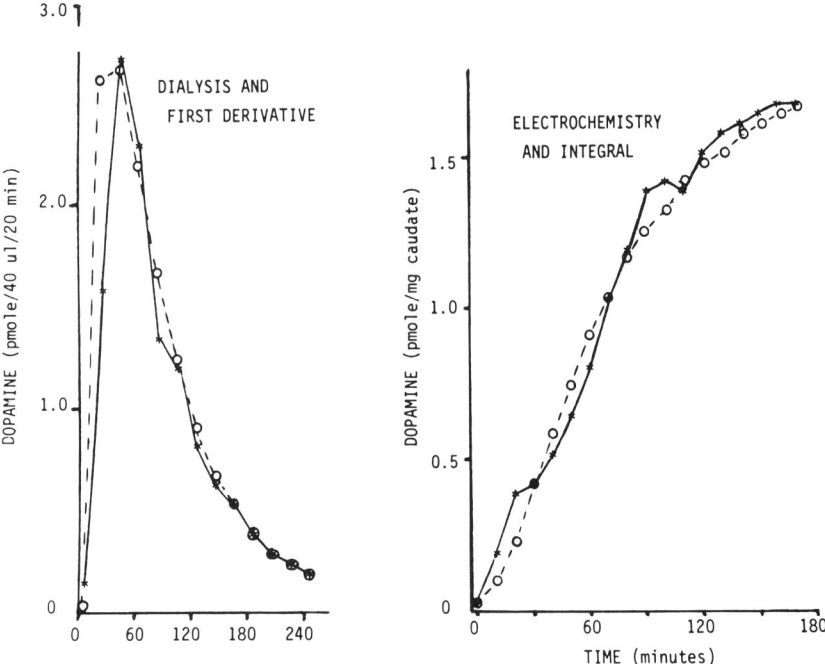

Fig. 4 – Dopamine release after amphetamine measured by *in vivo* dialysis and *in vivo* electrochemistry. Dialysis data adapted from Zetterström *et al.* (1983). The electrochemistry data was recorded from a 200 micrometre carbon paste electrode following amphetamine 5 mg/kg i.p. The solid lines are the actual data, the dashed lines represent the fit to the integral (electrochemistry) and the first derivative (dialysis) of a function described in the text.

data should correspond to the first derivative of the electrochemical signal. The model was fitted to the rising phase of the electrochemistry data, the later slow decay was ignored. The experimentally derived curves for extracellular fluid dopamine which fit both the integral and the first derivative are shown in Fig. 4 and the equation for the integral is given below.

$$DA_{ecf} = DA_{max} (1 - e^{-k_1 t}) (1 - e^{-k_2 t})$$

where $k_1 = 0.035$ min^{-1} and $k_2 = 0.013$ min^{-1} DA_{ecf} is extracellular fluid dopamine, and DA_{max} is the maximum extracellular fluid dopamine concentration achieved after 5 mg/kg amphetamine.

While it would be best to have incontrovertible evidence that the electrochemical electrode is measuring dopamine, such evidence is not available at this time. On the assumption that this integral-first derivative model is accurate, we can make some predictions about the actual time course of dopamine release during trained circling (see Fig. 3). The electrochemical peak at 30 minutes would represent the time at which release was actually slowing down. Peak release occurred when the slope of the integrated release curve was greatest. Thus we would predict that maximal release occurred during the first 5 to 10 minutes of circling. This prediction could be confirmed by direct measure of release with dialysis and by direct measurements of nigral firing during this behaviour.

If it is true that dopamine is released primarily during the first 5 or 10 minutes of trained circling, then it would follow that dopamine release is used to initiate behaviour rather than to sustain it.

4. DISCUSSION

The *in vivo* electrochemical electrode made it possible for us to discover that dopamine was dynamically used during normal motor behaviour. The increased release is accompanied by an increase in tyrosine hydroxylase activity and in dopamine and DOPAC production. Most experimenters using pharmacological techniques such as haloperidol to increase dopamine synthesis in caudate have found increases in DOPAC concentrations but no change in dopamine concentrations. In fact, the DOPAC/dopamine ratio is used to express this augmented turnover of dopamine and is useful particularly in lesion experiments in which dopamine concentrations are low because of destruction of dopamine nerve terminals (Hefti *et al.*, 1980). Our results in normal animals performing normal motor activity show that physiological activation of dopamine synthesis is much more extravagant than that produced by drugs or lesions. Dopamine synthesis appears to be in excess of that needed from motor behaviour since dopamine itself accumulates within 15 minutes of the onset of circling (Morgan *et al.*, 1984). Using tritiated tyrosine infusions into brain, we have found a 300% increase in dopamine synthesis in the first 20 minutes of circling (Bennett and Freed, 1983).

The identification of the chemical species being measured by *in vivo* electrochemistry remains a problem. Gonon and co-workers using electrically modified carbon fibre electrodes find they can measure ascorbic acid and DOPAC as discrete peaks. They do not measure dopamine, probably because the dopamine concentration in the extracellular fluid space is only a few per cent of the DOPAC concentration and their electrode has similar sensitivity for both compounds (Gonon *et al.*, 1981). Unmodified carbon paste electrodes have been said not to discriminate between dopamine, DOPAC and ascorbic acid. Inclusion of stearic acid in the carbon paste has been shown to provide an anionic barrier to exclude DOPAC and ascorbic acid and so enhance specificity for dopamine (Blaha and Lane, 1983). Similarly, the sulphated polymer Nafion has been used on carbon epoxy electrodes to provide selective sensitivity for dopamine over DOPAC and ascorbate (Gerhardt *et al.*, 1984). Carbon paste electrodes do not maintain their *in vitro* character after implantation into brain. We and others have found that there are shifts in oxidation potential and changes in electrode sensitivity for a number of compounds which occur within a few minutes of electrode placement (Freed and Echizen, 1983; O'Neill *et al.*, 1982). Ascorbic acid also affects the response of the electrode to dopamine by reducing the oxidized dopamine back to dopamine. At physiological concentrations of 300 micromolar ascorbic acid and using 200 micrometre brain-treated carbon paste electrodes, we have found a 3000% augmentation of the electrochemical response to dopamine (Freed and Echizen, 1983). While this amplification does introduce uncertainty about whether the apparent change in dopamine release is actually dopamine release or only a change in extracellular fluid ascorbic acid, the amplification has merit for increasing the electrode sensitivity for extracellular fluid dopamine.

In the trained circling rat studies, we used stearic acid modified electrodes to increase electrode selectivity for dopamine. We treated some of these animals with pargyline and found no reduction in the electrochemical signal. These results indicate that DOPAC probably did not contribute to the signal measured during circling. Because ascorbic acid amplification could modify the dopamine signal, we cannot say with certainty that the changes in catechol signal were not simply due to changes in tissue ascorbate concentration. However, the fact that we have seen lateralized changes in dopamine and DOPAC tissue concentrations and increases in caudate tyrosine hydroxylase activity during circling means that dopamine release is also occurring during movement.

The concentration of dopamine in the extracellular fluid space remains a subject of conjecture. Estimates have ranged from 1.0 to 50 micromolar. The problem with making such projections is that most are made from *in vitro* extrapolations of electrode sensitivity. Response to a known concentration of dopamine is measured in the beaker and the brain concentration is estimated by comparing the signal measured in brain with that determined in the beaker. We already know that some electrochemical electrodes are affected by the ascorbic acid concentration in brain. Other, unknown amplifier or inhibitor substances may be present in brain. Our best guess of the dopamine concentration in the extracellular fluid space is 1.0 micromolar. This estimate is based on the apparent dopamine peak height and the acetaminophen peak height following 75 mg/kg acetaminophen. Because we have measured the acetaminophen concentration in tissue and know that the maximal electrochemical peak height corresponds to a tissue concentration of about 200 micromolar (Morgan and Freed, 1981), we can estimate the dopamine concentration as a fraction of the acetaminophen response. The apparent dopamine peak is about 25% of the acetaminophen peak which implies a dopamine concentration of 50 micromolar. However, this estimate is almost certainly too high since the dopamine peak is amplified by tissue ascorbate while the acetaminophen peak is not. Thus, assuming a tissue concentration of 300 micromolar ascorbic acid, there will be a 30-fold augmentation of the dopamine peak relative to the acetaminophen. Correcting for this effect, the dopamine concentration estimate falls to 1.5 micromolar. Brain-treated electrodes are also intrinsically less responsive to acetaminophen than to dopamine, which makes the estimate of the actual dopamine concentration in brain even lower, 1.0 micromolar or less.

The physiological importance of dynamic dopamine release is great. Our results indicate that dopamine is actively used during normal movement. This means that Parkinson patients treated with drugs are unlikely to have normal movement since all drugs at present available supply a single level of dopamine agonist to all parts of brain. The level varies only with the time that the drug is taken. We have recently shown that dopamine utilization in caudate and nucleus accumbens is directly proportional to the intensity as well as direction of movement. Each nucleus has its individual response to each variable in movement—dopamine metabolism in nucleus accumbens changes with movement intensity as well as direction while dopamine metabolism in caudate is most affected by posture and direction of movement (Freed and Yamamoto, 1984). Again, pharmacological treatment of patients cannot supply the needs of discrete brain nuclei. Only a treatment such as transplantation with fetal substantia nigra is likely to restore selective function of nuclei and to produce fully normal motor behaviour.

ACKNOWLEDGEMENTS

This research was supported by US Public Health Service grants NS18639, NS09199 and an RCDA HL00782 (C.R.F.).

REFERENCES

Asmus, P. A. and Freed, C. R. (1979). Reversed-phase high-performance liquid chromatography of catecholamines and their congeners with simple acids as ion-pairing reagents. *J. Chromatogr.*, **1979**, 303–311.

Barbeau, A., Sourkes, T. L. and Murphy, G. F. (1962). In: *Monoamines et systeme Nerveux Centrale,* de Ajuriognevra (ed.), Masson, Geneva, p. 247.

Bennett, B. A. and Freed, C. R. (1983). Lateralized increase in caudate dopamine synthesis in the trained circling rat. *Fed Proc.* **42**(4), 1105, abstract 4766.

Blaha, C. D. and Lane, R. F. (1983). Chemically modified electrodes for *in vivo* monitoring of brain catecholamines. *Brain Res. Bull.,* **10**, 861–864.

Cotzias, G. C., Van Woert, M. H. and Schiffer, L. M. (1967). Aromatic amino acids and modification of parkinsonism. *N. Eng. J. Med.,* **276**, 374–378.

Echizen, H. and Freed, C. R. (1983). *In vivo* electrochemical detection of extra-neuronal 5-hydroxyindole acetic acid and norepinephrine in the dorsal raphe nucleus of urethane anaesthetized rats. *Brain Res.,* **277**, 55–62.

Ehringer, H. and Hornykiewicz, O. (1960). Verteilung von noradrenalin und dopamin (3-hydroxytyramin) im gehirn des menschen und ihr verhalten bei erkrankungen dex extrapyramidalen systems. *Klin. Wschr.,* **38**, 1236–1239.

Ewing, A. G., Dayton, M. A. and Wightman, R. M. (1981). Pulse voltammetry with microvoltammetric electrodes. *Anal. Chem.,* **53**, 1842–1847.

Freed, C. R. and Echizen, H. (1983). Factors affecting *in vivo* electrochemistry: Electrode modification by brain tissue and amplification of catecholamine responsed by ascorbic acid. *Soc. Neurosci. Abstracts,* **9**(2), 999, abstract 290.19.

Freed, C. R. and Yamamoto, B. K. (1984). Dopamine in nucleus accumbens and caudate is a marker for the speed, turning angle and direction of rats running on a rotating disk. IUPHAR 9th International Congress Pharmacology, London, July 1984.

Gerhardt, G. A., Oke, A. F., Nagy, G., Moghaddam, B. and Adams, R. N. (1984). Nafion-coated electrodes with high selectivity for CNS electrochemistry. *Brain Res.,* **290**, 390–395.

Gonon, F., Buda, M., Cespuglio, R., Jouvet, M. and Pujol, J.-F. (1980). *In vivo* electrical detection of catechol in the rat neostriatum: Dopamine or DOPAC? *Nature,* **286**, 902–904.

Gonon, F., Buda, M., Cespuglio, R., Jouvet, M. and Pujol, J.-F. (1981). Volt-ammetry in the striatum of chronic freely moving rats: Detection of cate-chols and ascorbic acid. *Brain Res.,* **223**, 69–80.

Hefti, F., Melamed, E. and Wurtman, R. J. (1980). Partial lesions of the dopa-minergic nigrostriatal system: Biochemical characterization. *Brain Res.,* **195**, 123–137.

Kissinger, P. T., Hart, J. B. and Adams, R. N. (1973). Voltammetry in brain tissue – a new neurophysiological measurement. *Brain Res.,* **55**, 209–213.

Lane, R. F., Hubbard, A. T. and Blaha, C. D. (1978). Brain dopaminergic neurons: *In vivo* electrochemical information concerning storage, meta-bolism and release processes. *Bioelectrochem. Bioenerg.,* **5**, 504–525.

Morgan, M. E. and Freed, C. R. (1981). Acetaminophen as an internal standard for calibrating *in vivo* electrochemical electrodes. *J. Pharmacol. Exp. Ther.,* **219**, 49–53.

Morgan, M. E., Yamamoto, B. K. and Freed, C. R. (1984). Unilateral activiation of caudate tyrosine hydroxylase during voluntary circling behavior. *J. Neurochem.,* **43**(3), 737–741.

O'Neill, R. D., Grunewald, R. A., Fillenz, M. and Albery, W. J. (1982). Linear sweep voltammetry with carbon paste electrodes in the rat striatum. *Neurosci.,* **7**, 1945–1954.

Ungerstedt, U. (1971). Striatal dopamine release after amphetamine or nerve degeneration revealed by rotational behavior. *Acta Physiol. Scand.,* **82,** Suppl. 367, 46–68.

Yamamoto, B. K. and Freed, C. R. (1982). The trained circling rat: A model for inducing unilateral caudate dopamine metabolism, *Nature,* **298,** 467–468.

Yamammoto, B. K., Lane, R. F. and Freed, C. R. (1982). Normal rats trained to circle show asymmetric caudate dopamine release. *Life Sci.,* **30,** 2155–2162.

Zetterström, T., Sharp, T., Marsden, C. A. and Ungerstedt, U. (1983). *In vivo* measurement of dopamine and its metabolites by intracerebral dialysis: Changes after *d*-amphetamine. *J. Neurochem.,* **41,** 1769–1773.

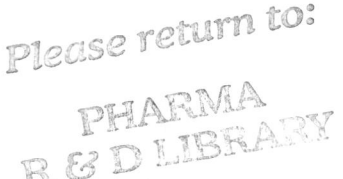

4

Commentary: Dopamine release and metabolism *in vitro*

D. F. Sharman
A.F.R.C. Institute of Animal Physiology, Babraham, Cambridge CB2 4AT

The discussion following the paper on the *in vivo* measurement of the auto-regulation of amine release and metabolism (Part III, Chapter 1 of this volume) centred on the problem of the correlation between the concentration of DOPAC measured in the brain and the release of dopamine from dopaminergic nerve terminals. It was suggested that the changes following treatment with haloperidol, which causes an increase in the concentration of DOPAC that appears to outlast the change in dopamine release, might be due to changes in receptor sensitivity or could reflect compensatory changes, possibly in other parts of the brain. In order to investigate the latter possibility, the experiment could be repeated using restrained animals because the compensation might require the animal to move. Dr. Marsden made it clear that he did not think that changes in the concentration of DOPAC in the brain simply reflected changes in the release of dopamine. Such changes could arise from leakage from the sites at which dopamine or DOPAC are formed. It is also known that changes in the meta-bolism of dopamine in the brain can occur without parallel, comparable changes in the release of dopamine from the nerve terminals. However, it was concluded that in the experiments described, an increase in the concentration of DOPAC would, at least in part, reflect a corresponding increase in the release of dopamine.

The use of neuroleptic drugs to induce changes in the metabolism of dopa-mine might not be the best approach to the analysis of this problem because the changes are large and could lead to saturation of removal mechanisms. It was considered likely that decreases, or physiological changes, might bear a closer relation to the release of dopamine. The work, reported at the meeting by Justice *et al.* shows that changes in the concentrations of the extracellular metabolites of dopamine lag behind the release of dopamine from nerve terminals and that, following the physiological stimulus of eating, the estimates of the concentration of DOPAC remained high for over two hours.

It was accepted that the concentration of DOPAC was not a good index of the size, or temporal relations, of the release of dopamine in the brain.

The questions raised by the results presented by T. Sharp *et al.* (Part III, Chapter 2 of this volume) were concerned with the problem of relating an increase in the concentration of dopamine in perfusates, obtained with dialysis perfusion cannulae placed in the brain, to the release of dopamine from dopaminergic neurons. The Chairman was of the opinion that the effect following treatment with amphetamine should not be described as increased release because the increase in the concentration of dopamine reflects an increase in the extracellular concentration of dopamine. This latter change does not necessarily arise from an increase in the release of dopamine but could be the result of changes in the biochemical equilibria of the processes concerned with the inactivation of the transmitter. Amphetamine inhibits the re-uptake of dopamine, is an inhibitor of monoamine oxidase and, in addition, causes a decrease in the firing rate of dopaminergic neurons. Thus, amphetamine appears to cause a decreased release of dopamine but its intervention in the inactivation processes results in an increase in the extracellular concentration.

It was queried whether dialysis perfusion would always detect a change in the release of dopamine in the brain since an increased release would, presumably, be balanced by increased re-uptake and catabolism. However, in order for increased inactivation to take place there must be an increased concentration of extracellular dopamine, provided that increased neuronal activity is not accompanied by significant changes in the kinetics of the inactivating mechanisms. It was concluded that the method might not be sufficiently sensitive to detect changes of the order of 20% but, in general, it would provide a good index of the synaptic release of dopamine.

Following the clear demonstration by C. Freed *et al.* (Part III, Chapter 3 of this volume) of the lateral differentiation in the cerebral neurochemistry of dopamine in rats moving in a circular path, it was observed that drug-induced behavioural responses, seen in rats treated centrally with 6-hydroxy-dopamine, were dependent on the stimulation or blockade of a bimodal system. The nucleus accumbens appears to be concerned with drive, influencing other parts of the brain, whereas the striatum appears to be concerned with posture. The effect of amphetamine in the 6-hydroxy-dopamine treated animal leads to activation with a bias on direction; the activation may be independent of the tendency to move laterally and it might be possible to separate the two components. The lateral differentiation might be better investigated in animals with a unilateral lesion of the median fore-brain bundle. Evidence for 'lateral function' in the nucleus accumbens was that the injection of dopamine unilaterally into this brain region does not cause locomotion, but locomotion is observed when dopamine is injected into both nuclei. C. Freed replied that laterality was observed in the nucleus accumbens in his experiments and that it was most pronounced at low speeds.

The possibility that the electrochemical signal represents the integral of the release of dopamine could be further investigated using electrochemical and dialysis-perfusion methods in animals treated with amphetamine to see if the relation still holds when the inactivation mechanisms are modified. Experiments carried out by T. Zetterström appear to indicate that the relation is not as good in this case. Dr. Zetterström said that the experiments were open to other interpretations and that the effect might depend on localization. Dr. Freed concurred and observed that the changes he had reported occurred in the anterior and dorsal part of the striatum and that different results were obtained in the posterior striatum.

Dr. Freed, commenting on the persistence of the electrochemical signal after the behaviour had ceased, described how this could be explained by assuming that the electrochemical signal represented the integral of the dopamine release and that there appeared to be a large release of dopamine near the start of the behaviour. He also confirmed that the experiments with tyrosine hydroxylase had been carried out with the soluble form of the enzyme under sub-saturating conditions. The kinetics of the enzyme activity showed, as expected, a curvilinear relation and it had been concluded that the kinetics did not follow the Michaelis—Menten equation.

Dr Fillenz asked whether increased synthesis of dopamine leads to a leakage of dopamine from the neurons. Dr. Freed suggested that under these conditions some DOPAC might be formed from dopamine that had never been released from a nerve terminal but the situation was not entirely clear. In experiments on the release of dopamine from the dopaminergic nerve endings in the neurohypophysis, it has been observed that there can be an increased release of dopamine per impulse when the synthesis of dopamine is increased (Holzbauer, Racké and Sharman, to be published).

The Chairman observed that, in his view, the striatal dopaminergic neuronal system seemed to be designed to remain constant, whereas Dr. Freed was impressed by its variability, particularly in the size of the changes he observed. This might be the way in which the system overcomes the restraints exerted upon it by the several feedback systems which are known to control dopamine synthesis and release in this region of the brain and that a sudden, large increase in synthesis might be necessary for the required release of dopamine.

It was asked whether the adaptation in the synthesis of dopamine that occurs only three minutes after the animal started circling, reflected the response of brain that had previously learned the task. Dr. Freed's reply was that the response could be seen in rats, running on a sandpaper disk during the second exposure, so that they could not really be regarded as trained animals. There was some evidence that changes in DOPAC on the ipsilateral side in circling rats are larger in trained animals. It has also been reported that dopamine metabolism can be conditioned using drug treatment as the unconditional stimulus (Perez-Cruet, J. (1976) *Pav. J. Biol. Sci.,* **11**, 237–250).

The changes in the activity of tyrosine hydroxylase seem to be a function of use in the striatal dopaminergic neuronal system.

The problem of the damage caused, in the brain, by the different electrodes and cannulae was discussed. Because of the size of the dialysis—perfusion cannulae, it was suggested that it would be best if these were placed just outside the brain region or nucleus under investigation. Dr. Kruk said that the small carbon fibre electrodes used for single unit recording appear to do less damage than other electrodes as they pass through the brain.

With regard to electrochemical recording in the brain, Dr. Knott stated that the peak which he observed at the potential at which dopamine is oxidized was not entirely due to dopamine but he was convinced that it could be employed as an index for the release of dopamine in the brain.

5

Monitoring brain amine metabolism using CSF: Validation of method and use in the investigation of relationships with social behaviour

G. Curzon, P. H. Hutson, A. Jackson, B. J. Sahakian and **G. S. Sarna**
Department of Neurochemistry, Institute of Neurology,
33 John's Mews, London WC1N 2NS, UK

1. INTRODUCTION

The use of conventional methods for studying brain amines in small laboratory animals has led to many advances in our understanding of their roles in the brain. However, these methods have various limitations deriving from the necessity to kill the animals before determinations can be made. This prevents many kinds of investigation while others become both effort-intensive and cost-intensive. A standard method for measuring rat brain 5HT turnover (Neff and Tozer, 1968) may be used as an example. Probenecid is given to block egress of the acid metabolite 5HIAA and its rate of accumulation then measured. At least 8–12 rats are needed and the end result is one turnover value and a group of dead rats. There are many fundamental questions to which such methods cannot readily be applied. For example, how is the metabolism of the transmitter related to behaviour in the normal animal? This is difficult to study because turnover values cannot be obtained for individual rats. Also, as these methods involve killing the animals, their behaviour can only be observed prior to determination of turnover. Similar difficulties prevent us from making neurochemical measurements in the same rat at different times after altering its environment or after giving food or drugs. So investigating time courses becomes labour-intensive and needs large numbers of animals.

One method by which the above problems can be avoided has been recently developed in our laboratory and involves the repeated withdrawal of small volumes of CSF from freely moving rats (Sarna *et al.*, 1983). Rather similar procedures have been concurrently described by Elghozi *et al.* (1983) though they have mostly if not invariably (see Danguir *et al.*, 1982) been applied to anaesthetized rats. Also, Joseph *et al.* (1981) and Griauzde and Radulovacki (1976) have previously collected successive CSF samples from primates and cats respectively while Nielsen and Moore (1982) have measured amine metabolites in cerebroventricular perfusates from freely moving rats. The present chapter describes our method, its validation and its application in a behavioural study.

2. METHOD

The method of catheter implantation and CSF withdrawal was largely as described by Sarna *et al.* (1983) (see Fig. 1). Male Sprague-Dawley rats, weight range 170 ± 5 g (Charles-River U.K. Ltd.), were singly housed for at least 7 days prior to implantation and allowed food and water *ad lib.* The animals were anaesthetized with Sagatal (BDH Chemicals Ltd, Poole, Dorset) 60 mg/kg i.p. and placed in a stereotaxic frame using ear bars only. A midline incision was made between lambda and the external occipital crest and the skin and underlying tissues retracted. A burr hole was drilled 2–3 mm lateral to the midline and approximately 5 mm caudal to lambda for the placement of a stainless steel keying screw (8BA). Two more burr holes were drilled on the midline 2 and 3 mm dorsal to the external occipital crest, care being taken to leave the dura intact. These two holes were joined together, forming a slot approximately 3 mm long.

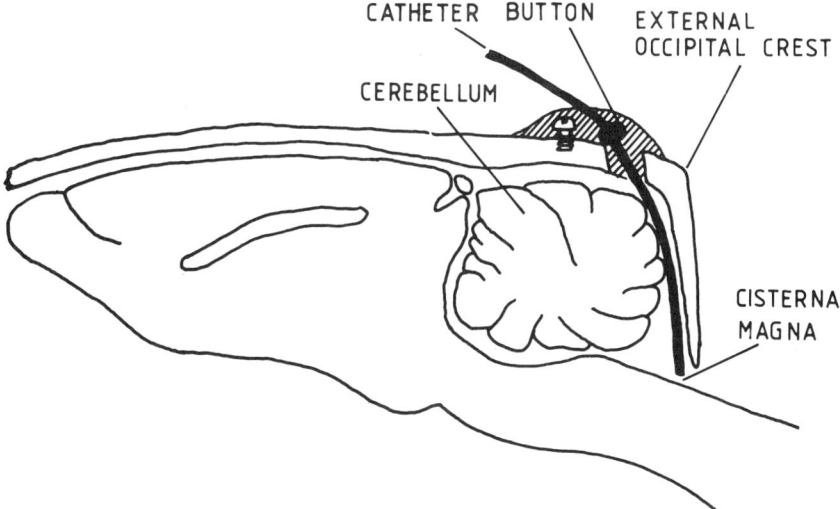

Fig. 1 – Schematic illustration of catheter placement in the cisterna magna of rat. See text for details. (From Sarna *et al.*, 1983).

Catheters were formed from 10 cm lengths of PP10 polyethylene tubing (Portex Ltd, Hythe, Kent). During implantation each catheter contained a 12 cm length of 34G enamelled copper wire (Scientific Wire Co., P.O. Box 30, London) to give it rigidity and to aid puncture of the dura. A button was formed 6.5 mm from one end of the catheter by gentle heating over a soldering iron. This served as a depth stop and also helped to secure the catheter in place. Implantation was achieved by pushing the catheter caudally along the slot, puncturing the dura, until the button rested on the skull surface (Fig. 1). After withdrawal of the wire the catheter was secured in place with dental acrylic (DeTrey, Weybridge). Gentle negative pressure on the catheter induced CSF to flow. The catheter was then cut to approximately 3 cm and heat-sealed. The rats were sutured and the wound sprayed with terramycin (Pfizer Ltd., Sandwich).

CSF was sampled in conscious rats by connecting the implanted catheter to a cannula made from approximately 20 cm PP10 tubing joined to approximately 20 cm PP50 polythene tubing which was attached by a 23 G needle to a 1 ml syringe. The cannula was then passed through a hole in the centre of the cage lid and allowed to hang over the side of the cage. The weight of the syringe was sufficient to keep the cannula taut when the rat moved. CSF samples (30–55 μl) were collected in 0.75 ml Sarstedt tubes and 25–50 μl transferred to tubes containing 5–10 μl of 0.1% cysteine for analysis by HPLC. After each sample was taken the CSF remaining in the cannula was slowly flushed back into the cisternal space.

X-ray studies confirmed that the catheters did not penetrate the cerebellum and were accurately located in the cisterna magna. About 60% were patent for use 3 days following implantation and half of these were still patent 4 days later.

The catheters were easily implanted and their flexibility enabled placement in the cisterna magna without damage to brain tissue. The volumes of CSF withdrawn were more than sufficient for analysis by high pressure liquid chromatography and as the rate of sampling (typically 30–55 μl each 30 min) was less than the rate of production of CSF in the rat (2–3 μl min^{-1}) and only 10–20% of the CSF volume (Cserr, 1965; Burns et al., 1976), sampling was unlikely to affect CSF concentrations of amine metabolites. In practice, serial samples taken from rats in a quiet environment showed reasonably steady concentrations.

3. VALIDATION OF USE OF RAT CISTERNAL CSF TO MONITOR BRAIN AMINE METABOLISM

The CSF method was validated insofar as it was shown in the following investigations to give results which paralleled findings on whole brain.

3.1 Turnover measurements

5HT and DA turnover values were obtained in individual rats (Hutson et al., 1984a) by measuring the rates of accumulation of 5HIAA, DOPAC and HVA in cisternal CSF samples taken from each rat three days after catheter implantation and 0, 30 and 60 min after probenecid (200 mg/kg i.p.) administration.

Determinations were made by HPLC. Considerable fractions of the DOPAC and HVA in rat CSF occur as acid hydrolysable conjugates (Hutson *et al.,* 1984a; Sarna *et al.,* 1984) and the CSF samples were therefore acid hydrolysed essentially as Dedek *et al.* (1979) before determinations were made. Results in Fig. 2 show that 5HIAA concentration and total (DOPAC + HVA) concentration rose approximately linearly in the CSFs of individual rats after probenecid was given and that rats pretreated with a dose of the decarboxylase inhibitor DL-α-monofluoromethyl-DOPA (MFMD) sufficient to partially inhibit 5HT and DA synthesis showed smaller increases than did vehicle-treated rats.

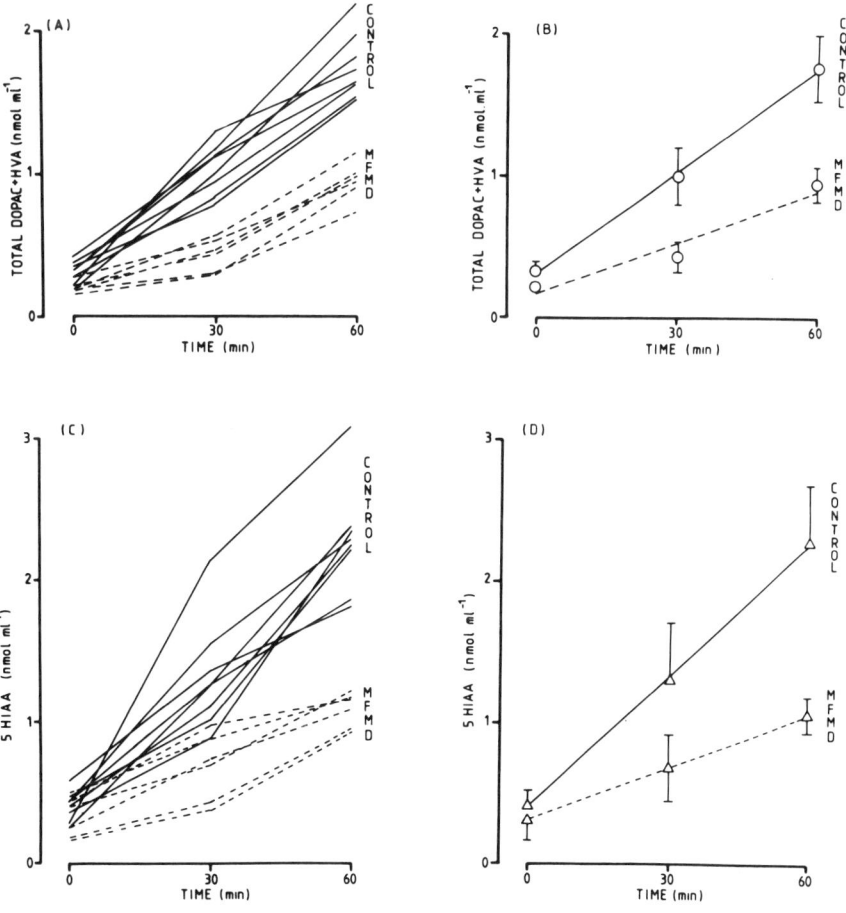

Fig. 2 – Central DA and 5HT turnovers determined in individual rats given either vehicle (1 ml/kg p.o., *n* = 8) or DLα-monofluoromethyldopa (MFMD) (100 mg/k p.o., *n* = 6) and injected 16 h later with probenecid (200 mg/kg i.p.). A: Total DOPAC + HVA concentrations of CSF of individual rats taken 0, 30 and 60 min after probenecid. B: Corresponding mean values ± S.D. C: 5HIAA concentrations of CSF of individual rats taken 0, 30 and 60 min after probenecid. D: Corresponding mean values ± S.D. (From Hutson *et al.,* 1984a).

A separate experiment was made to investigate whether differences of turnover are proportionately reflected in CSF and brain. Rats were given either 100 mg/kg MFMD p.o. or vehicle and injected 16 h later with 200 mg/kg probenecid i.p. CSF was sampled immediately or 30 or 60 min after probenecid injection (i.e. only one CSF sample was taken from each rat). The animals were decapitated immediately after sampling and amine metabolites determined on CSF and brain after acid hydrolysis. 5HIAA and total (DOPAC + HVA) rose linearly over 1 h after probenecid in the brain and CSF of vehicle- and MFMD-treated rats. Calculation of turnover values from these results showed that MFMD caused very comparable percentage decreases of turnover whether this was determined using CSF or brain (Table 1). Similar findings were previously obtained in a study of the effect of the tryptophan hydroxylase inhibitor p-chlorophenylalanine (PCPA) on 5HT synthesis (Sarna et $al.$, 1983). Therefore 5HT and DA turnover determinations based on cisternal CSF measurements proportionately reflect changes of whole brain turnover of these transmitters. This proportionality was only obtained if the samples were subjected to acid hydrolysis (Hutson et $al.$, 1984).

Table 1 – Effect of partial inhibition of synthesis on amine turnover as measured using CSF and brain

	CSF $(nmol.ml^{-1}.h^{-1})$	Brain $(nmol.g^{-1}.h^{-1})$
5HT		
Saline (22)	1.49 ± 0.13	1.51 ± 0.14
MFMD (21)	0.79 ± 0.11	0.81 ± 0.23
% decrease	47	47
Saline (14)	1.57 ± 0.15	1.12 ± 0.20
PCPA (21)	0.52 ± 0.07	0.29 ± 0.06
% decrease	67	74
DA		
Saline (21)	1.74 ± 0.09	2.14 ± 0.28
MFMD (21)	0.82 ± 0.09	0.89 ± 0.22
% decrease	53	58

Amine turnover was determined in individual animals by measuring the accumulation of metabolites in brain and CSF, 30 or 60 min after probenecid, 200 mg/kg, i.p. (see text). Animals were treated with MFMD, 100 mg/kg, p.o., or appropriate saline control, 16 h previously or with PCPA, 150 mg/kg, or appropriate saline control, 24 h previously. Results are given ± SD, with the numbers of animals in brackets. Results from Hutson et $al.$ (1984a) and Sarna et $al.$ (1983).

3.2 Effect of tryptophan administration

The above investigations indicated that 5HT and DA turnovers as indicated by CSF analysis paralleled those indicated by determinations on brain. However, this does not necessarily mean that transient changes of transmitter amine

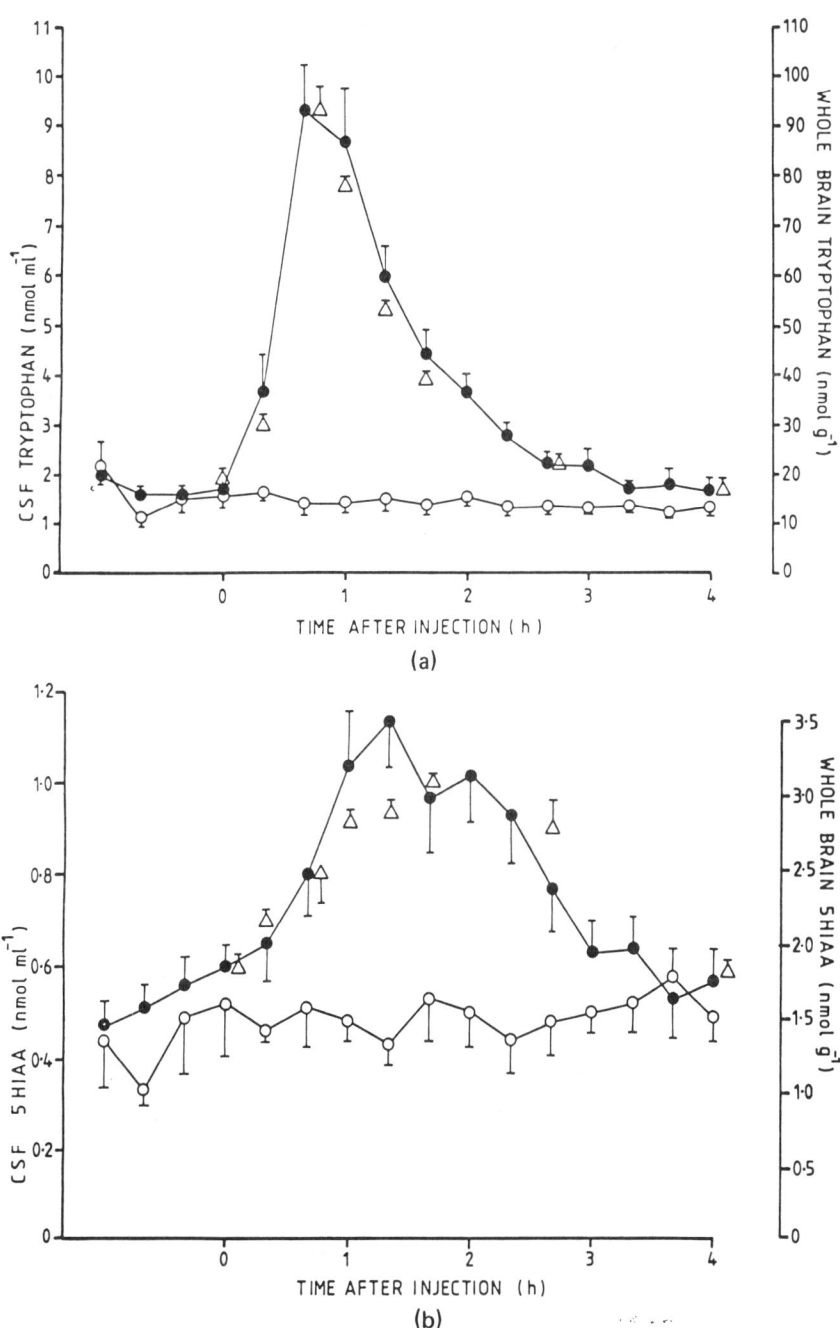

Fig. 3 – (a) Mean time courses of tryptophan concentration after i.p. injection of 0.9% NaCl or L-tryptophan 50 mg/kg. ○, CSF, NaCl injected; $n = 5$; ●, CSF, tryptophan injected, $n = 9$, △, whole brain, tryptophan, $n = 5$ at each time. (b) Mean time courses of 5HIAA concentration after i.p. injection of 0.9% NaCl or L-tryptophan 50 mg/kg. Symbols, numbers of determinations etc. as shown in (a) above. (From Hutson *et al.*, 1985).

synthesis in rat brain are closely paralleled in the CSF. We therefore compared the time-course of the effects of a L-tryptophan load (50 mg/kg i.p.) on central tryptophan concentration and on 5HT metabolism as indicated by 5HIAA values using (a) successively withdrawn CSF samples and (b) a conventional method i.e. killing groups of rats at intervals and determining the above substances in their brains (Hutson *et al.,* 1985). Results showed that tryptophan changes in the CSF were proportionate to those in whole brain and followed essentially identical time courses. Similarly, results for 5HIAA showed reasonable proportionality between CSF and brain values (Fig. 3a, b).

4. INTER-INDIVIDUAL DIFFERENCES OF 5HT AND DA TURNOVER

Fig. 4 shows 5HT and DA turnover values for each of 28 rats as determined by the CSF probenecid method. The animals were male Sprague-Dawley 200 g non-litter-mates which had been obtained from suppliers at 21–22 days and housed singly for 4–5 weeks on a reversed lighting schedule before catheter

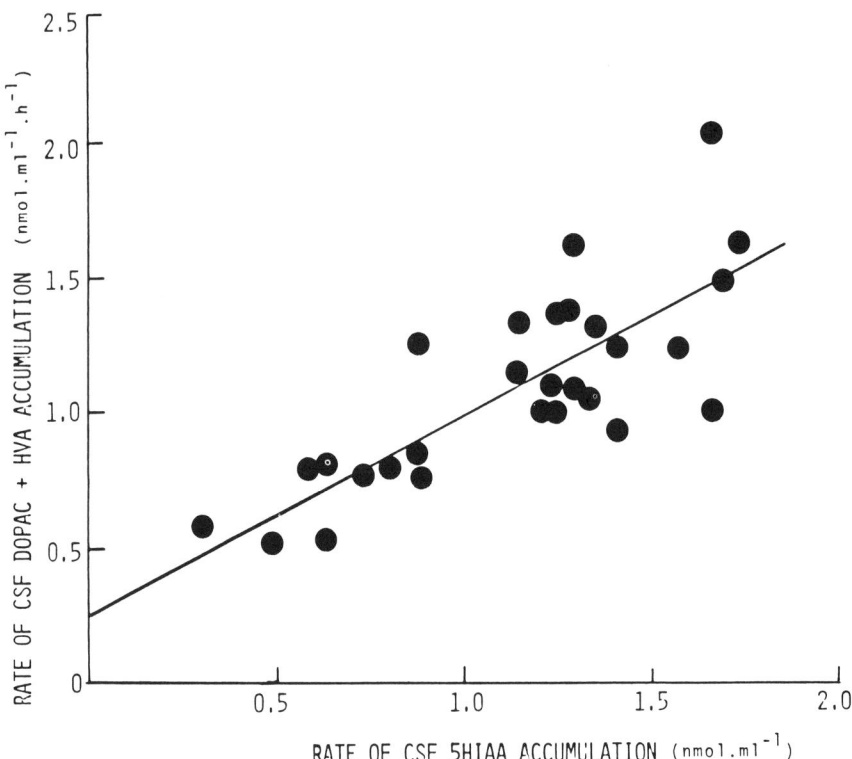

Fig. 4 – Correlation between individual DA and 5HT turnover values as indicated by accumulations of acid metabolites in cisternal CSF in 1 h after probenecid injection (200 mg/kg i.p.). Correlation coefficient $r = 0.79, p < 0.001, n = 28$, $y = 0.73x + 0.28$. (From Curzon *et al.,* 1985).

implantation. The CSF samples were taken 7 days after implantation and during the dark (red light) phase when rats are most active and when we have shown higher turnovers of both 5HT and DA than during the white-light relatively quiescent period (Hutson *et al.*, 1984b). Between-rat variation of turnover was considerable and 5HT and DA turnovers correlated with each other significantly and positively with the relationship representing about 60% of the variance.

The large range of turnover values found suggested the possibility of investigating whether there are associations between turnovers and behaviour within this group of apparently normal rats. It was therefore of interest to know whether the turnover values were relatively fixed characteristics of the individual rats. Unfortunately, when serial turnover determinations were made on a separate group of rats, using repeated probenecid injections, there were marked delayed but transient toxic effects of previous probenecid treatment; these were indicated by a striking fall of food intake during the initial 2–3 days after probenecid injection. The considerable variability of turnover with time shown by some of the rats may well have been due to this toxicity (Hutson *et al.*, 1984a).

However, other findings suggest that the between-rat differences were not merely of transient significance or due to experimental error. Firstly, duplicate determinations on the same CSFs differed from means by only ±5%. Secondly, the striking proportionality between the frequency with which rats bit each other on pairing and their individual 5HT turnovers even though these were determined three weeks before the rats were paired (see below) is consistent with individual turnovers being closely controlled over considerable periods. Furthermore, repeated determinations of amine metabolites in the lateral ventricles of cats over periods of up to 5 months indicated large intra-individual variations but individual constancy (Degrell *et al.*, 1983).

5. 5HT TURNOVER AND SOCIAL BEHAVIOUR

Conventional neurochemical methodology is particularly restrictive when studying social behaviour. The limitations indicated in the introduction imply that it is not possible to perform experiments in which the transmitter metabolism of individual rats is first characterized and animals with, for example, markedly different turnovers then put together for behavioural observation. Therefore, most previous work has been based on the behavioural effects of drug treatments or brain lesions. Whether normal behavioural roles for the transmitters can be deduced from such experiments alone is unclear. As well as obvious problems related to drug specificity we cannot be sure that the gross neurochemical changes commonly induced are relevant to normal behaviour and normal regulatory mechanisms.

Making use of the group of rats for which turnover values in the red light phase are shown in Fig. 4 we were able to investigate associations between turnovers and social behaviour by pairing rats with markedly different turnover values. Two weeks after the CFSs were taken for turnover measurements, 18 rats were selected for subsequent pairing in an observation chamber. Each pair was weight-matched and contained one animal with a 5HT turnover value markedly higher than that of the other. The overall association between 5HT and DA turnover (Fig. 4), implies that the DA turnovers of the pairs had a similar but less close relationship. Before the rats were paired they were habituated to the observation chamber in the red light phase by placing them in it individually for 30 min/day for 2 days. During these periods, motor activity was scored on video tape by square crossings. These values did not show significant correlations with either 5HT or DA turnover.

Social interactions during pairing for 30 min in the red light phase were scored using videotape by an observer who was not aware of the turnover values. and included durations of body contact, dominant and submissive postures, allogrooming, mounting and boxing and numbers of neck and body bites. The only behaviour which correlated with turnover values was neck and body bites. The total number of bites/pair correlated very strikingly with 5HT turnover (n = pairs), i.e. bites vs higher 5HT turnover of pair, $r = -0.83, p <$ 0.01; bites vs lower 5HT turnover of pair, $r = -0.95, p < 0.001$; bites vs higher 5HT turnover of pair/lower 5HT turnover of pair, $r = 0.97, p < 0.001$. As in general, one rat of each pair did most of the biting, the corresponding correlations between bites by the principal biter and 5HT turnover are also significant ($r = -0.77, p < 0.02; r = -0.90, p < 0.001; r = 0.93, p < 0.001$). As the animals were selected for pairing so that absolute difference between each pair of 5HT turnovers was approximately constant, a correlation of bites with the higher 5HT turnover of each pair implies a tendency towards a correlation with the lower 5HT turnover of each pair. Biting correlated less strikingly with DA turnover and it must be taken into account that because of the overall positive correlation between 5HT turnover and DA turnover (Fig. 4) a correlation between bites and 5HT turnover necessarily tends to lead to a correlation between bites and DA turnover. Values were as follows: bites vs higher DA turnover of pair, $r = -0.45$, n.s.; bites vs lower DA turnover of pair, $r = -0.93$, $p < 0.001$; bites vs higher DA turnover of pair/lower DA turnover of pair, $r = 0.52$, ns.

Fig. 5 illustrates the motor activities of the rats in the observation box before pairing and their biting activities after pairing. The following comments may be made:

(1) Except in the case of one pair (see below) there is no obvious indication that the relative amounts of biting by the paired rats simply reflects their relative motor activities when alone.

(2) The five pairs on the left have high ratios of 5HT turnovers and the principal biter has the higher turnover of the pair.

(3) The two pairs on the right have small ratios of 5HT turnovers and show very little biting at all.

(4) In the two intermediate pairs, the principal biter has the smaller turnover. However, in one of these pairs, this finding could reflect the fact that the rat with the smaller 5HT turnover was much more active than its partner when they were placed individually in the observation box. This three-fold difference was greater than that found for any other pair; the more active rat being the most active one of the whole experiment.

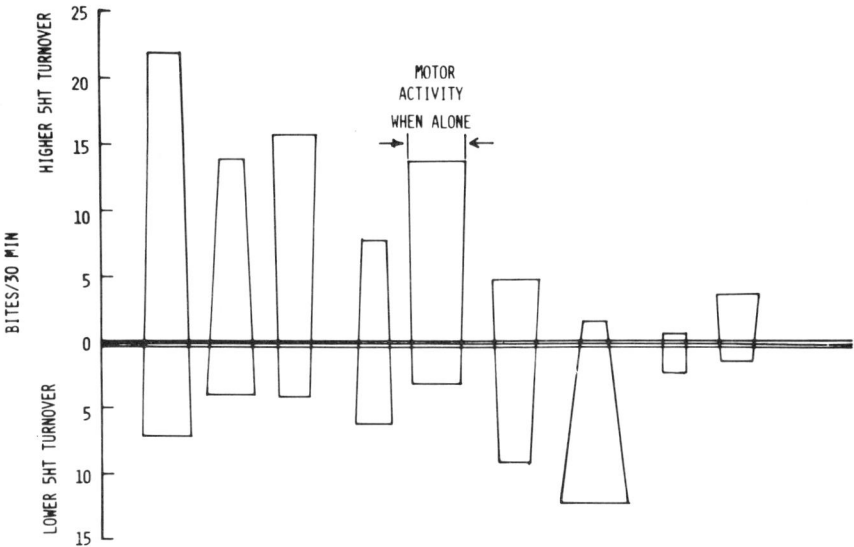

Fig. 5 – Motor activities (square crossings) of rats in the observation box before pairing and numbers of bites after pairing. Each rhombus shows results for one pair of rats. Bites by the partners with the higher and lower 5HT turnovers are shown above and below the x-axis respectively. The ratios of the 5HT turnovers of the pairs were as follows (left to right): 2.6, 2.0, 2.0, 1.8, 1.8, 1.8, 1.9, 1.5, 1.5. The widths of the parallel upper and lower sides of each rhombus are proportional to the respective motor activities of the partners when placed separately in the observation box.

In general, these results suggest that this rather ritualized biting (in which blood is never drawn and which may be a component of the development of dominance behaviour) tends to be predicted by higher 5HT turnover. The results might be thought to go against evidence that aggressive behaviour (albeit shown against an intruder) is precipitated by low 5HT synthesis. However, there are numerous problems in interpreting such evidence and it is by no means all on one side. Thus work by Sheard (1973), Hodge and Butcher (1974), Paxinos and Atrens (1977), Gibbons *et al.* (1978), Valzelli *et al.* (1981), Brown *et al.* (1982) and Morand *et al.* (1983) is consistent with low 5HT function leading to aggression but findings by Kostowski and Valzelli (1974), Malick and Barnett (1976), Weinstock and Weiss (1980), Payne and Wilson (1981) and Matter (1982) point in the other direction.

Furthermore, we cannot assume that all behaviour that can be categorized as aggression is mediated in the same way. Neurochemical mechanisms which in animals mediate the killing of an intruder or in man are implicated in impulsive violence (Brown *et al.*, 1982; Morand *et al.*, 1983) may well have little in common with mechanisms responsible for biting which does not lead to physical trauma and possibly mediates the establishment of dominance patterns within a social group. The present results might perhaps be compared with those obtained by McGuire *et al.* (1983) on 5HT metabolism in a colony of male vervet monkeys as the dominant monkeys had significantly higher CSF 5HIAA and blood platelet 5HT than non-dominant animals. However, the platelet difference disappeared on housing singly for three weeks while our results suggested that central 5HT turnover values of singly housed rats predicted future social behaviour.

6. SUMMARY

The main conclusions are as follows:

(a) Rat whole brain amine metabolism is paralleled in cisternal CSF.
(b) The CSF withdrawal method is applicable to neurochemical–behavioural investigations.
(c) 5HT turnover in the central nervous system within its normal range may have predictive value for the social behaviour of rats. In particular, the results indicate that previously determined turnover values correlate with biting in a social situation structured to elicit dominant/aggressive behaviour.

These behavioural findings suggest many possible further experiments. Furthermore, the present experiments indicate that neurochemical–behavioural studies of a new kind are now possible in which neurochemical characteristics of individual rats are determined using CSF (or dialysis or *in vivo* voltammetry) without killing the animals and the predictive value of the results for subsequent behaviour then assessed.

REFERENCES

Brown, G. L., Goodwin, F. K. and Bunney, W. E. (1982). Human aggression and suicide: their relationship to neuropsychiatric diagnosis and serotonin metabolism. *Adv. Biochem. Psychopharmacol.*, **34**, 287–307.

Burns, D., London, J., Brunswick, D. J., Pring, M., Garfinkel, D., Rabinowitz, J. L. and Mendels, J. (1976). A kinetic analysis of 5-hydroxyindoleacetic acid excretion from rat brain and CSF. *Biol. Psychiat.*, **11**, 125–157.

Cserr, J. (1965). Potassium exchange between cerebrospinal fluid, plasma and brain. *Am. J. Physiol.*, **209**, 1219–1226.

Curzon, G., Hutson, P. H., Kantamaneni, B. D., Sahakian, B. J. and Sarna, G. S. (1985). Dopamine and 5-hydroxytryptamine metabolism in the rat: acidic metabolites in cisternal cerebrospinal fluid before and after giving probenecid. *J. Neurochem.*, **45**, 508–604.

Danguir, J., LeQuan-Bui, K. H., Elghozi, J. L., Devynck, M. A. and Nicolaidis, S. (1982). LCEC monitoring of 5-hydroxyindolic compounds in the cerbrospinal fluid of the rat related to sleep and feeding. *Brain Res. Bull.*, **8**, 293–297.

Dedek, J., Baumes, R., Tien-Duc, N., Gomeni, R. and Korf, J. (1979). Turnover of free and conjugated (sulphonyloxy) dihydroxyphenylacetic acid and homovanillic acid in rat striatum. *J. Neurochem.*, **33**, 687–695.

Degrell, I., Zenner, K., Kummer, P. and Stock, G. (1983). Monoamine metabolites in the CSF of conscious unrestrained cats. *Brain Res.*, **277**, 283–287.

Elghozi, J. L., Mignot, E. and LeQuan-Bui, K. H. (1983). Probenecid sensitive pathway of elimination of dopamine and serotonin metabolites in CSF of the rat. *J. Neural Trans.*, **57**, 85–94.

Gibbons, J. L., Barr, G. A., Bridger, W. H. and Leibowitz, S. F. (1978). Effects of para-chlorophenylalanine and 5-hydroxytryptophan on mouse killing behaviour in killer rats. *Pharmacol. Biochem. Behav.*, **9**, 91–98.

Griauzde, M. and Radulovacki, M. (1976). Increase of 5-hydroxyindoleacetic acid and homovanillic acid in cisternal fluid of cats subjected to stress. *J. Neurochem.*, **26**, 1301–1302.

Hodge, G. K. and Butcher, L. L. (1974). 5-hydroxytryptamine correlates of isolation-induced aggression in mice. *Eur. J. Pharmacol.*, **28**, 326–337.

Hutson, P. H., Sarna, G. S., Kantamaneni, B. D. and Curzon, G. (1984a). Concurrent determination of brain dopamine and 5-hydroxytryptamine turnovers in individual freely moving rats using repeated sampling of cerebrospinal fluid. *J. Neurochem.*, **43**, 151–159.

Hutson, P. H., Sarna, G. S. and Curzon, G. (1984b). Determination of daily variation of brain 5-hydroxytryptamine and dopamine turnovers and of the clearance of their acidic metabolites in conscious rats by repeated sampling of cerebrospinal fluid. *J. Neurochem.*, **43**, 291–293.

Hutson, P. H., Sarna, G. S., Kantamaneni, B. D. and Curzon, G. (1985). Monitoring the effect of a tryptophan load on brain indole metabolism in freely moving rats by simultaneous cerebrospinal fluid sampling and brain dialysis. *J. Neurochem.*, **44**, 1266–1273.

Joseph, M. H., Baker, H. F. and Ridley, R. M. (1981). Analysis of CSF amine metabolites and precursors including tryptophan, 5HIAA and HVA by HPLC using fluorescence and electrochemical detection in primates: effect of probenecid. In: *Central Transmitter Turnover,* Pycock, V. J. and Taberner, P. V. (eds.), Croom Helm, pp. 162–167.

Kostowski, W. and Valzelli, L. (1974). Biochemical and behavioural effects of lesions of raphe nuclei in aggressive mice. *Pharmacol. Biochem. Behav.*, **2**, 277–280.

Mackintosh, J. H., Chance, M. R. A. and Silverman, A(1977). The contribution of ethological techniques to the study of drug effects. In: *Handbook of Psychopharmacology,* Vol. 7, Iversen, L. L., Iversen, S. D. and Snyder, S. H. (eds.), Plenum, pp. 3–35.

Malick, J. B. and Barnett, A. (1976). The role of serotonergic pathways in isolation-induced aggression in mice. *Pharmacol. Biochem. Behav.*, **5**, 55–61.

Matte, A. C. (1982). The effect of 5,7-dihydroxytryptamine on motor activity, aggression, and 'emotionality' in isolated wild male mice. *Aggress. Behav.*, **8**, 198–200.

McGuire, M. T., Raleigh, M. J. and Johnson, C. (1983). Social dominance in adult vervet monkeys: behaviour–biochemical relationships. *Soc. Sci. Inf.*, **22**, 311–328.

Morand, C., Young, S. N. and Ervin, F. R. (1983). Clinical response of aggressive achizophrenics to oral tryptophan. *Biol. Psychiat.,* **18**, 575–578.

Neff, N. H. and Tozer, T. N. (1968). *In vivo* measurement of brain serotonin turnover. *Adv. Pharmacol.,* **6A**, 97–109.

Nielsen, J. A. and Moore, K. E. (1982). Measurement of metabolites of dopamine and 5-hydroxytryptamine in cerebroventricular perfusates of unanaes-thetized freely-moving rats: selective effects of drugs. *Pharmacol. Biochem. Behav.,* **16**, 131–137.

Paxinos, G. and Atrens, D. M. (1977). 5-7-dihydroxytryptamine lesions: effects on body weight, irritability, and muricide. *Aggrsss. Behav.,* **3**, 107–118.

Payne, A. P. and Wilson, C. A. (1981). Effect of living conditions and aggression on neural biogenic amine metabolism in male golden hamsters. In: *The Biology of Aggression,* Brain, P. F. and Benton, D. (eds.), Syjthoff and Noordhoff, pp. 147–154.

Sarna, G. S., Hutson, P. H., Tricklebank, M. D. and Curzon, G. (1983). Deter-mination of brain 5-hydroxytryptamine turnover in freely moving rats using repeated sampling of cerebrospinal fluid. *J. Neurochem.,* **40**, 383–388.

Sarna, G. S., Hutson, P. H. and Curzon, G. (1984). Effect of α-methylfluorodopa on dopamine metabolites: importance of conjugation and egress. *Eur. J. Pharmacol.,* **100**, 343–350.

Sheard, M. H. (1973). Brain serotonin depletion by p-chlorophenylalanine or lesions of raphe neurons in rats. *Physiol. Behav.,* **10**, 809–811.

Valzelli, L., Bernasconi, S. and Dalessando, M. (1981). Effect of tryptophan administration on spontaneous and p-CPA induced muricidal aggression in laboratory rats. *Pharmacol. Res. Comm.,* **13**, 891–897.

Weinstock, M. and Weiss, C. (1980). Antagonism by propranolol of isolation induced aggression in mice: correlation with 5-hydroxytryptamine receptor blockade. *Neuropharmacology,* **19**, 653–656.

6

Serotonin metabolism and blood pressure regulation: Insights from brain tissue assays and *in vivo* electrochemical recording

Curt R. Freed, Hirotoshi Echizen and **Devarajan Bhaskaran**

Division of Clinical Pharmacology and Toxicology, Box C237, University of Colorado Health Sciences Center, 4200 East Ninth Avenue, Denver, Colorado 80262, USA

1. INTRODUCTION

Both serotonin and norepinephrine are known to play a role in the regulation of blood pressure. A number of anti-hypertensive agents work by reducing sympathetic outflow from the brain probably by a mechanism which increases presynaptic inhibition of noradrenergic neurons. The developing understanding of alpha-2 presynaptic inhibitory receptors coupled with the recognition that compounds such as alpha-methylnorepinephrine and clonidine are selective and potent alpha-2 agonists has supported this model. The role of serotonin in blood pressure regulation is less certain. Acute single doses of 5-HTP have been shown to lower blood pressure in experimental animals (Henning and Rubenson, 1971; Nolan, 1977). This result suggests that increasing serotonin production in brain reduces blood pressure. Conflicting with this fact is the observation that stimulation of serotonergic cell bodies in the dorsal raphe nucleus causes hypertension and also leads to release of serotonin from terminal fields such as the anterior hypothalamus (Kuhn *et al.*, 1980). Direct application of serotonin onto anterior hypothalamus also causes an increase in blood pressure (Wolf *et al.*, 1981).

There also appear to be direct interactions between serotonin and norepine-phrine. Norepinephrine has been shown to inhibit serotonin release from rat brain slices and synaptosomes by stimulation of alpha receptors located on serotonergic nerve terminals (Frankhuyzen and Mulder, 1980; Maura *et al.,* 1982). Noradrenergic nerve terminals directly synapse on serotonin neurons in raphe (Baraban and Aghajanian, 1981). Blockade of norepinephrine input suppresses serotonergic nerve firing and iontophoretic application of norepine-phrine will restore firing. Clonidine causes a reduction in serotonergic cell firing in raphe although the reduction is probably due to an indirect effect primarily involving inhibition of noradrenergic neurons in locus coeruleus (Svensson *et al.,* 1975). With this experimental background, we decided to explore the relation-ship between serotonin and norepinephrine during blood pressure regulation using pharmacologic manipulations of serotonin concentration. We have also changed peripheral blood pressure with vasodilators and vasopressors and then looked at central norepinephrine and 5-HIAA concentrations using direct *in vivo* electrochemical techniques.

2. MATERIALS AND METHODS

Male Sprague-Dawley rats 300–400 g were used for all experiments. In studies of the effect of long-term infusions of the serotonin precursors TP and 5-HTP, animals anaesthetized with chloral hydrate-pentobarbital had arterial and venous catheters implanted in the aorta below the level of the renal arteries and in the right jugular vein. Animals were placed in restraining cages and allowed to recover from anaesthesia for 24 hours. They were then infused with doses of 5-HTP 2 to 20 mg/kg/h with and without the peripheral decarboxylase inhibitor, carbidopa, 2.5 mg/kg/h. TP was administered in doses of 5 to 40 mg/kg/h. Blood pressure was measured in the conscious, restrained animals before and after 24 hours of drug administration. Following the drug infusion, animals were sacrificed and brain tissue and heart were removed. Norepinephrine, dopamine, serotonin and 5-HIAA were measured by HPLC with electrochemical detection as previously described (Echizen and Freed, 1982).

For the studies using *in vivo* electrochemistry, animals were anaesthetized with urethane and a 250 micrometer unmodified carbon paste electrode made from Ultra F Carbon and mineral oil was implanted under stereotaxic control in the dorsal raphe nucleus, nucleus tractus solitarius or locus coeruleus. Electrode position was determined by histologic examination of the tissue in each case. Blood pressure was measured by an intra-arterial line in either the tail artery or femoral artery. Drugs were infused intravenously or given intraperitoneally as noted below.

In vivo electrochemistry was performed using a DCV-5 cyclic voltammetry apparatus (Bioanalytical Systems) with a linear ramp from -0.2 to $+0.5$ V at a rate of 10 millivolts per second. The signal was processed by semiderivative techniques and two peaks were seen in all brain regions. The first peak was recorded at 0.15 volts (peak 1) and the second peak at 0.3 volts (peak 2).

Characterization of these electrochemical peaks was by pharmacologic techniques including the tyrosine hydroxylase inhibitor alpha-methylparatyrosine, the monoamine oxidase inhibitor pargyline, and the dopamine beta hydroxylase inhibitor fusaric acid. In addition to monitoring the changes in electrochemical peaks, we also dissected individual nuclei after pharmacologic treatments and assayed them for dopamine, DOPAC, norepinephrine, serotonin and 5-HIAA using HPLC with electrochemical detection. Phenylephrine was infused intravenously at a dose to cause a blood pressure increase of 50–60 mm Hg for 50–60 min and sodium nitroprusside was given intravenously to lower blood pressure by 20 mm Hg.

3. RESULTS

Infusions of 5-HTP caused a dose-related reduction in blood pressure while TP infusions did not lower blood pressure (Echizen and Freed, 1982). The pressure reduction associated with 5-HTP was directly related to the serotonin and 5-HIAA concentrations in hypothalamus and brainstem. These increases were very large compared to the modest changes produced by TP infusions. Fig. 1 shows the relationship between brain 5-HIAA concentration and blood pressure. There is a highly significant correlation between the two. In additional experiments we demonstrated that the hypotensive effect of 5-HTP was due to a central rather than peripheral effect since 5-HTP administered without carbidopa

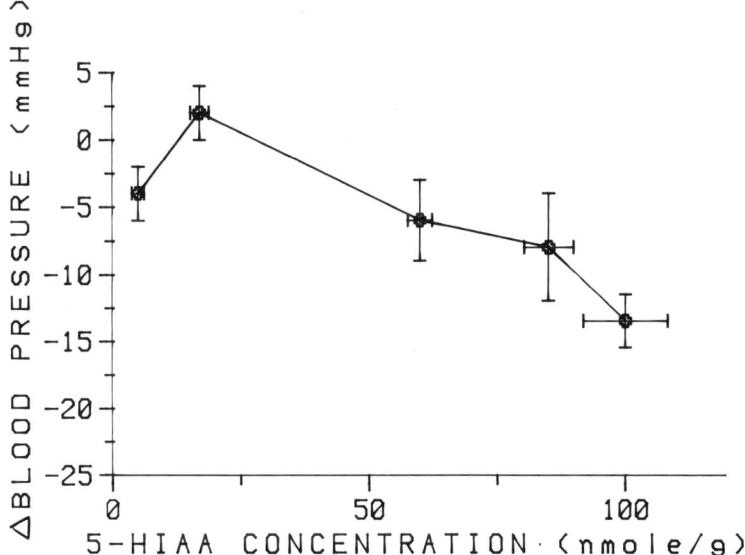

Fig. 1 – Correlation between hypothalamic 5-HIAA concentration and change in blood pressure in rats receiving 5-hydroxytryptophan. Each data point represents $n = 5$ animals. $r^2 = 0.73$; $p < 0.05$. Doses of 5-hydroxytryptophan of 0, 2, 5, 10 and 20 mg/kg/h for 24 h poduced the progressive increases in 5-HIAA concentration.

led to greater concentrations of serotonin and 5-HIAA in heart; however, the hypotensive effect of the drug was less.

We also examined the effect of the amino acid infusions on norepinephrine and dopamine concentrations. We found that both 5-HTP and TP caused a dose-dependent reduction in dopamine and norepinephrine in hypothalamus and brainstem regions. The reduction in both catecholamines was equivalent for the two amino acids suggesting that a selective reduction in catecholamine concentration was not the explanation for the greater hypotensive effect of 5-HTP. It is likely that the catecholamine reductions were due to competition for tyrosine uptake by the competing neutral amino acids.

The *in vivo* electrochemical electrode was first studied in the dorsal raphe nucleus. Enzyme inhibition with alpha-methylparatyrosine, pargyline and fusaric acid indicated that peak 1 appeared to be norepinephrine rather than dopamine or DOPAC since the peak was reduced by alpha-methylparatyrosine and fusaric acid but not affected by pargyline. Ascorbate was not detected using these electrodes (Echizen and Freed, 1983). Peak 2 was largely composed

Table 1 — Dorsal raphe nucleus: Changes in electrochemical signals and tissue concentrations of catechols and indoles.

Drug treatment		% control electrochemical peak		% control concentration
Alpha-methylparatyrosine	Catechol	78 ± 6	NE	53 ± 9^a
300 mg/kg			DA	22 ± 5^a
	Indole	97 ± 2	5-HT	117 ± 4
			5-HIAA	100 ± 9
Pargyline	Catechol	94 ± 3	NE	178 ± 9^b
75 mg/kg			DA	187 ± 22^a
	Indole	42 ± 2^b	5-HT	430 ± 38^b
			5-HIAA	44 ± 6^b
Fusaric acid	Catechol	72 ± 3^b	NE	42 ± 8^a
100 mg/kg			DA	153 ± 22^b
	Indole	177 ± 31^b	5-HT	156 ± 6^a
			5-HIAA	172 ± 19^b
Parachlorophenylalanine	Catechol	78 ± 6^b	NE	106 ± 8
300 mg/kg			DA	75 ± 3
	Indole	86 ± 2^b	5-HT	97 ± 8
			5-HIAA	77 ± 5

All drugs were given i.p. and electrochemical and tissue results are at 2 hours after drug injection.
Results are mean ± S.E.M.; $n = 5$ or 6.
[a] $= p < 0.05$, [b] $= p < 0.01$, different from control.

of 5-HIAA rather than serotonin since it was reduced by pargyline (Echizen and Freed, 1983) although a contribution from uric acid cannot be excluded at this time. Table 1 shows the changes in the electrochemical signal coupled with the reductions in tissue concentrations of norepinephrine, dopamine, serotonin and 5-HIAA actually observed.

Results of experiments with phenylephrine-induced hypertension and nitroprusside-induced hypotension are presented in Figs. 2 and 3. These results indicate that hypertension is associated with an increase in extracellular fluid

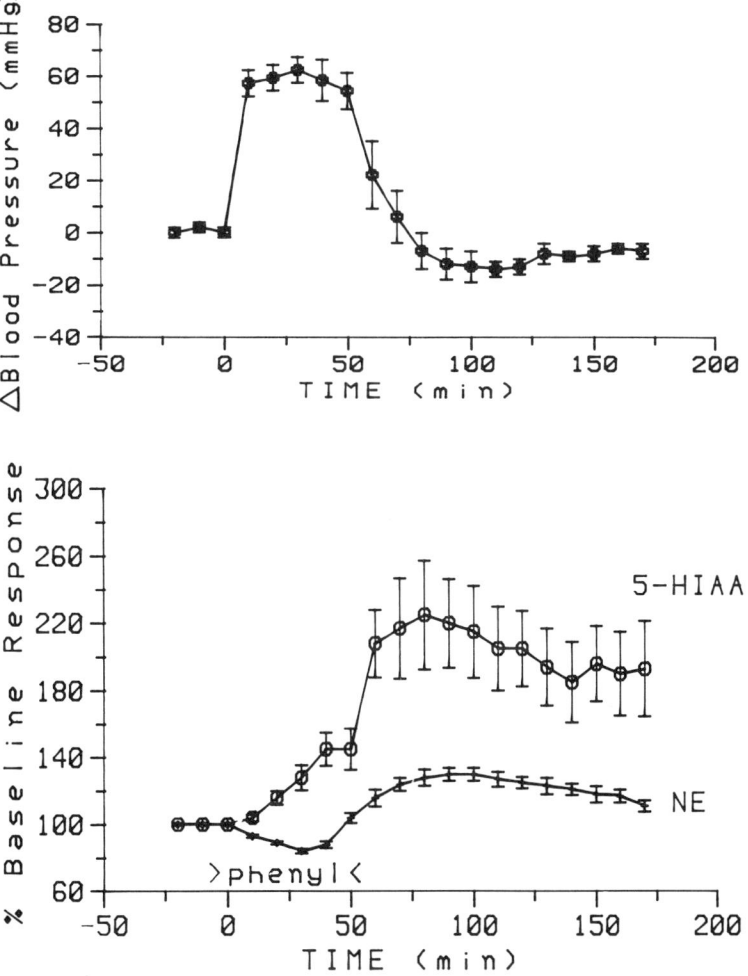

Fig. 2 – Phenylephrine hypertension and changes in dorsal raphe norepinephrine and 5-HIAA electrochemical responses. Blood pressure was raised 50 mm Hg by a 50-minute infusion of phenylephrine. 5-HIAA signal rose within 20 minutes of the onset of hypertension and continued to increase even after discontinuation of the drug infusion ($p < 0.01$). Norepinephrine showed a small reduction during hypertension and then a significant increase following the drug infusion ($p < 0.05$).

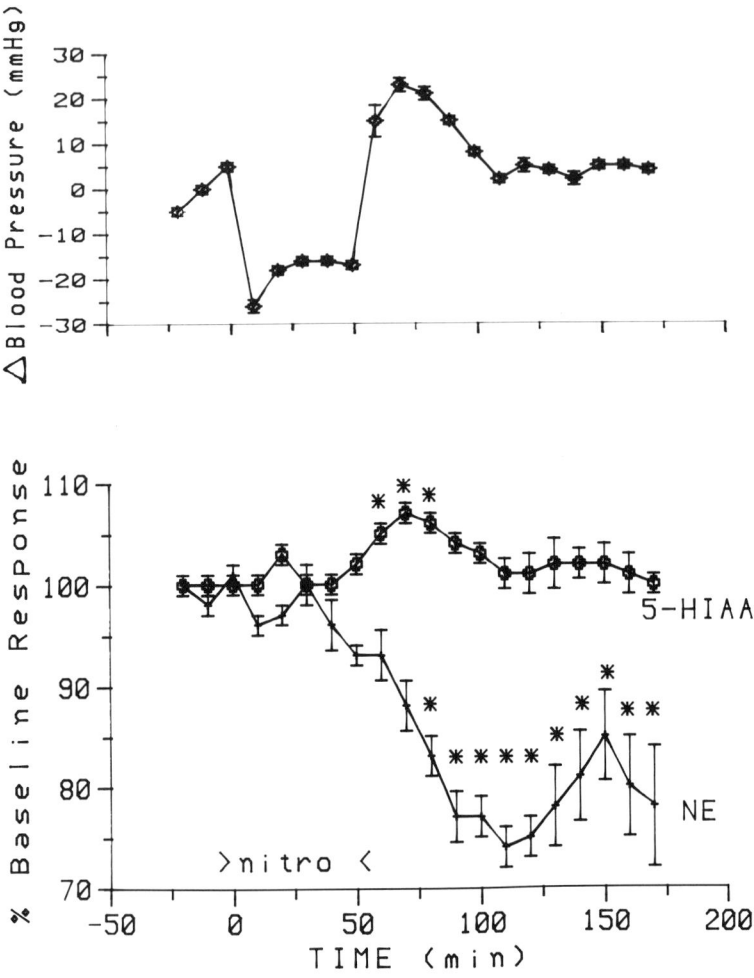

Fig. 3 – Nitroprusside hypotension and changes in dorsal raphe norepinephrine and 5-HIAA electrochemical responses. Blood pressure was reduced 20 mm Hg by sodium nitroprusside. During the infusion there was no change in 5-HIAA and a small reduction in norepinephrine when the infusion was stopped. After the infusion, there was a period of rebound hypertension during which 5-HIAA increased and norepinephrine concentration fell (* = p < 0.05).

5-HIAA concentration which began immediately after the increase in blood pressure and persisted after the infusion was stopped. Norepinephrine, by contrast, showed an initial fall in signal but then a subsequent rise even as the phenylephrine infusion was continued. The norepinephrine signal continued to rise following the discontinuation of the pressor agent. With nitroprusside-induced hypotension (Fig. 3) there was no change in the electrochemical signal seen during the hypotensive phase. However, during the reflex hypertension which followed the infusion there was a reduction in norepinephrine release and an increase in 5-HIAA concentration (Echizen and Freed, 1984).

The same experimental paradigm was repeated in nucleus tractus solitarius and locus coeruleus. In nucleus tractus solitarius as in dorsal raphe, there was an increase in the 5-HIAA signal during phenylephrine-induced hypertension (Bhaskaran and Freed, 1984). The norepinephrine response was somewhat different, however. As shown in Fig. 4, there was a reduction in norpinephrine concentration which persisted throughout the hypertensive period and only when the drug was discontinued was there an increase in norepinephrine signal. Fig. 5 shows that during nitroprusside-induced hypotension, the 5-HIAA concentration did not change in nucleus tractus solitarus. However, there was a reduction in the norepinephrine signal. On discontinuation of the nitroprusside there was an increase in the 5-HIAA signal while the norepinephrine signal was even more reduced. Tissue concentrations measured after these physiologic manipulations confirmed the increases in 5-HIAA and the reductions in norepinephrine concentrations (Bhaskaran and Freed, 1984).

Electrochemical responses in locus coeruleus were strikingly different from dorsal raphe and nucleus tractus solitarius. First, pharmacologic characterization of peak 1 showed that it was reduced after pargyline and alpha-methylparatyrosine but was not affected by fusaric acid. Thus the peak appears to be DOPAC as others have noted (Buda *et al.*, 1983). Phenylephrine hypertension produced a reduction in the DOPAC peak during the 40 minutes of infusion followed by an increase during the last 20 minutes of infusion and thereafter.

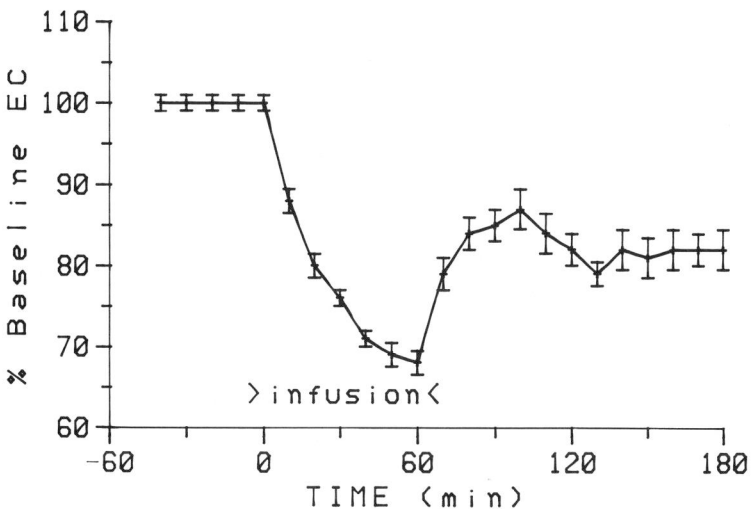

Fig. 4 – Phenylephrine hypertension and norepinephrine signal in nucleus tractus solitarius. Blood pressure was increased by 50 mm Hg for 60 minutes. There was a highly significant decrease (*p* < 0.001) in the norepinephrine signal. Following the infusion the norepinephrine signal partially recovered toward baseline.

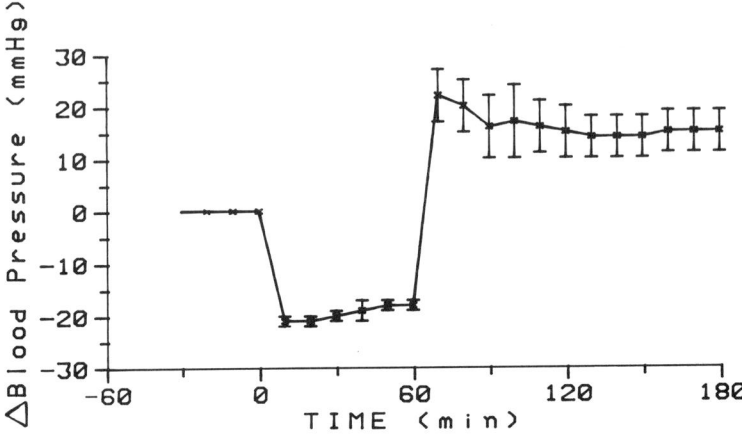

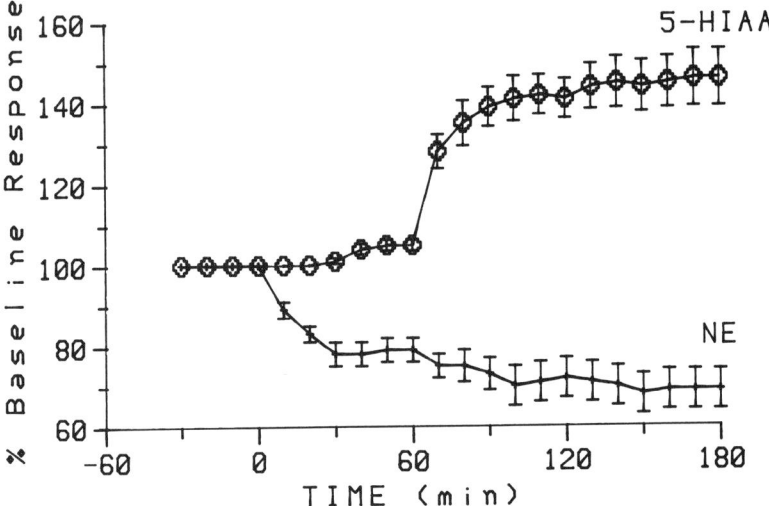

Fig. 5 – Nitroprusside hypotension and changes in electrochemical peaks in nucleus tractus solitarius. Blood pressure was reduced by 20 mm Hg for 60 minutes. Norepinephrine fell immediately and remained low even after the infusion ($p < 0.01$, all points after 30 min different from baseline). 5-HIAA rose only during post-infusion reflex hypertension ($p < 0.01$, all points after 70 minutes).

Nitroprusside hypotension was associated with a modest decrease in the apparent DOPAC signal during the hypotensive phase with an increase during the reflex hypertension which followed the infusion. In contrast to the dorsal raphe and nucleus tractus solitarius, the 5-HIAA signal rose during hypotension and kept increasing during the reflex hypertensive phase.

4. DISCUSSION

Infusions with 5-HTP produced blood pressure reductions which were proportional to the increases in serotonin turnover induced in brainstem (Echizen and Freed, 1982). Tadepalli and co-workers have shown that when 5-HTP is restricted to the region of the fourth ventricle, the drug produces hypotension (Tadepalli *et al.*, 1977). When the drug is confined to anterior portion of brain with infusion to the lateral ventricles, no hypotension is observed. This result indicates that the probable site of action of 5-HTP is the region of the serotonin cell bodies. Since serotonin is known to auto-inhibit serotonergic cell firing (Wang and Aghajanian, 1978), it is likely that the increase in serotonin turnover in brainstem leads to reduced cell firing. Slower cell firing would be associated with less serotonin release from nerve terminals in pressor regions such as anterior hypothalamus.

Our experiments with *in vivo* electrochemical measurements during induced hypertension and hypotension show that there are changes in serotonin turnover in different brain nuclei in response to increases and decreases in blood pressure. The data indicate that with phenylephrine-induced hypertension there is an increase in the 5-HIAA signal in all nuclei which we have studied. In dorsal raphe, the increase might represent auto-inhibition of serotonergic neurons (Echizen and Freed, 1984).

We propose that the increase in 5-HIAA is related to pressure information alone rather than the state of sympathetic nervous system since we see the increased 5-HIAA both during induced hypertension when sympathetic activity is low and during reflex hypertension when sympathetic activity is high. Thus, there appears to be little relationship between the 5-HIAA signal and sympathetic activity. To see whether baroreceptor afferents are responsible for the observed changes in 5-HIAA, we are conducting experiments with animals which have undergone sino-aortic denervation.

The reasons for the differences in norepinephrine and 5-HIAA responses in dorsal raphe nucleus and nucleus tractus solitarius are uncertain. Both are areas with noradrenergic nerve terminals and yet norepinephrine release is depressed throughout the hypertensive phase in nucleus tractus solitarius while only transiently depressed in dorsal raphe nucleus. During hypotension, nucleus tractus solitarius showed a reduction in norepinephrine release while in dorsal raphe nucleus there was no change in norepinephrine signal during the hypotensive phase but the signal did fall during the reflex hypertensive period that followed the nitroprusside infusion.

The locus coeruleus differs from the other two nuclei studied since the catechol signal at that site appears to be DOPAC rather than norepinephrine. Others have noted the presence of DOPAC in the locus coeruleus (Buda *et al.*, 1983). The changes in catechol signal in locus coeruleus are also different from those seen in either dorsal raphe or nucleus tractus solitarius. Rather than a decrease in the DOPAC signal during hypotension there appeared to be a slight increase during the first 30 minutes of nitroprusside infusion. The 5-HIAA response during hypotension was also different in locus coeruleus. The 5-HIAA signal rose only after hypotension in dorsal raphe and nucleus tractus solitarius while it increased in locus coeruleus right at the onset of hypotension.

It is premature to assign meaning to the electrochemical changes seen in brainstem during manipulations of peripheral blood pressure. If we accept the hypothesis that presynaptic dopamine and norepinephrine release inhibits noradrenergic cell firing then we might suppose that the increased DOPAC signal in the noradrenergic cells of the locus coeruleus would represent greater inhibition of those cells. Conversely, a rise in the norepinephrine signal in dorsal raphe nucleus might be a marker for increased serotonergic cell firing. Further experiments with other nuclei will let us see a broader part of the interplay between catechol and serotonin and will, we hope, make it easier to unravel a pattern relating the norepinephrine and 5-HIAA signals to changes in blood pressure.

ACKNOWLEDGEMENTS

This research was supported by US Public Health Service Grants HL30722, NS18639, RCDA HL00782 (C.R.F.), and a grant from Merck, Sharp & Dohme.

REFERENCES

Baraban, J. M. and Aghajanian, G. K. (1981). Noradrenergic innervation of serotonergic neurons in the dorsal raphe: Demonstration by electron microscopic autoradiography. *Brain Res.*, **204**, 1–11.

Bhaskaran, D. and Freed, C. R. (1984). Changes in systemic blood pressure alter norepinephrine release and serotonin turnover in nucleus tractus solitarius as measured by *in vivo* electrochemistry. *Society of Neurosciences*, **10**(1), 299, abstract 91.1.

Buda, M., DeSimoni, G., Gonon, F. and Pujol, J.-F. (1983). Catecholamine metabolism in the rat locus coeruleus studied by *in vivo* differential pulse voltammetry. I. Nature of origin of contributors to the oxidation current at $+0.1$ V. *Brain Res.*, **273**, 197–206.

Echizen, H. and Freed, C. R. (1982). Long-term infusion of L-5-hydroxytryptophan increases brain serotonin turnover and decreases blood pressure in normotensive rats. *J. Pharmacol. Exp. Ther.*, **200**(3), 579–584.

Echizen, H. and Freed, C. R. (1983). *In vivo* electrochemical detection of extraneuronal 5-hydroxyindoleacetic acid and norepinephrine in the dorsal raphe nucleus of urethane-anaesthetized rats. *Brain Res*, **277**, 55–62.

Echizen, H. and Freed, C. R. (1984). Altered serotonin and norepinephrine metabolism in rat dorsal raphe nucleus after drug-induced hypertension. *Life Sci.*, **34**(16), 1581–1585.

Frankhuyzen, A. L. and Mulder, A. H. (1980). Noradrenaline inhibits depolarization-induced ³H-serotonin release from slices of rat hippocampus. *Eur. J. Pharmacol.*, **63**, 179–182.

Henning, M. and Rubenson, A. (1971). Effects of 5-hydroxytryptophan on arterial blood pressure, body temperature and tissue monoamines in the rat. *Acta Pharmacol. Toxicol.*, **29**, 145–154.

Kuhn, D. M., Wolf, W. A. and Lovenberg, W. (1980). Pressor effects of electrical stimulation of the dorsal and median raphe nuclei in anaesthetized rats. *J. Pharmacol. Exp. Ther.*, **214**, 403–409.

Maura, G., Gemignani, A. and Raiteri, M. (1982). Noradrenaline inhibits central serotonin release through alpha-2 adrenoceptors located in serotonergic nerve terminals. *Naunyn-Schmiedeberg's Arch. Pharmacol.*, **320**, 272–274.

Nolan, P. L. (1977). The effects of serotonin precursors on the pressor response to intravenous clonidine in conscious rats. *Clin. Exp. Pharmacol. Physiol.*, **4**, 579–583.

Svensson, T. H., Bunney, B. S. and Aghajanian, G. K. (1975). Inhibition of both noradrenergic and serotonergic neurons in brain by the alpha-adrenergic agonist clonidine. *Brain Res.*, **92**, 291–306.

Tadepalli, A. S., Mills, E. and Schanberg, S. M. (1977). Central depression of carotid baroreceptor pressor response, arterial pressure and heart rate by 5-hydroxytryptophan: Influence of supracollicular areas of the brain. *J. Pharmacol. Exp. Ther.*, **202**, 310–319.

Wang, R. Y. and Aghajanian, G. K. (1978). Collateral inhibition of serotonergic neurones in the rat dorsal raphe nucleus: Pharmacological evidence. *Neuropharmacology*, **17**, 819–825.

Wolf, W. A., Kuhn, D. M. and Lovenberg, W. (1981). Pressor effects of dorsal raphe stimulation and intrahypothalamic application of serotonin in the spontaneously hypertensive rat. *Brain Res.*, **208**, 192–197.

7

Changes in extracellular brain ascorbate concentration as an index of excitatory aminoacid release

Marianne Fillenz, Robert D. O'Neill[†] **and Richard A. Grunewald**
University Laboratory of Physiology, Parks Road, Oxford, OX1 3PT, UK

Ascorbic acid is present in high concentration in the mammalian brain; only the adrenal cortex (Damron *et al.*, 1952; Hornig, 1975) and the pituitary (Schaus, 1957) have higher concentrations. In species such as guinea pig and man, ascorbate comes entirely from the diet, whereas in rats it is synthesized in the liver at the rate of 70 mg/day.

Plasma concentration of ascorbate, which is affected by drugs and stress (Sebrell and Harris, 1967), is normally about 50 μM (Grunewald *et al.*, 1983). The blood–brain barrier has a low permeability to ascorbate, which is transferred from plasma to cerebrospinal fluid (CSF) by an active, saturable transport mechanism (Spector *et al.*, 1977). The site of this transport mechanism (K_m = 55 μM) is the choroid plexus (Spector and Lorenzo, 1974); normally, therefore, the transport mechanism is half-saturated. The extracellular concentration in the brain and in the CSF is estimated at 100–500 μM (Gonon *et al.*, 1981; O'Neill *et al.*, 1982a; Shenk *et al.*, 1982). There is a second active transport mechanism across the neuronal, and possibly glial, cell membrane whose K_m is 33 μM and which is therefore normally fully saturated. The operations of this transport system results in an intracellular ascorbate concentration of 1–2 mM. There

---

†Beit Memorial Research Fellow, Present address: Department of Chemistry, University College. Belfield, Dublin 4, Eire

have been a number of studies which have demonstrated that brain ascorbate *in vivo* is kept constant by a homeostatic mechanism (Spector, 1981; Spector Lorenzo, 1973, 1974). More recently, Shenk *et al.* (1982) suggested that there is a second homeostatic mechanism which keeps ascorbate in the brain extracellular fluid within narrow limits, and that this occurs at the expense of intracellular ascorbate.

1. MEASUREMENT OF EXTRACELLULAR BRAIN ASCORBATE

Ascorbate is electroactive and the development of voltammetry *in vivo* provides a method for the continuous monitoring of extracellular brain ascorbate. Because the voltammetric technique was developed primarily to monitor the release of the monoamine transmitters, the detection of ascorbate, whose oxidation potential is close to those of dopamine and its metabolites, has been widely regarded merely as an obstacle to the study of dopamine release; there has been, therefore, little systematic study of changes in extracellular ascorbate concentration.

We have used microcomputer-controlled linear sweep voltammetry with carbon-paste electrodes to monitor the ascorbate signal simultaneously in up to four discrete brain regions of the unrestrained rat. The applied voltage is

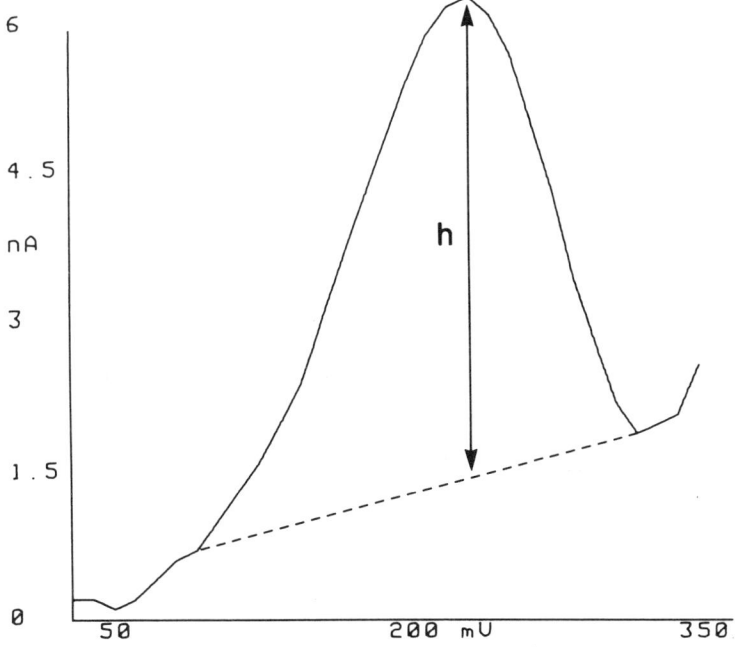

Fig. 1 – Peak 1 of a striatal voltammogram recorded with a carbon-paste electrode in the unrestrained rat. The height of the peak, h, was measured as indicated and is proportional to the extracellular concentration of ascorbic acid around the electrode tip.

increased linearly at a rate of 5 mV/s from, typically, 0 to 650 mV with respect to a Ag reference electrode (O'Neill *et al.*, 1983d). Voltammograms recorded at 12-min intervals consist of a number of separate peaks. A wide variety of approaches have been used to identify the ascorbate signal obtained with this technique. Oxidation potentials *in vitro* (O'Neill *et al.*, 1982b), micro-injections of ascorbate beside electrodes implanted in the brain (O'Neill *et al.*, 1983b), and the use of ascorbate oxidase (Brazell and Marsden, 1982) all indicate that peak 1 recorded with carbon-paste electrodes is due to the oxidation of ascorbic acid at the electrode tip; changes in the height of this peak (measured as indicated in Fig. 1) are proportional to changes in the extracellular concentration of ascorbate (O'Neill *et al.*, 1983b).

2. VARIATIONS IN EXTRACELLULAR ASCORBATE CONCENTRATION

Using this technique we found that a number of drugs produced substantial changes in the ascorbate signal (Fig. 2). For example, the dopamine mimetics amphetamine (Grunewald *et al.*, 1983) and apomorphine (O'Neill and Fillenz, unpublished results) administered systemically lead to an increase in the

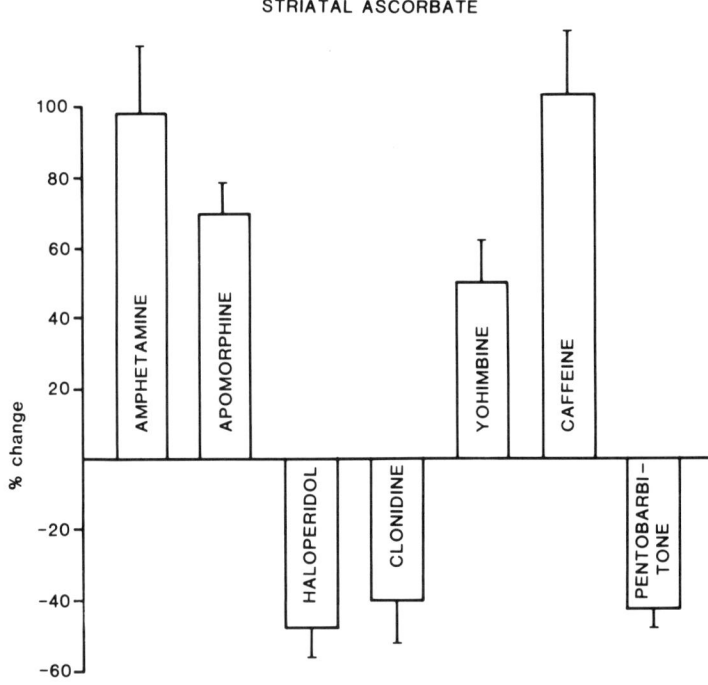

Fig. 2 – The effect of a variety of drugs, administered intraperitoneally, on the ascorbate signal recorded in the striatum. The results are expressed as a percentage change, 60–90 min after injection, compared with the pre-injection value. Amphetamine (5 mg/kg); apomorphine (2 mg/kg); haloperidol (0.5 mg/kg); clonidine (0.1 mg/kg); yohimbine (10 mg/kg); caffeine (50 mg/kg); and pentobarbitone (20 mg/kg).

ascorbate signal recorded in the striatum; haloperidol, a dopamine-receptor antagonist, causes a decrease in the striatal ascorbate signal (O'Neill *et al.,* 1983c). In contrast, the alpha$_2$-adrenoceptor agonist, clonidine, reduces, and the alpha$_2$-antagonist, yohimbine, enhances the ascorbate signal in the striatum. Caffeine, a CNS stimulant, increases while the anaesthetic, pentobarbitone, reduces ascorbate concentration.

The drug-induced changes in ascorbate show considerable variation between brain regions. Fig. 3 shows the changes in ascorbate, 60 min after an i.p. injection of 2 mg/kg apomorphine, in the frontal cortex, nucleus accumbens, striatum and hippocampus. A decrease in hippocampal ascorbate, with an increase in

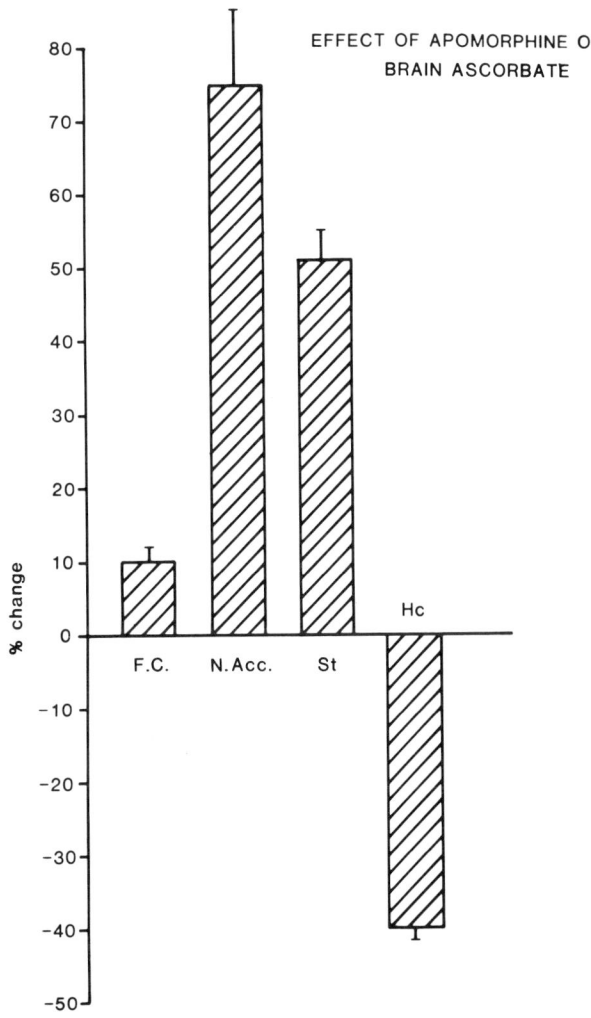

Fig. 3 — The effect of apomorphine (2 mg/kg i.p.) on the ascorbate signal recorded in the frontal cortex (F.C.), nucleus accumbens (N.Acc.), striatum (St.) and hippocampus (Hc.). The results are expressed as a percentage change, 60 min after injection, compared with the pre-injection value.

striatal ascorbate, is also seen after i.p. administration of amphetamine (Grune-wald *et al.*, 1983).

Even in the absence of drug administration, extracellular ascorbate shows fluctuations, which are closely correlated with the animal's motor activity (O'Neill, 1983. O'Neill *et al.*, 1983c). Both these changes have a major circadian rhythm, with a high level of motor activity and extracellular ascorbate at night and a low level during the daytime. Superimposed on this major rhythm are secondary changes, such as the decrease seen in both these variables around midnight (Fig. 4).

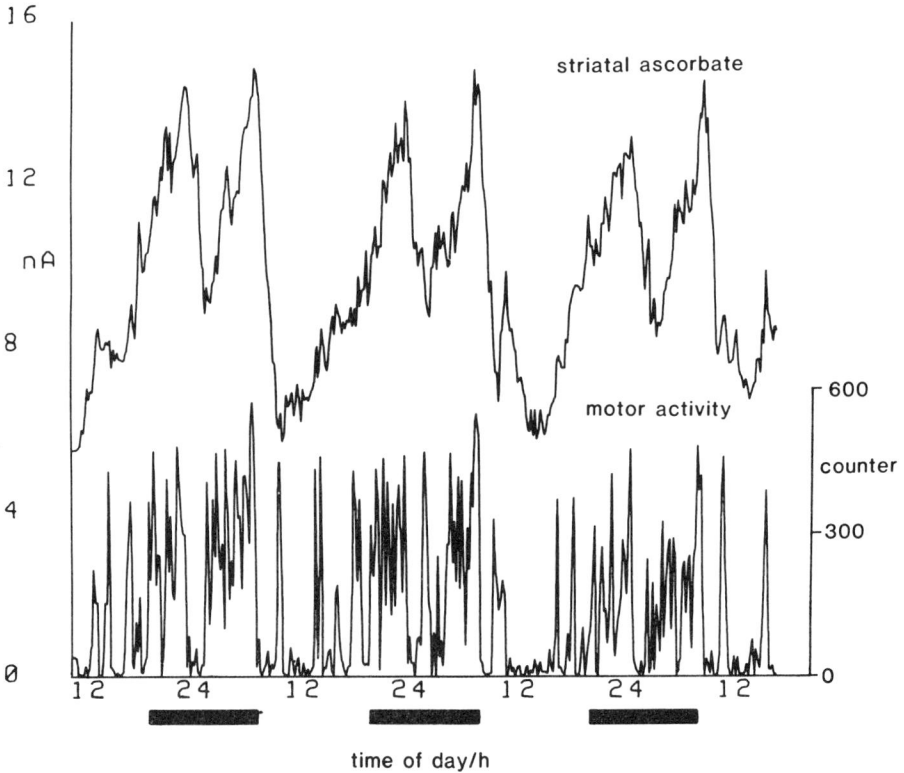

Fig 4 – Circadian changes in striatal ascorbate and total motor activity recorded over a 3-day period.

3. ORIGIN OF CHANGES IN EXTRACELLULAR BRAIN ASCORBATE CONCENTRATION

The finding that drug-induced changes in ascorbate differ between brain regions makes it very unlikely that they reflect changes in the supply of ascorbate from the blood. However, we have carried out additional experiments to eliminate this possibility. The concentration of ascorbate in plasma withdrawn through chroni-cally implanted intra-atrial cannulae was measured at 6-h intervals during the

24-h cycle. Plasma ascorbate at 4 p.m. was 45 ± 4 μM. It showed considerable fluctuation with a minimum at 10 a.m. and a maximum at 10 p.m. 76% higher. The changes in brain ascorbate were found to be out of phase with those of plasma ascorbate (Fig. 5).

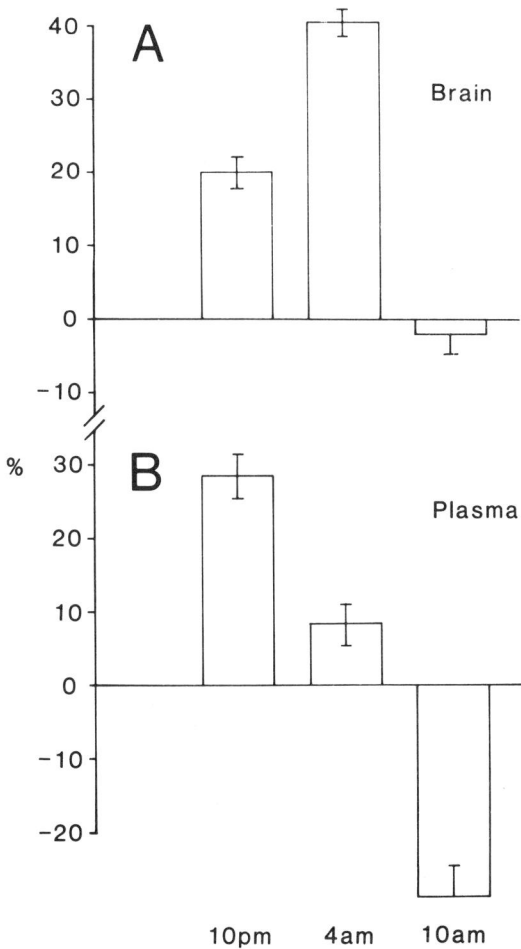

Fig. 5 – Circadian changes in ascorbate measured in the exttacellular fluid of the brain (A) and in the plasma (B). Results expressed as a percentage of the value measured at 4 p.m. (From Grünewald *et al.*, 1983, with permission).

Ascorbate, when injected i.p., leads to an increase in the ascorbate signal measured in the extracellular fluid (ECF) by voltammetry. However, such increases are seen only when the dose of ascorbate is greater than 500 mg/kg body weight. Two approaches were used to see whether amphetamine had any effect on the transport of ascorbate from blood to ECF: in one, the increase in the ascorbate voltammetric signal after i.p. ascorbate was compared in the presence and absence of amphetamine. In the second approach, ^{14}C-ascorbate was administered and the distribution of radioactivity in different brain regions was compared in the presence and absence of amphetamine. With neither of these approaches was there any evidence that ascorbate changes are secondary to changes in the supply of ascorbate from the blood stream: they must therefore arise from the modulation of ascorbate release and/or uptake by neurons or glia (Grunewald *et al.*, 1983).

4. RELEASE OF ASCORBATE *IN VITRO*

Milby *et al.* (1981) demonstrated a depolarization-dependent release of ascorbate, both *in vitro* from synaptosomal preparations and in experiments *in vivo* using a corticol cup method. In addition to K^+- and veratridine-dependent depolarization, electrical stimulation of the lemniscus, which activates the thalamocorticol pathway, led to release of ascorbate into the cortical cup. The K^+-evoked release of ascorbate was Ca^{2+} independent, but was paralleled by Ca^{2+}-dependent release of noradrenaline or dopamine. However, 6-hydroxy-dopamine (6-OHDA) lesions of the cerebellum, which largely removed the noradrenergic input, had little effect on the release of ascorbate. From this the authors concluded that ascorbate release was a consequence of neuronal depolarization.

Our results, showing such a wide variety of effects on ascorbate with different drugs, led us to look for the possibility of a more specific mechanism for the control of ascorbate release.

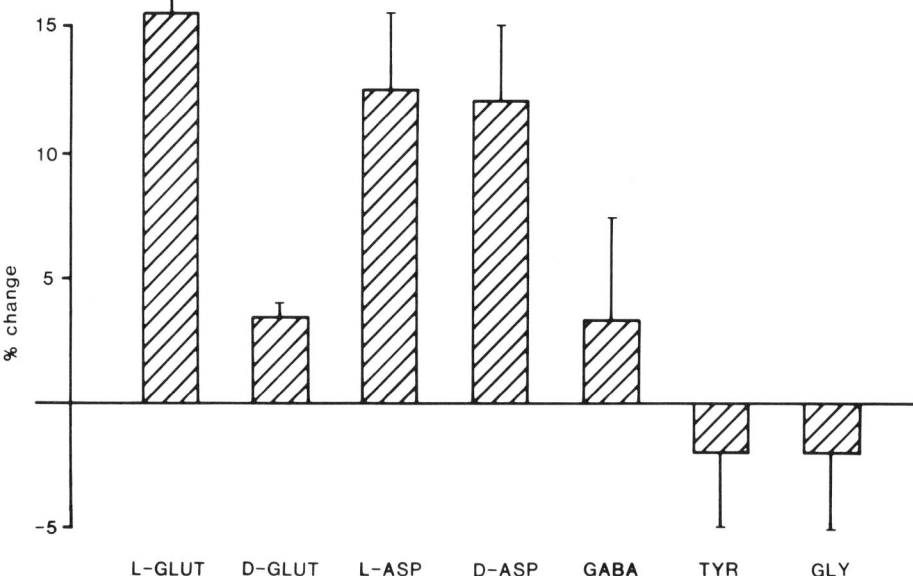

Fig. 6 — The effect of a variety of amino acids on the efflux of ascorbate from cortical synaptosomes. The final concentration of the amino acid was 50 μM. (From Grünewald and Fillenz, 1984, with permission).

We used a crude synaptosomal pellet and measured ascorbate release (Grune-wald and Fillenz, 1984). There was a temperature-dependent release of ascorbate; this was subtracted from any evoked release. Dopamine, noradrenaline and acetylcholine had no effect on ascorbate efflux; neither did GABA or glycine. L-glutamate, however, increased ascorbate release above the baseline level. The effect was dose-dependent between 10^{-6} and 10^{-4} M glutamate, and was stereoselective, since D-glutamate was very much less effective. A similar releasing effect was produced by the excitatory amino acids L- and D-asparate (Fig. 6).

Examination of the ionic requirements of glutamate-evoked release of ascorbate showed that it was Ca^{2+}-independent: replacement of Ca^{2+} in the medium with Mg^{2+}, Mn^{2+} or Co^{2+} had no effect on ascorbate release. This is consistent with the subcellular localization of ascorbate: differential centrifugation of brain tissue shows that very little of the ascorbate is associated with subcellular particles, most of it being in the soluble cytoplasmic compartment. Although Ca^{2+} removal has no effect, the substitution of sucrose for Na^+ in the incubation medium caused a 63% depression of the glutamate-evoked release of ascorbate from cortical synaptosomes (Fig. 7).

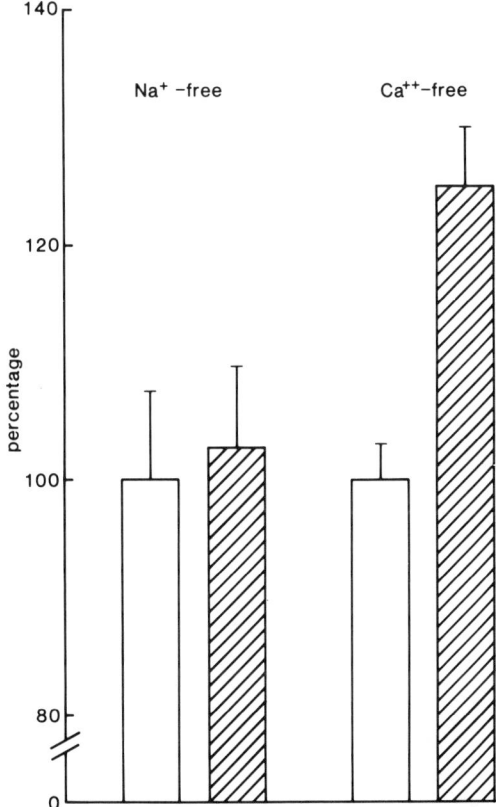

Fig. 7 – The effect of removing Na^+ or Ca^{2+} from the incubation medium on the glutamate-evoked release of ascorbate from cortical synaptosomes. Results expressed as a percentage of non-stimulated efflux.

In order to elucidate the mechanism of the ascorbate release evoked by the excitatory amino acids, the actions of a number of drugs were tested. Antagonists of excitatory amino acid receptors *cis*-2,3-piperidine dicarboxylate and 2-amino-5-phosphonovalerate had no effect on glutamate-evoked release of ascorbate from corticol synaptosomes; nor was there any effect of specific excitatory amino acid agonists N-methyl-D-L-aspartate (NMDA) of kainic acid at 50-μM concentrations. These findings suggested that the glutamate effect was not receptor-mediated (Grunewald and Fillenz, 1984).

5. ASCORBATE RELEASE AS AN INDEX OF EXCITATORY AMINO ACID RELEASE

The finding that glutamate-evoked release of ascorbate was sensitive to changes in extracellular Na^+ concentration raised the possibility that it involved the high-affinity glutamate uptake mechanism, which is Na^+-dependent, and led us to put forward the hypothesis illustrated in Fig. 8. The release of ascorbate is linked to the activity of neurons releasing excitatory amino acids in the following way: the arrival of an impulse at the nerve terminal leads to the Ca^{2+}-dependent

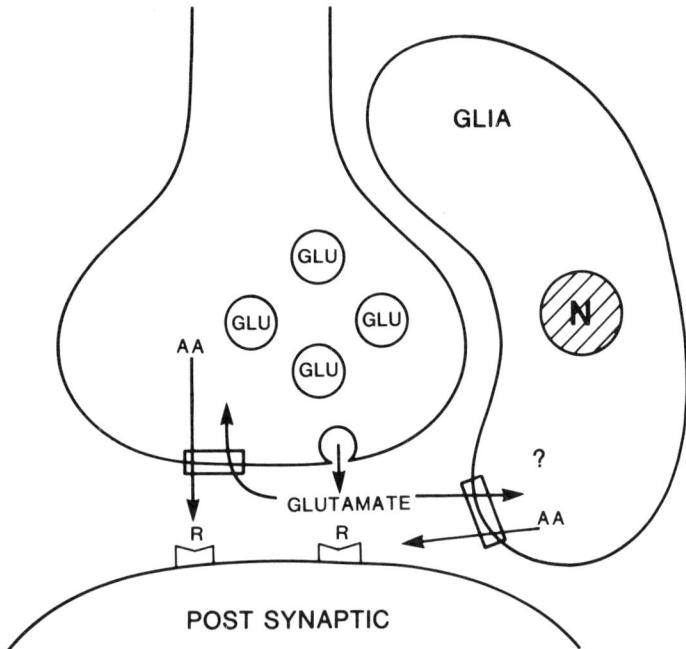

Fig. 8 – Model for the origin of the changes in the extracellular concentration of brain ascorbate. Ca^{2+}-dependent impulse-evoked release of glutamate (or aspartate) is followed by its re-uptake; this is accompanied by the release of ascorbate from the cytoplasmic compartment of the glutamatergic nerve terminals and, possibly, from glial cells. Glu = glutamate; AA = ascorbate.

release of glutamate (or aspartate), which is followed by its re-uptake. The uptake of glutamate occurs by a Na^+-dependent mechanism and is coupled to the outward transport of ascorbate from the cytoplasmic compartment. Although the release of glutamate is from nerve terminals, its re-uptake may be into nerve terminals or glial cells.

The uptake of glutamate is inhibited by two classes of drugs; the first are competitive uptake blockers, which themselves are substrates for the uptake process. Among these are L-aspartate-beta-hydroxamate, D,L-threo-beta-hydroxyaspartate and L-cysteate; all these drugs slightly enhanced rather than inhibited glutamate-evoked ascorbate release. Kainic acid, at high concentration, is an example of the second class, the non-competitive uptake inhibitors; 5 mM kainate completely abolished glutamate-evoked release of ascorbate (Grunewald and Fillenz, 1984).

A number of glutamate uptake systems have been described in nervous tissue, which can be distinguished on the basis of kinetic parameters, localization, ionic dependence, substrate specificity and susceptibility to inhibitors. There is a high affinity glutamate uptake, first described for cortical synaptosomes (Logan and Snyder, 1971). This uptake has a K_m of 20 μM, shows an absolute dependence on sodium ions (Bennett et al., 1972; Balcar and Johnston, 1972); L-glutamate, L- and D-aspartate are taken up with equal efficiency (Davies and Johnston, 1976; Takagaki, 1978) whereas D-glutamate is a very much less effective substrate (Takagaki, 1976). Kainate and dehydroxykainate are not taken up, and they are true inhibitors (Johnston et al., 1979; Lodge et al., 1979) in contrast to the competitive inhibitors which themselves are taken up.

A second, low affinity, glutamate uptake system can be identified with a K_m greater than 500 μM; it has a low sensitivity to changes in extracellular Na^+ (Bennett et al., 1972; Balcar and Johnston, 1972), and does not discriminate between L- and D-glutamate.

The characteristics of the glutamate-evoked ascorbate release suggests that it is mediated largely or exclusively by the high-affinity uptake system. The localization of this high-affinity uptake transport for excitatory amino acids has been studied by a number of different methods (Storm-Mathisen, 1981). All these methods show that this transport mechanism is restricted to a specific population of nerve endings; these are the nerve endings which, by other criteria, have been shown to release excitatory amino acids. However, high-affinity glutamate uptake is also found in glial cells (Hosli and Hosli, 1978). Whether and how this differs from the high affinity neuronal uptake is at present not clear. Electron microscopy of ^{3}H-glutamate uptake in the hippocampus showed most of the label over the profiles of boutons and unmyelinated axons, with the labelling of glial profiles not significantly different from background. Similarly, lesion of glutamatergic pathways has been reported to result in a reduction of glutamate uptake, although such lesions normally result in the replacement of the degenerating nerve terminals by proliferating glial cells.

The changes in extracellular brain ascorbate in response to drug administration showed regional variation. This raises the question whether the proposed model, which is based on experiments with cortical synaptosomes, is generally applicable. In order to answer this question, synaptosomes prepared from a number of brain regions were compared. Those from striatum and hippocampus had the same characteristics as cortical synaptosomes: cerebellar synaptosomes, however, showed no release of ascorbate in response to glutamate or aspartate; however kainate (5 μM) did induce release of ascorbate. This was reduced by the glutamate receptor antagonist 2,3-PDA.

Recently, Biglow *et al.* (1984) have reported the release of ascorbate from striatal synaptosomes by GABA. This appears to be receptor-mediated, but occurs only in the presence of K^+-depolarization. The effect may therefore be due to receptor-mediated GABA enhancement of K^+-stimulated glutamate release (Mitchell, 1980).

6. PREDICTIONS OF THE HYPOTHESIS TESTED

The model in Fig. 8 gives rise to a number of predictions, and some of these have been tested.

6.1 Injections of excitatory amino acids

We first tested the prediction that raising the extracellular concentration of

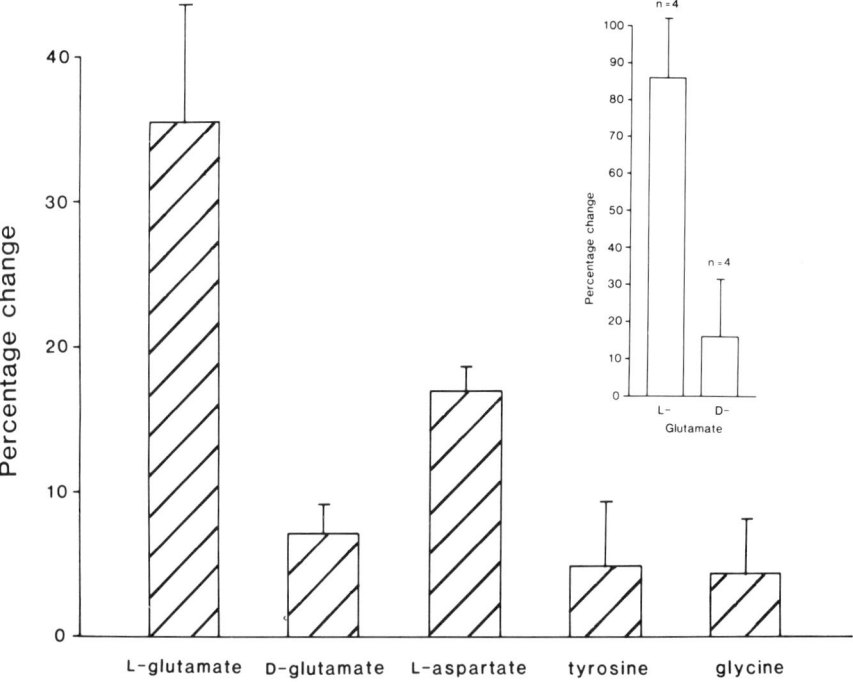

Fig. 9 – The effect of the administration of a variety of amino acids (500 mg/kg i.p.) on the ascorbate signal recorded in the striatum of the unrestrained rat. Results (4 h after injection) are expressed as a percentage of the pre-injection value and were corrected for circadian changes in the ascorbate signal.

Inset. The effect on the ascorbate signal of 35 μg/2μl of D- and L-glutmate injected directly into the striatum. The difference between the 2 isomers was significant; $p < 0.05$, $n = 4$. (From O'Neill *et al.*, 1984, with permission).

excitatory amino acids in the brain would lead to an increase in the ascorbate signal. Rats implanted with carbon-paste electrodes in the striatum were given 500 mg/kg L-glutamate by i.p. injection. This resulted in an increase in the ascorbate signal. To test the specificity of this effect a number of other amino acids were injected: L-asparate led to an increase in ascorbate, D-glutamate had a similar but much smaller effect and glycine and tyrosine were without effect on ascorbate. Fig. 9 shows the effects on the voltammetric ascorbate signal of i.p. administration of these amino acids; these are to be compared with their effect *in vitro* on ascorbate release from synaptosomes shown in Fig. 6.

In another set of experiments (O'Neill *et al.*, 1984), micro-infusion of 35 μg glutamate in 2 μl carrier directly into the striatum through chronically implanted cannulae led to an increase in the ascorbate signal of 87 ± 17% (*n* = 4) in response to L-glutamate and only 17 ± 15% (*n* = 4) in response to D-glutamate (inset Fig. 9).

Since glutamate is a product of carbohydrate metabolism, it is found throughout the brain. Only a small proportion of this glutamate has a transmitter function, and so the density of glutamate innervation cannot be assessed

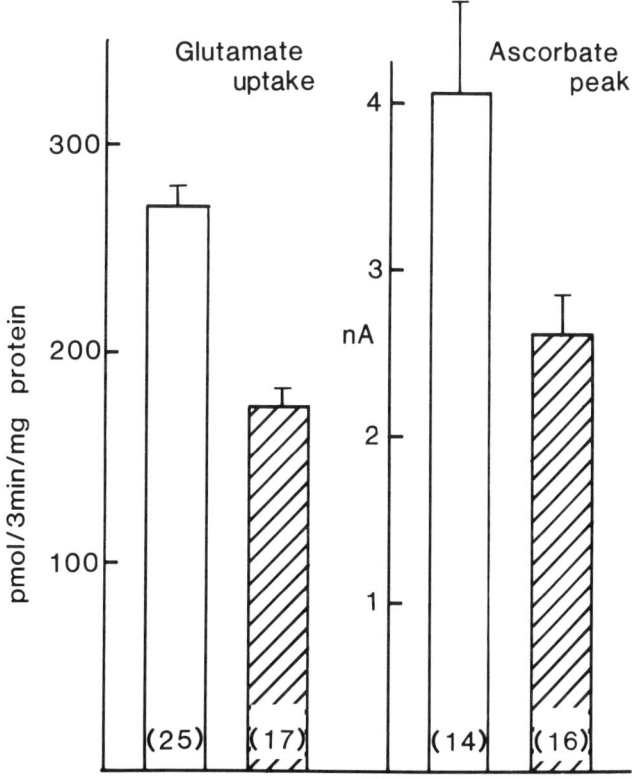

Fig. 10 — A comparison of the uptake rate of glutamate by tissue from accumbens and striatum (Walaas, 1981) with the height of the ascorbate signal recorded in these brain regions. Within the experimental errors, the ratio of uptake in the accumbens and striatum is the same as the ratio of peak heights measured in the two regions. Open histograms = striatum; hatched histograms = nucleus accumbens.

from the distribution of glutamate. Instead, high-affinity glutamate uptake has been used as a measure of terminal density (Walaas, 1981). Fig. 10 shows the relative magnitude of glutamate uptake in the striatum and nucleus accumbens, comparing it with the relative size of the ascorbate signal in these two brain regions. As the hypothesis predicts, the ratio of uptake and the ratio of extracellular ascorbate are similar.

6.2 Effect of lesions

There is extensive evidence that the corticostriatal pathway uses glutamate as a transmitter. Cortical lesions result in a reduction in the level of endogenous glutamate in the striatum (Hassler et al., 1982), in the Ca^{2+}-evoked release of endogenous glutamate (Rowlands and Roberts, 1980) and in the high-affinity uptake of glutamate and aspartate (Walaas, 1981). If fluctuations in extracellular striatal ascorbate reflect changes in glutamate uptake following its release, a lesion of the cortico-striatal pathway should affect changes in striatal ascorbate.

A unilateral lesion of the cortex overlying the striatum caused a 55% reduction of the ascorbate signal on the lesioned, compared to the unlesioned, side. This closely resembled the reduction in high-affinity uptake in the striatum after lesions of the overlying cortex (Walaas, 1981). When the circadian changes in the ascorbate signal were compared, the nocturnal increase on the lesioned side was similarly found to be only 20% of that on the unlesioned side (O'Neill et al., 1983d). Finally, administration of amphetamine produced an increase on the lesioned side which was only 26% of that seen on the unlesioned side (Table 1)

Table 1 — The effect of unilateral cortical lesion on the height of the ascorbate peak recorded in both striata. In circadian experiments, min = day and max = night-time values; in the amphetamine (5 mg/kg i.p.) experiments, min = pre-injection and max = maximum post-injection value (90 min after injection).

		INTACT	LESIONED
Circadian (n = 6)	min	6.4 ± 1.3	2.9 ± 1.3
	max	10.9 ± 1.8	3.8 ± 1.8
Amphetamine (n = 6)	min	7.0 ± 1.4	3.9 ± 1.0
	max	12.8 ± 1.9	5.4 ± 1.0

The effect of amphetamine on the ascorbate signal, suggested that dopamine may play a role in these changes. We therefore looked at changes in ascorbate in animals in which 6-OHDA had been injected into the substantia nigra on one side; this produces a lesion of the cells of origin of the dopaminergic projection to the striatum. In such animals the dopaminergic terminals degenerate and are partially replaced by proliferating glial cells. Comparison of the lesioned with the unlesioned side showed no significant difference in the size of the ascorbate signal in the nocturnal increase of the ascorbate peaks or the increase after amphetamine administration. Several conclusions can be drawn from the 6-OHDA experiments: the dopaminergic nerve terminals in the striatum make little or no contribution to the basal extracellular ascorbate concentration or its circadian fluctuation. It has been shown previously that amphetamine when applied to slices or synaptosomes, or when given by local micro-injection into the striatum, does not cause release of ascorbate (O'Neill *et al.*, 1983b). Its effect, when given by intraperitoneal injection, must therefore be indirect; if its effect is mediated by dopamine, it must be a pathway other than the nigrostriatal dopaminergic pathway.

We investigated the effect on striatal ascorbate of a third lesion: kainic acid was injected into the striatum on one side. This causes the degeneration of the intrinsic neurons and their terminals, which is accompanied by glial proliferation; terminals of extrinsic neurons are unaffected. In kainic acid lesioned animals there was no difference between the lesioned and unlesioned sides in either the size of the ascorbate peak or its circadian or amphetamine-induced increase.

These three kinds of lesion experiments demonstrate that there is a strong link between the concentration of extracellular ascorbate in the striatum and the glutamatergic cortico-striatal pathway; they suggest furthermore that the basal level as well as the circadian changes in extracellular ascorbate are due to fluctuations in the release of glutamate by this pathway. However, although ascorbate is dependent on glutamate release, its source could be either glutamatergic nerve terminals or glia, since both of these have a high-affinity glutamate uptake.

6.3 Stimulation of putative glutamatergic pathways
Finally, since lesioning a glutamatergic pathway produced a marked reduction both in the ascorbate signal and its circadian and drug-induced changes, the question remained whether stimulation of a glutamatergic pathway produced an increase in the ascorbate signal.

The first attempt to test this prediction consisted of stimulating the cortex overlying the striatum, using bipolar electrodes, in rats anaesthetized with chloral hydrate. There was no change in the ascorbate signal recorded with a carbon-paste electrode in the striatum with stimulus parameters ranging from 10—50 V, 0.5—1 ms, 50—100 Hz and 1 s — 5 min duration.

Since all the other experiments on changes in ascorbate were carried out in the absence of anaesthetics, the possibility existed that anaesthesia could interfere with one of the processes involved in glutamate-evoked ascorbate release. We therefore decided to repeat these experiments in a brain region where electrical stimulation without anaesthesia is acceptable. Cotman and Nadler (1981) have reviewed the biochemical and pharmacological evidence that glutamate serves as the transmitter of perforant path fibres which project from the entorhinal cortex to the dentate gyrus. Although the evidence is not conclusive, the role of glutamate as a transmitter for this pathway is more firmly established than for any other.

Rats anaesthetized with chloral hydrate were implanted with carbon-paste electrodes in the dentate gyrus; a bipolar stimulating electrode was implanted in the perforant path, using stereotaxic coordinates; the depth of the stimulating electrode during insertion was monitored by recording the evoked population spike in the dentate gyrus with the carbon paste electrode. The position of the carbon-paste electrode was confirmed histologically after termination of the experiment. The animals were given at least 2 days to recover from the anaesthesia and surgery, and experiments on the effects of electrical stimulation were then carried out.

In three out of six rats stimulation of the perforant path resulted in an increase in the ascorbate signal (Fig. 11). Subsequent histology (see Fig. 12) showed that only in these three rats was the carbon-paste electrode correctly placed in the dentate gyrus (O'Neill *et al.*, 1984).

Single or double stimuli produced no changes in the ascorbate signal, and there was no significant difference between the increase in ascorbate produced by 100 stimuli or by 500 stimuli. The increase in ascorbate could be seen

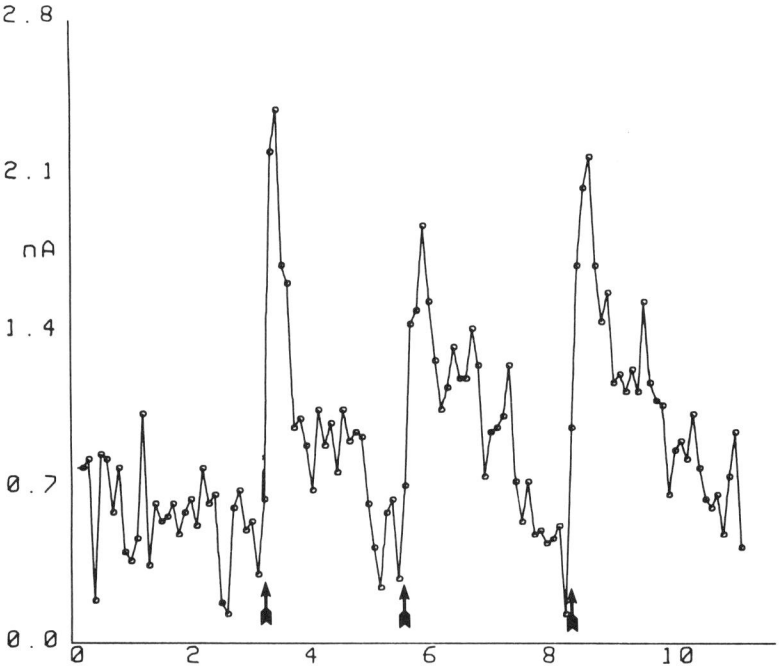

Fig. 11 – The effect of electrical stimulation (200 Hz, 0.5 ms, 1 s duration) of the perforant path on the ascorbate signal recorded in the dentate gyrus of the hippocampus over an 11-h period. Stimulus given at arrows, 1 min before the scan.

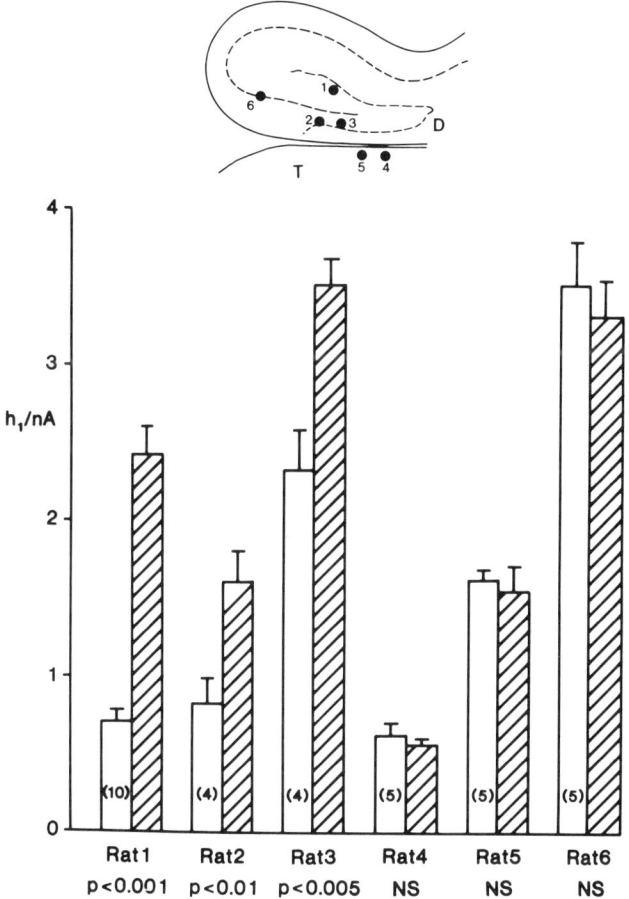

Fig. 12 – The effect of electrical stimulation (200 Hz, 0.2–0.5 m.s, 0.5–2.5 s duration) of the perforant path on the ascorbate signal recorded near the dentate gyrus of the hippocampus. Only in rats where the carbon-paste electrode was close to the terminal region of this glutamatergic input was there any effect (see inset). Figures in brackets = number of stimulations.

Inset. Diagrammatic representation of the position of the carbon-paste recording electrode. T = thalamus; D = dentate gyrus. 1–6 = rat number. (From O'Neill *et al.*, 1984, with permission).

1 min after the end of stimulus; it was not possible to monitor the ascorbate at shorter intervals because the trains of stimuli interfered with the recording of voltammograms.

In order to see whether the earlier failure of cortical stimulation to produce a change in striatal ascorbate could be attributed to the anaesthetic, we examined the effect of chloral hydrate on stimulation of the perforant path. Fig. 13 shows that intraperitoneal administration of this anaesthetic completely suppressed the stimulation-evoked increase in ascorbate. The effect was reversible, as a normal response was obtained 27 h later.

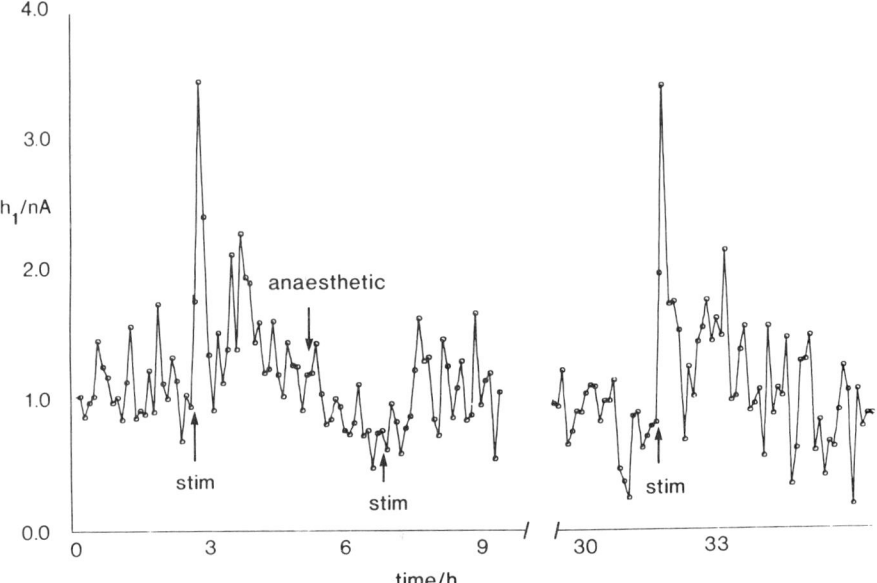

Fig 13 – The effect of chloral hydrate (7 ml/kg 5% solution i.p.) on the stimulus-evoked release of ascorbate in the dentate gyrus. Stimulations were given before, during and after anaesthesia at the arrows. (From O'Neill *et al.*, 1984, with permission).

It is interesting to compare the present results showing an increase in ascorbate in response to electrical stimulation with the release of dopamine in response to electrical stimulation in the whole animal; such release has been monitored *in vivo* both by voltammetry (Ewing *et al.*, 1983) and by brain dialysis (Imperato and Di Chiara, 1984). In these studies also, 300–600 stimuli were required before any increase in dopamine could be detected. Thus the sensitivity of ascorbate as an index of excitatory aminoacid release is comparable to the methods available for monitoring dopamine release *in vivo*.

REFERENCES

Balcar, V. J. and Johnston, G. A. R. (1972). Glutamate uptake by brain slices and its relation to the depolarization of neurones by acidic amino acids. *J. Neurobiol.*, **3**, 295–301.

Bennett, J. P., Logan, W. J. and Snyder, S. H. (1972). Amino acid transmitter candidates: sodium-dependent high-affinity uptake by unique synaptosomal fractions. *Science*, **178**, 997–999.

Bigelow, J. C., Brown, D. S. and Wightman, R. M. (1984). Gamma-aminobutyric acid stimulates the release of endogenous ascorbic acid from rat striatal tissue. *J. Neurochem.*, **42**, 412–419.

Brazell, M. P. and Marsden, C. A. (1982). Intracerebral injection of ascorbate oxidase – effects on *in vivo* electrochemical recordings. *Brain Res.*, **249**, 167–172.

Cotman, C. W. and Nadler, J. V. (1981). Glutamate and aspartate as hippo-campal transmitters: biochemical and pharmacological evidence. In: *Gluta-mate: Transmitter in the Central Nervous System'* Roberts, P. J., Storm-Mathisen, J. and Johnston, G. A. R. (eds.), John Wiley, Chichester.

Damron, C. M., Monier, M. M. and Roe, J. H. (1952). Metabolism of L-ascorbic acid, dehydro-L-ascorbic acid and diketo-L-gulonic acid in guinea pig. *J. Biol. Chem.,* **195,** 599–606.

Davies, L. P. and Johnston, G. A. R. (1976). Uptake and release of D- and L-aspartate by rat brain slices. *J. Neurochem.,* **26,** 1007–1014.

Ewing, A. G., Bigelow, J. C. and Wightman, R. M. (1983). Direct *in vivo* moni-toring of dopamine released from two striatal compartments in the rat. *Science,* **221,** 169–171.

Gonon, F., Buda, M., Cespuglio, R., Jouvet, M. and Pujol, J.-F. (1981). Voltam-metry in the striatum of chronic freely moving rats: detection of catechols and ascorbic acid. *Brain Res.,* **223,** 69–80.

Grunewald, R. A. and Fillenz, M. (1984). Release of ascorbate from synapto-somal fraction of rat brain. *Neurochem. Inter.,* **6,** 491–500.

Grunewald, R. A., O'Neill, R. D., Fillenz, M. and Albery, W. J. (1983). The origin of circadian and amphetamine-induced changes in the extracellular concentration of brain ascorbate. *Neurochem. Inter.,* **5,** 773–778.

Hassler, R., Haug, P., Nitch, C., Kim, J. S. and Paik, K. (1982). Effect of motor and premotor cortex ablation on concentrations of amino acids, mono-amines and acetylcholine and on the ultrastructure in the rat striatium. A confirmation of glutamate as the specific corticostriatal transmitter. *J. Neurochem.,* **38,** 1087–1098.

Hornig, D. (1975). Distribution of ascorbic acid, metabolites and analogs in man and animals. *Ann. N.Y. Acad. Sci.,* **258,** 103–118.

Hösli, L. and Hösli, E. (1978). Action and uptake of neurotransmitters in CNS tissue culture. *Rev. Physiol. Biochem. Pharmac.,* **81,** 135–188.

Imperato, A. and Di Chiara, G. (1984). Trans-striatal dialysis coupled to reverse phase HPLC with electrochemical detection: a new method for the study of the *in vivo* release of endogenous dopamine and metabolites. *J. Neurosci.,* **4,** 966–977.

Johnston, G. A. R., Kennedy, S. M. E. and Twitchin, B. (1979). Action of the neurotoxin kainic acid on high affinity uptake of L-glutamic acid in rat brain slices. *J. Neurochem.,* **32,** 121–127.

Lodge, D., Johnston, G. A. R., Curtis, D. R. and Bornstein, J. C. (1979). Kainate neurotoxicity and glutamate inactivation. *Neurosci. Lett.,* **14,** 343–348.

Logan, W. J. and Snyder, S. H. (1971). Unique high affinity uptake systems for glycine, glutamic and aspartic acids in central nervous tissue of the rat. *Nature (Lond.),* **234,** 297–299.

Milby, K. H., Mefford, I. N., Chey, W. and Adams, R. N. (1981). *In vitro* and *in vivo* depolarization-coupled efflux of ascorbic acid in rat brain preparations. *Brain Res. Bull.,* **7,** 237–242.

Mitchell, R. (1980). A novel GABA receptor modulates stimulus-induced gluta-mate release from cortico-striatal terminals. *Eur. J. Pharmac.,* **67,** 119–122.

O'Neill, R. D. (1983). Electrochemistry in brain tissue – a developing technique in neurobiology. *J. Instit. Chem. Ire.,* 5–10.

O'Neill, R. D., Fillenz, M. and Albery, W. J. (1982a). Circadian changes in homovanillic acid and ascorbate levels in the rat striatum using microprocessor-controlled voltammetry. *Neurosci. Lett.,* **34,** 189–193.

O'Neill, R. D., Grunewald, R. A., Fillenz, M. and Albery, W. J. (1982b). Linear sweep voltammetry with carbon paste electrodes in the rat striatum. *Neurosci.,* **7,** 1945–1954.

O'Neill, R. D., Fillenz, M. and Albery, W. J. (1983a). The development of linear sweep voltammetry with carbon paste electrodes *in vivo. Neurosci. Methods,* **8,** 263–273.

O'Neill, R. D., Fillenz, M., Albery, W. J. and Goddard, N. J. (1983b). The monitoring of ascorbate and monoamine transmitter metabolites using microprocessor-controlled voltammetry. *Neurosci.,* **9,** 87–93.

O'Neill, R. D., Fillenz, M., Grunewald, R. A. and Albery, W. J. (1983c). Simultaneous monitoring of motor activity and neurotransmitter release in the rat striatum. *Neurosci. Lett.,* Suppl. **14,** S268.

O'Neill, R. D., Grunewald, R. A., Fillenz, M. and Albery, W. J. (1983d). The effect of unilateral cortical lesions on the circadian changes in rat striatal ascorbate and homovanillic acid levels measured *in vivo* using voltammetry. *Neurosci. Lett.,* **42,** 105–110.

O'Neill, R. D., Fillenz, M., Sundstrom, L. and Rawlins, J. N. P. (1984). Voltammetrically measured brain ascorbate as an index of excitatory amino acid release in the unrestrained rat. *Neurosci. Lett.,* **52,** 227–233.

Rowlands, G. J. and Roberts, P. J. (1980). Specific calcium-dependent release of endogenous glutamate from rat striatum is reduced by destruction of the corticostriatal tract. *Expl. Brain Res.,* **39,** *239–240.*

Shenk, J. O., Miller, E., Gaddis, R. and Adams, R. N. (1982). Homeostatic control of ascorbate concentration in the CNS extracellular fluid. *Brain Res.,* **253,** 353–356.

Sebrell, W. H. and Harris, R. S. (1967). *The Vitamins,* Vol. 1, Academic Press, New York and London.

Spector, R. (1981). Penetration of ascorbic acid from cerebrospinal fluid into brain. *Exp. Neurol.,* **72,** 645–653.

Spector, R. and Lorenzo, A. V. (1973). Ascorbic acid homeostasis in the central nervous system. *Amer. J. Physiol.,* **225,** 757–763.

Spector, R. and Lorenzo, A. V. (1974). Specificity of ascorbic acid transport system of the central nervous system. *Amer. J. Physiol.,* **226,** 1468–1473.

Spector, R., Spector, A. Z. and Snodgrass, S. R. (1977). Model of transport in the central nervous system. *Amer. J. Physiol.,* **232,** R73–79.

Storm-Mathisen, J. (1981). Autoradiographic and microchemical localization of high affinity glutamate uptake. In: *Glutamate: Transmitter in the Central Nervous System,* Roberts, P. J., Storm-Mathisen, j. and Johnston, G. A. R. (eds.), John Wiley, Chichester.

Takagaki, G. (1976). Properties of the uptake and release of glutamic acid by synaptosomes from rat cerebral cortex. *J. Neurochem.,* **27,** 1417–1425.

Takagaki, G. (1978). Sodium and potassium ions and accumulation of labelled D-aspartate and GABA in crude synaptosomal fraction from rat cerebral cortex. *J. Neurochem.*, **30**, 47–56.

Walaas, I. (1981). Biochemical evidence for overlapping neocortical and allocortical glutamate projections to the nucleus accumbens and rostral caudatoputamen in the rat brain. *Neurosci.*, **6**, 399–405.

CHAPTER

Transmitter release from cerebral cortex and olfactory bulb *in vivo* monitored by chronic superfusion in freely moving animals

H. F. Bradford, A. S. Abdul-Ghani*, J. Coutinho-Netto**, C. M. Thanki and **D. W. Peterson**
Department of Biochemistry, Imperial College of Science and Technology, Imperial College Road, London SW7 2AZ, UK

1. INTRODUCTION

There are currently several approaches to the study of neurotransmitter release and turnover *in vivo*. They include following biogenic amine release by voltammetry, monitoring neurotransmitter release, or turnover, by taking continual small samples of CSF, or by collecting neurotransmitters and their metabolites from cerebral ventricles by perfusion. Other approaches involve inserting push–pull cannulae into various brain structures, with or without an attached dialysis tubing, or collecting neurotransmitters from various regions of the brain surface by a continuous or batch washing procedure using so-called cortical cups. The present account deals with the latter technique employed to continuously

*Present address: Department of Biology and Biochemistry, Birzeit University, P.O. Box 14 Birzeit, West Bank, Israel
**Present address: Faculdade de Medicina, Departmento de Bioquimica, 14.100 – Ribeirae Preto – S.P. Brazil.

monitor neurotransmitter release from the cortical surface of awake, unrestrained, and behaviourally normal animals over periods of hours, days or weeks (Abdul-Ghani *et al.,* 1981).

In terms of their efficiency in collecting aminoacids from extracellular spaces, push—pull dialysis and surface-washing procedures seem to be in the same range as judged by the content of aminoacid in the superfusion stream per unit time (Table 1), with about twice as much of the principal aminoacids being collected by the cup techniques. Washing the ventricles by a push—pull method resulted in the collection of 4- to 5-fold more amino acid, which would include contributions from CSF collected in the superfusion stream.

Table 1 — Comparison of superfusion methods pmoles/10 min)

Amino acid	Hippocampal dialysis	Ventricular push—pull	Cortical cup
Taurine	146 ± 16	278 ± 69	ND
Aspartate	30 ± 4	61 ± 9	103 ± 35
Threonine	39 ± 9	280 ± 39	190 ± 24
Serine	70 ± 12	372 ± 51	ND
Glutamate	26 ± 3	101 ± 21	48 ± 4
Glutamine	134 ± 27	568 ± 59	204 ± 12
Glycine	53 ± 8	315 ± 61	48 ± 4
Alanine	56 ± 8	350 ± 57	119 ± 6
Valine	27 ± 4	167 ± 33	46 ± 4
Methionine	6 ± 4	59 ± 14	ND
Isoleucine	14 ± 1	84 ± 15	64 ± 5
Leucine	24 ± 3	144 ± 27	100 ± 9
Tyrosine	ND	93 ± 17	55 ± 4
Phenylalanine	14 ± 4	78 ± 13	32 ± 2
Arginine	32 ± 5	199 ± 13	ND
Flow rate (μL/min)	2.00	15.00	15.00

$N = 5$ for each group. Values represent mean ± SEM for each amino acid determined in artificial CSF superfusate collected from a 1 mm loop of dialysis tubing in the ventral hippocampus, a concentric push—pull cannula in the lateral ventricle or a 4 mm diameter plastic cup placed over the sensorimotor cortex.

2. EXPERIMENTAL PROCEDURES

2.1 Superfusion technique

A so-called swivel-cannula (4 mm diameter) made from non-toxic materials (e.g. Teflon), and having a small internal volume (15 μl) was implanted under anaesthesia in the skull of Sprague-Dawley rats over small regions of cortex from which the dural membrane had been carefully removed under microscopic control. Measurements employing the Oldendorf technique (Oldendorf, 1970) with [^{14}C]-sucrose and [^{3}H]-H$_2$O as probes have shown that the cannula perfuses an area which is inside the blood—brain barrier. Its construction is such that the basic 'cup' structure allows free rotation within it of the section which carries the tubing delivering the superfusion fluid. This arrangement is leak-proof and allows the animal to move freely within the cage whilst preventing the tubing leads from twisting. The small size of the cannula (4 mm dia.) allows superfusion of small discrete areas of the brain surface, and therefore permits study of the effects of specific forms of sensory stimulation on the release of neurotransmitters from localized regions such as sensorimotor cortex, visual cortex and olfactory bulb surface. Full details of the cannula, its construction and surgical implantation have been previously described (Dodd *et al.,* 1974). Continuous superfusion with gassed (O$_2$, 95%, CO$_2$, 5% v/v) 0.8% saline containing Ca^{2+} (1.2 or 1.85 mM), or with artificial CSF at neutral pH, was allowed for periods of at least 24 hours in acute experiments, and for 2 or 3 days in chronic experiments, before starting to monitor neurotransmitter release. The flow of superfusion fluid (5—12 ml/h) and the hydrostatic pressure were adjusted to provide a 2% to 3% net loss of fluid into the brain to minimize any contribution made to the superfusion fluid from CSF flowing from the subarachnoid space into the cortical field being superfused. Pressure measurements showed that approximately normal rat CSF pressure was maintained. When artificial CSF was employed, neutral pH was maintained by gassing with a 5% CO$_2$; 95% O$_2$ gas mixture, and the colloidal osmotic pressure was maintained by adding 20 mg% inulin, instead of protein, which made it slightly hyperosmotic.

All surgery and subsequent experiments were performed in a temperature-stabilized room (24°C) which was also on a 12 h 'light-on', 12 h 'light-off' cycle. Superfusion fluid was continuously collected on a fraction collector whose tubes contained small quantities of 1.25 M H$_2$SO$_4$ to act as fixative (final conc. 12.5 mM). All chronic experiments were carried out under conditions of complete sterilization to avoid bacterial contamination, and in many experiments superfusate samples were daily incubated on Agar plates to search for bacterial contamination. Histological investigation of the superfused cortex using light microscopy and a range of tissue stains showed that superfused tissue (7 days) was relatively normal. No changes in the cellular composition of the cortex could be seen, and there was no obvious loss of neurons or other structural changes in the tissue compared with the contralateral homotopic control cortex. Throughout the experiments the animals appeared to be behaviourally normal as judged by their exploratory and grooming behaviour, their food and water intake, and by the normal rhythm of the oestrus cycle in females. Brachial plexus electrodes were implanted as described elsewhere (Abdul-Ghani *et al.,* 1980a).

2.2 Analyses

Amino acids were measured by autoanalysis using a very sensitive analyser (5 pmol) as described in detail elsewhere (Norris *et al.,* 1980). Acetylcholine was bioassayed using the guinea pig ileum preparation as described by Abdul-Ghani *et al.* (1980a).

3. RESULTS AND DISCUSSION

3.1 Spontaneous release of amino acids

During the normal working day no significant changes were observed in the rates of spontaneous release of glutamate, or of any other amino acid, from sensorimotor cortex of awake, behaviourally normal animals. This spontaneous release did, however, show a clear diurnal rhythm (day/night cycle) for some amino acids, the largest amounts being released at night when the rats were most active, and correspondingly lower rates of release occurred during the day when the rats were normally resting (Fig. 1). This pattern applied in particular to lysine, glutamine, alanine, glycine, serine, valine and leucine. Glutamate, together with histidine, phenylalanine, methionine and tyrosine, showed only insignificant changes over a typical 24-hour period.

GABA is usually present in superfusates at levels which are close to the threshold levels for detection. These basal levels can be increased substantially by systemic administration of GABA-transaminase inhibitors such as γ-vinyl or γ-acetylenic GABA (Abdul-Ghani *et al.,* 1980b).

3.2 Application of depolarizing agents to the corticol surface

By introducing depolarizing agents into the stream of superfusion fluid, it is possible to evoke release of neurotransmitters from the underlying region of cerebral cortex. We have, in particular, used a purified scorpion venom toxin for this purpose, namely tityustoxin, a polypeptide (mol.wt. 6,995) from *Tityus serrulartus,* the Brazilian scorpion. At low concentrations (50 nM to 1 μM) this peptide selectively releases physiologically active amino acids (glutamate, aspartate, GABA) from sensorimotor cortex, and this evoked release can be prevented by including tetrodotoxin (0.1 μM) with the depolarizing peptide, which indicates that Na^+- channel activation is its mode of action, and that the released substances most likely originated in neurons. (Figs. 2 and 3). Acetylcholine, too, was released from sensorimotor cortex by this agent, and this response could also be blocked by tetrodotoxin (Fig. 3). About 5 min after beginning infusion of tityustoxin, the rats showed characteristic movements, which included frequent scratching at the cannulae, intensive grooming movements and chattering of the jaw. Myoclonic jerks of the contralateral limb began about 15 min after infusion began, and their frequency increased with time. These responses stopped entirely after introducing toxin-free saline Coutinho-Netto *et al.,* 1980). No doubt this kind of general stimulation of the cortex by direct application of depolarizing agents releases a large proportion of the neurotransmitters present in a non-selective way, and these agents stimulate a range of uncoordinated responses. Thus, although direct topical stimulation of the cortex by this method is useful in identifying the range of neurotransmitters present, it clearly lacks selectively. In contrast, sensory stimulation of the same cortical regions via the appropriate neural pathways should evoke

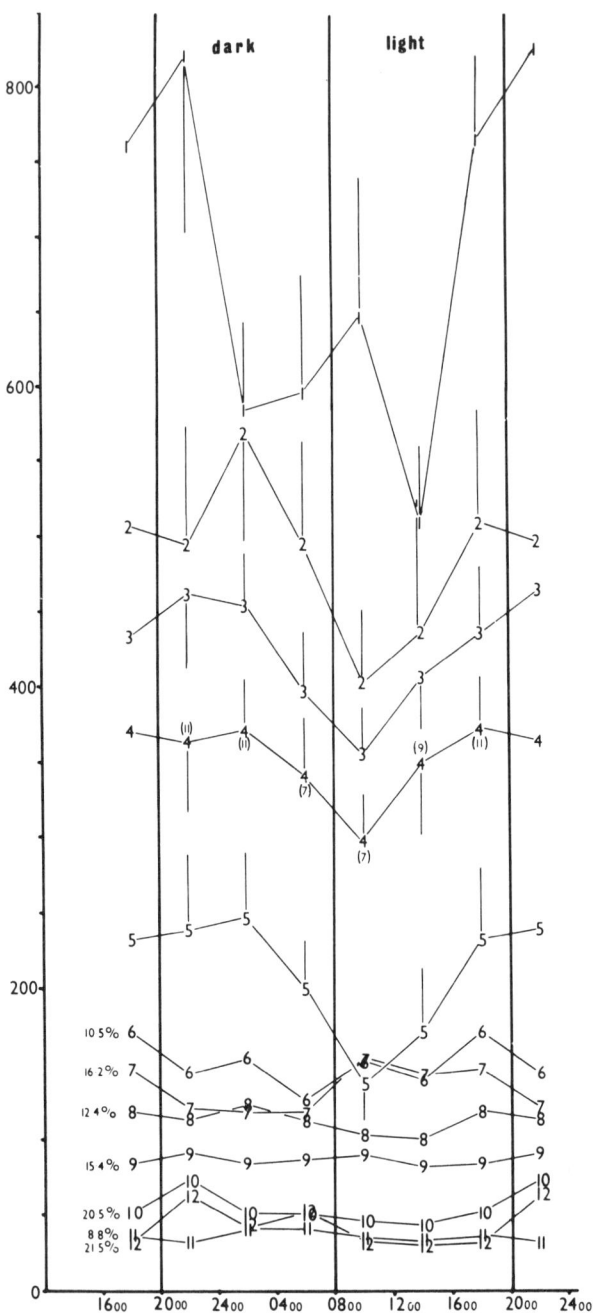

Fig. 1 – Average daily cycle of amino acid release. Amino acids: (1) lysine; (2) glutamine (+ threonine); (3) alanine; (4) glycine; (5) serine; (6) valine; (7) leucine; (8) glutamate (+ citrulline); (9) histidine; (10) phenylanaline; (11) methionine (as the sulphoxide); (12) tyrosine. Values are means ± SEM of the number of experiments given in parentheses next to the glycine values. Figures to the left of amino acids 6–12 give the average SEM for each as a percentage of the mean. Values from four different rats have been used, with a total superfusion time of 10.5 days. (From Dodd *et al.*, 1974, with permission).

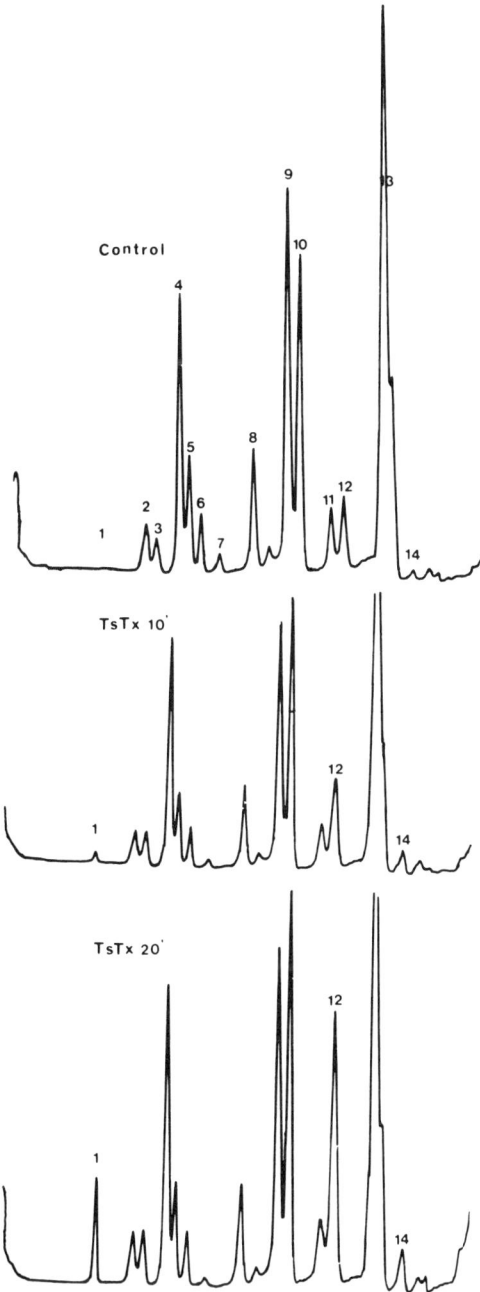

Fig. 2 – Patterns of amino acids released from superfused rat sensorimotor cortex. Representative chromatograms of control and stimulated samples collected 10 min and 20 min after beginning superfusion with saline containing tityustoxin (TsTx) (1 µM) are shown. Amino acids: 14, aspartate; 13, threonine, glutamine and serine; 12, glutamate; 11, citrulline; 10, glycine; 9, alanine; 8, valine; 7, methionine; 6, isoleucine; 5, leucine; 4, norleucine (50 pmol/100 µl of sample); 3, tyrosine; 2, phenylalanine; 1, GABA. (From Coutinho-Netto *et al.*, 1980, with permission).

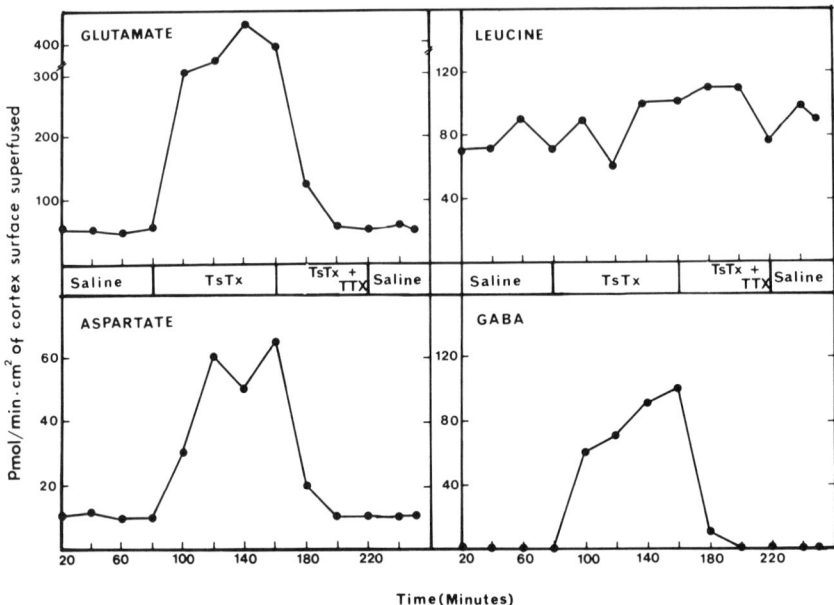

Fig. 3 — Effect of tetrodotoxin on the amino acid-releasing action of tityustoxin. In each animal eight 1-ml control samples were collected (10 min each) from sensorimotor cortex before tityustoxin (1 μM final concentration) was added to the superfusion fluid for 80 min. Then, both tetrodotoxin (0.1 μM) and tityustoxin (1 μM) were introduced for 60 min. This superfusate mixture was then replaced by saline. The values given represent the mean of three values from three animals superfused. Only alternate samples were analysed for amino acid content. (From Coutinho-Netto *et al.*, 1980, with permission).

release of only those neurotransmitters which are directly involved in the normal, physiologically relevant, synaptic processes occurring in the cortical columns concerned.

3.3 Brachial plexus stimulation

Small currents (1–3 mA; 1 ms duration; 2–3 Hz; 3–6 V amplitude, square-wave pulses) passed into the implanted brachial plexus electrodes, evoked clearly visible muscular jerking of the ipsilateral forelimb of anaesthetized animals, without visible movement of other body musculature. Analysis of the superfusion fluid after 5 min periods of contralateral brachial plexus stimulation revealed enhanced release of glutamate and of glutamine, other amino acids showing much smaller changes (Table 2). Stimulation of the brachial plexus ipsilateral to the cannula was without significant effect on amino acid release. These responses were fully reversible, reducing to control levels immediately after cessation of stimulation. GABA was not readily detectable in superfusates unless GABA levels in the brain were elevated by administering a GABA-transaminase inhibitor such as γ-acetylenic (or γ-vinyl) GABA (Lippert *et al.*, 1977;

Table 2 — Amino acid release from sensorimotor ortex during contralateral stimulation of anaesthetized animals (release rate pmol/cm^2/min).

Amino acids	No. experiments	Control	Stimulated	Difference between control and stimulated release	Changes %
Glutamine	(18)	204 ± 27	240 ± 30	36 ± 6[b]	18
Glutamic acid	(27)	48 ± 9	61 ± 11	12 ± 6[a]	27
Glycine	(19)	156 ± 22	166 ± 21	12 ± 7	7
Alanine	(25)	119 ± 14	130 ± 15	8 ± 5	7
Valine	(18)	46 ± 8	48 ± 8	2 ± 3	5
Threonine	(17)	190 ± 24	203 ± 27	12 ± 11	7
Isoleucine	(22)	64 ± 12	69 ± 12	4 ± 2	7
Leucine	(20)	100 ± 20	103 ± 19	3 ± 2	3
Phenylalanine	(19)	32 ± 4	36 ± 4	3 ± 3	12
Tyrosine	(17)	55 ± 10	58 ± 10	2 ± 6	5

Release of amino acids from sensorimotor cortex was determined in 8-min fractions (0.8 ml) of superfusate collected immediately prior to (control) or during contralateral stimulation of the brachial plexus. Values are mean ± SEM for the number of experiments indicated. Differences are expressed as means ± SEM for the number of pairs shown, each stimulus being paired with its own control. (From Abdul Ghani *et al.*, 1978, with permission).
[a] $p < 0.05$, paired comparison t-test.
[b] $p < 0.001$, paired comparison t-test.

Adbul-Ghani *et al.*, 1980b). Contralateral stimulation of the brachial plexus under these conditions caused a significant increase in the release of both GABA and glutamate, ipsilateral stimulation being ineffective (Fig. 4). Acetylcholine was similarly released only from contralateral cortex by brachial plexus stimulation (Fig. 5). Similar patterns of neurotransmitter release from ipsilateral cortex could be expected to occur, even if at lower levels, due to transfer of excitation via the corpus callosum. In this context, it is important to emphasize that changes in transmitter content in the superfusion fluid represent the balance between the true extent of release and the subsequent uptake to neurons and glial cells by high-affinity transport processes (or hydrolysis in the case of acetylcholine). The absence of a significant detectable response following ipsilateral stimulation rules out the possibility that the observed changes in neurotransmitter release are due to changes in whole cerebral blood flow, blood pressure, or other bodily stresses induced by the stimulation.

3.4 Photic stimulation of the retina

With the cannula positioned over the primary visual area of the occipital cortex, the animals (Hooded Rowett rats) were left in complete darkness to adapt for 18 h. They were then anaesthetized with Avertin and given γ-acetylenic GABA

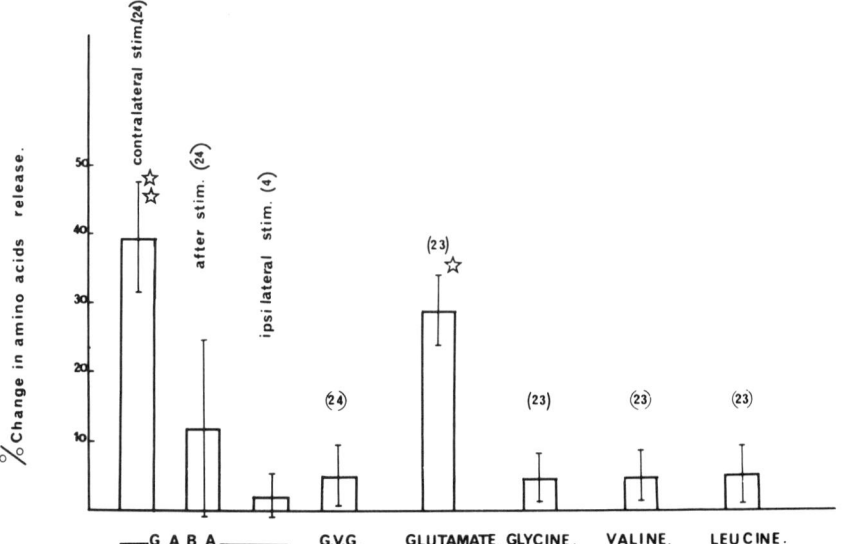

Fig. 4 – Release of GABA from sensorimotor cortex during brachial plexus stimulation. Fractions of superfusate (8 min, 1 ml) were collected from animals after single intraperitoneal injection of γ-vinyl-GABA (1500 mg/kg). After at least 60 min, brachial plexus stimulation (5–12 V, 3–7 mA, 1 ms pulse duration, 2–3 or 50 Hz) was applied either side as indicated. Histograms represent percentage changes relative to unstimulated levels. Values are mean ± SEM for the number of stimulations indicated in brackets *$p < 0.05$ **$p < 0.001$. (From Abdul-Ghani et al., 1980, with permission).

(100 mg/kg) when GABA release was monitored. Weak photic stimulation of the retina for 6-min periods was followed by equivalent periods of dark adaptation. A dry cell battery torch (1.2 W), the front covered with thin black chequered paper to project a 'line-and-edge' structured image, provided the photic (2 flashes/s). This form of sensory stimulation evoked significant and selective release of glutamate and GABA (plus γ-acetylanic GABA). In 20 photic stimulation sessions with associated controls, performed in 5 animals, 7 stimulations evoked an increase in glutamate release of more than 40%, on 7 occasions a change between 15% and 40% was evoked and on 6 occasions only small changes between ± 5% were evoked. GABA (plus γ-acetylenic-GABA) showed enhanced release (8% to 30%) in 11 out of 13 stimulations (Abdul-Ghani et al., 1978).

3.5 Morphine inhibition of evoked and spontaneous neurotransmitter release *in vivo*

When morphine (10 mg/kg) was given (i.p.) 30 min before superfusion samples were collected, it was found to depress the spontaneous release of acetycholine in awake, freely moving animals, an effect which lasted for at least 3 h; but it did not effect the spontaneous release of glutamate, nor for any other amino

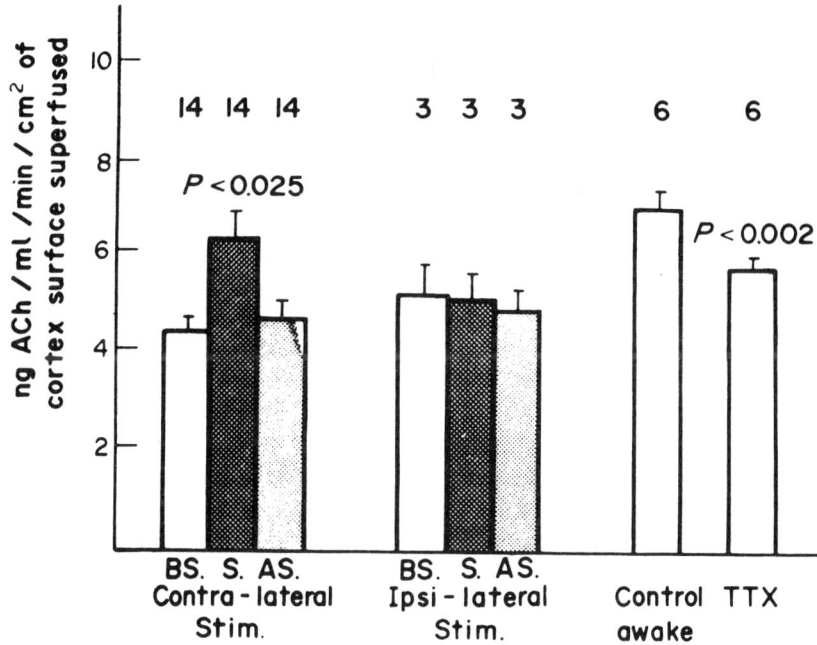

Fig. 5 – *In vivo* release of acetylcholine from sensorimotor cortex at rest and during periods of sensory stimulation via the brachial plexus. Data are Ach levels in 10 min fractions. Histobars represent the mean ± SEM for the number of observations indicated above them. These observations were collected from five animals for contralateral stimulation, three for ispilateral stimulation, three for control awake and three for tetrodotoxin. Animals were lightly anaesthetized during brachial plexus stimulation. Code is as follows: BS = before stimulation; S = during stimulation; AS = after stimulation. In other experiments tetrodotoxin (TTX; 0.1 μM) was infused through the cannula using awake animals (From Abdul-Ghani *et al.*, with permission).

acid measured (aspartate, GABA, glutamine, and nine other amino acids). Morphine-treated rats given naloxone (2 mg/kg) showed a large 'rebound' effect, with levels of spontaneous acetylcholine release exceeding the original control levels. Again, no effect on amino acid release was detected. The level of acetylcholine detected in the superfusion fluid was only 25% of that for glutamate, and it seems likely that a large part of the glutamate detected in control samples is related to general metabolism rather than to synaptic processes, and is being released from various non-synaptic cellular compartments, and is therefore, not modulated by drugs (e.g. morphine) acting at synaptic sites. In contrast, the release of both acetylcholine, and of glutamate, evoked by tityustoxin (Figs. 2 and 3) is completely suppressed by morphine, and this action is prevented by naloxone (Fig. 6). In addition, morphine shows a naloxone-sensitive inhibition of both acetylcholine and glutamate released from cerebral cortex during stimulation of the brachial plexus (Figs. 7 and 8). Thus, morphine, which has been widely demonstrated to inhibit release of acetylcholine and other neurotransmitters in the PNS and CNS (Jhamandas *et al.*, 1970, Mathews *et al.*, 1973; Jhamandas and Sutak, 1974), prevented glutamate release evoked both by sensory stimulation and by surface application of depolarizing agents, which emphasizes the possible neurotransmitter function of glutamate in the cortical areas being superfused.

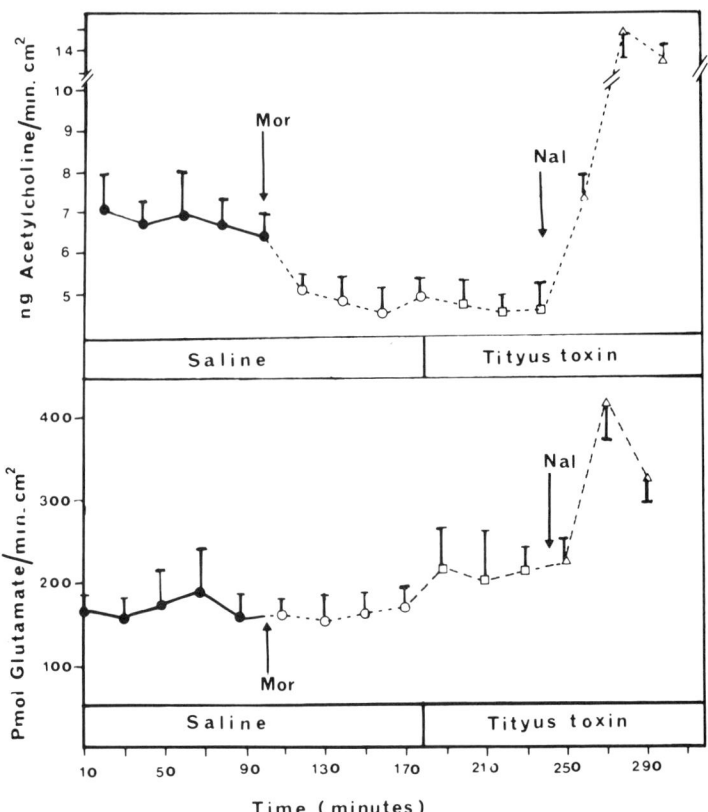

Fig. 6 – Effect of morphine and naloxone on tityustoxin-evoked release of acetylcholine (A) and glutamate (B) from superfused rat sensorimotor cortex. Superfusion was started with saline + Ca^{2+} and the same plus tityustoxin (1 μM) was introduced into the superfusion stream where indicated. Morphine (Mor; 10.mg/kg) and naloxone (Nal; 3 mg/kg) were administered intraperitoneally when indicated by the arrows ●, control ($N = 7$); 0, morphine-treated ($N = 7$); □, tityustoxin added ($N = 3$); △, naloxone ($N = 2$). Data represent the amount of each transmitter collected during 10 min of superfusion ± SEM (flow rate = 6 ml/h). (From Coutinho-Netto *et al.*, 1980, with permission).

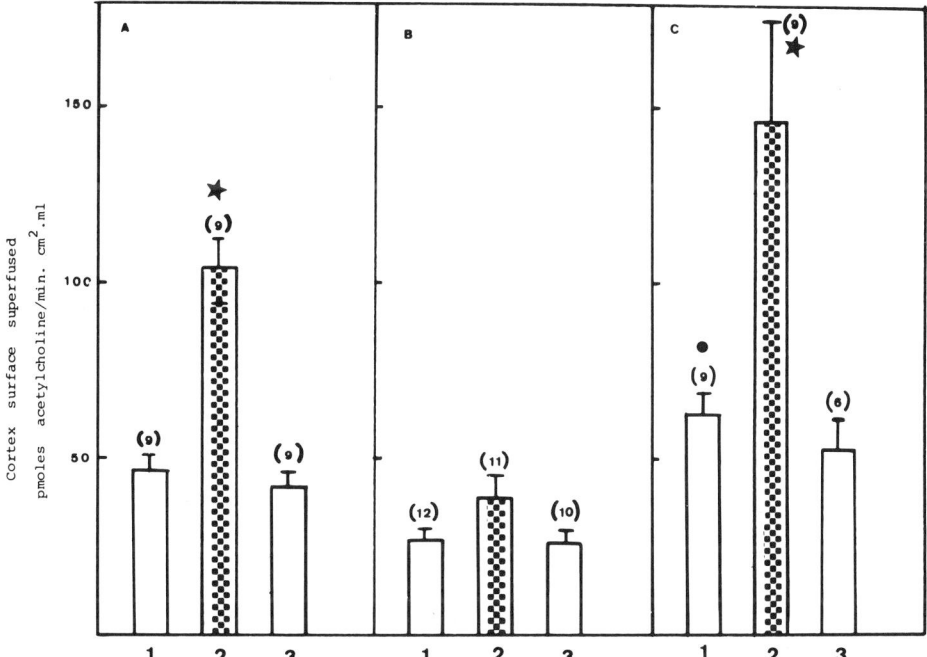

Fig. 7 – *In vivo* release of acetylcholine evoked from sensory stimulation via brachial plexus from superfused sensorimotor cortex in the drug-free condition and after administration of morphine and naloxone; the details are exactly as described in the caption to Fig. 8. Histobars represent the mean ± SEM for the number of observations indicated above them; these were obtained from four animals. The star indicates ACh release in A and C are significantly different from ACh release in B with $p > 0.001$. The black spot in C indicates naloxone effect in releasing ACh in C is significantly different from control (A) with $p > 0.01$. The two black spots in B indicate that spontaneous release is reduced due to morphine with $p > 0.001$. (From Coutinho-Netto *et al.*, 1980, with permission).

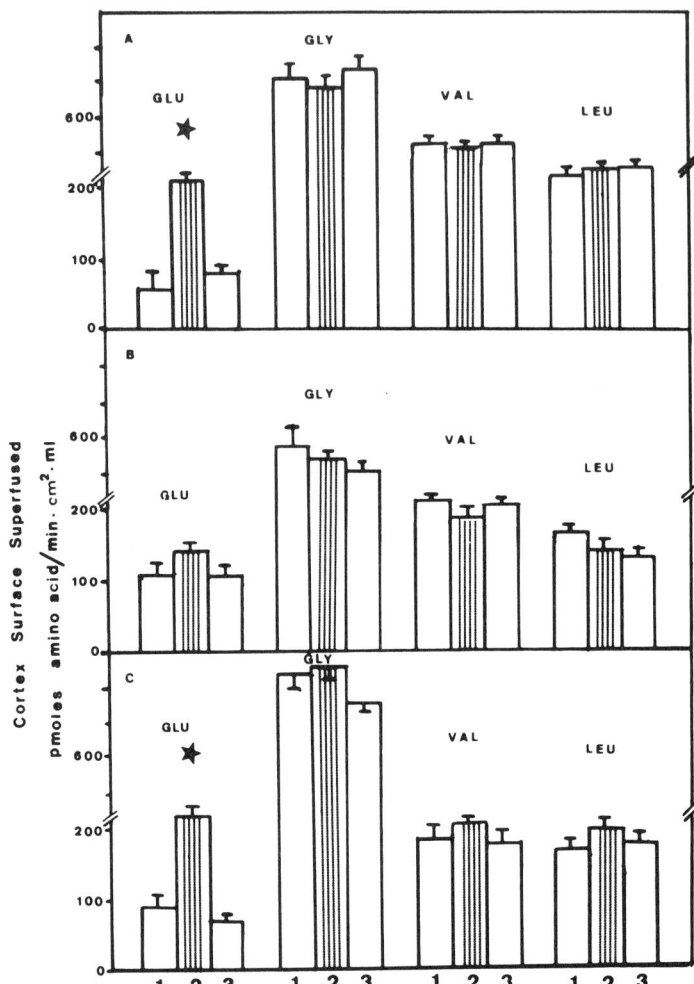

Fig. 8 – *In vivo* release of amino acids from superfused sensorimotor cortex during control preriods and during periods of stimulation of the contralateral brachial plexus. (A) drug-free, (B) after morphine, and (C) after naloxone. Histograms are as follows: (1) 10 min smaples before stimulation, (2) 10 min sample during stimulation, and (3) 10 min sample after stimulation. Morphine (20 mg/kg) was injected intraperitoneally after morphine administration. Histobars represent the mean ± SEM of 12 observations in 4 animals. Glu, glutamate; gly, glycine; val, valine; leu, leucine. The star indicates glutamate release in A and C is significantly different from glutamate release in B with $p > 0.001$. (From Coutinho-Netto *et al.*, 1980, with permission).

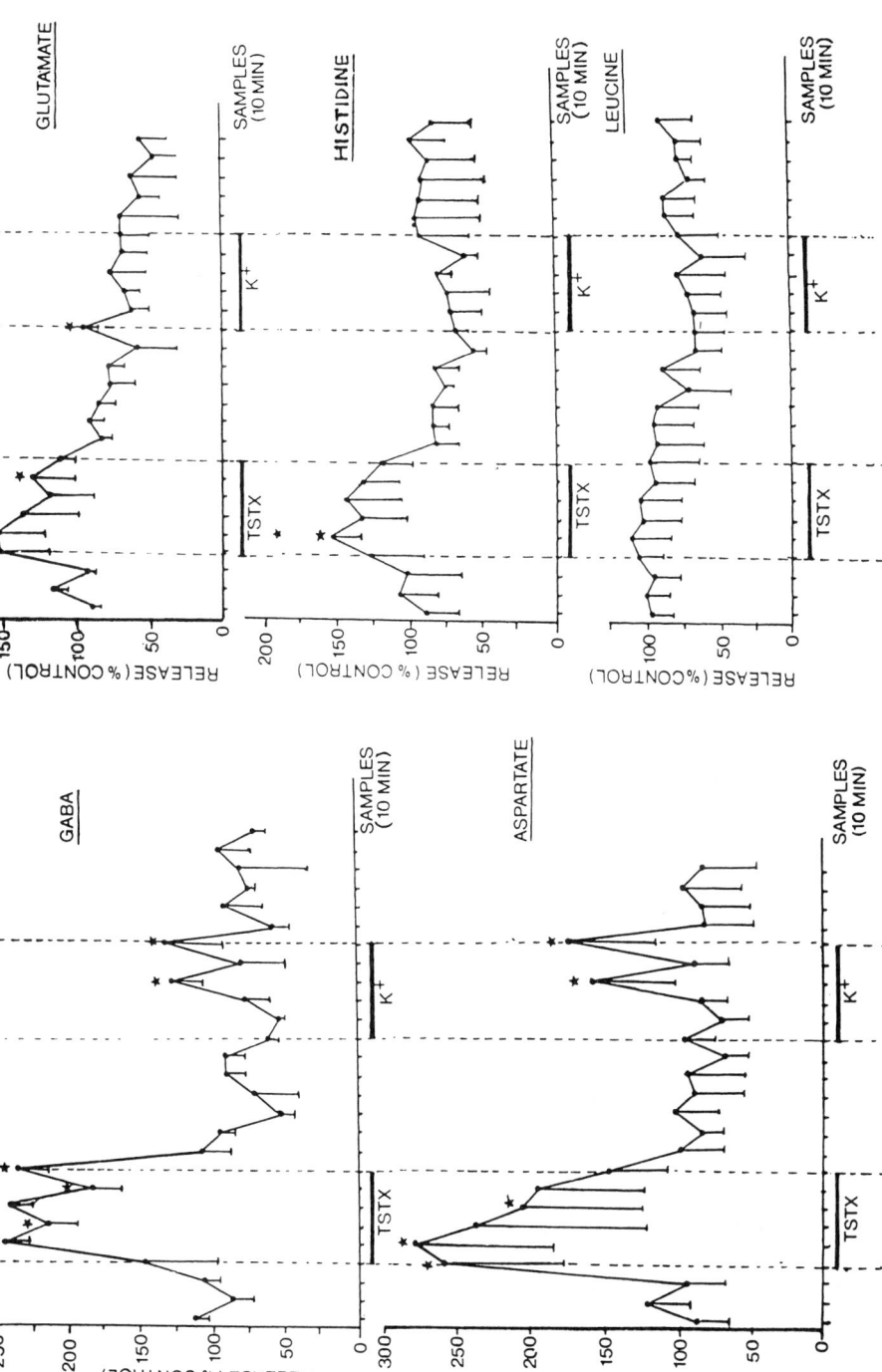

Fig. 9 – Release of amino acids from olfactory bulb surface was determined in 10 min samples (0.2 ml) of superfusate collected immediately prior to (control) or during stimulation of the olfactory bulb surface with tityustoxin (TsTx 1 μM) or K⁺ (56 mM). Values represent percentage changes relative to mean control levels. Values are mean ± SEM for four experiments. Basal levels of amino acid release were as follows: glutamate, 200—400; aspartate, 50—100; leucine, 200—300; GABA, histidine, 175—275. (From Thanki *et al.*, 1984, with permission).

3.6 Release from olfactory bulb

With the cannula positioned over the right olfactory bulb infusion of tityustoxin (1 μM) or K^+ (56 mM) into the dorsal surface evoked selective release of glutamate, aspartate, and GABA, with histidine also showing a response (30% above control, data not shown). Other amino acids measured showed little or no change (Fig. 9). The size of response was in the sequence: aspartate = GABA > glutamate > histidine. Carnosine, which was at the limit of detection in the present system, showed no responses.

3.7 Sensory stimulation of olfactory bulb

The animals (awake and freely moving) were placed in an airtight cage into which was delivered a stream of air (or oxygen/$CO_2$95:5% v/v) from a gas cylinder. The gas stream passed through tubes containing either water (as control) or a range of organic solvents used as smell stimuli (i.e. ethylacetate, toluene or 70% ethanol). The gas stream could be switched between the water or the solvent tubes. After a period of accommodation in the control gas stream (30–60 min), the smell stimulus was introduced for a period of 10 min. The control gas stream was then re-introduced. At least 30–50 min was allowed between smell stimuli. The olfactory bulb was superfused throughout with sterile saline-Ca^{2+} (1.85 mM) medium. Both ethylacetate and toluene produced very clear behavioural responses, the animals showing a marked increase in exploratory behaviour accompanied with sniffing and grooming, as if trying to seek the source of the smell. In contrast, alcohol produced little behavioural response, though the smell was clearly detectable by the experimenter. In terms of changes in amino acid release to superfusion fluid, both ethylacetate and toluene induced substantial responses. Glutamate and aspartate showed the largest and most consistent changes (Table 3). They involved a 2- to 3-fold increase in the extent of their release, and the responses were reversible when the smell stimulus ceased. GABA, however, showed a much smaller response (1- 2-fold) though this was consistent and significant ($p < 0.05$). Alcohol on the other hand, which produced much less of a behavioural response, had little detectable action on amino acid release.

Carnosine which was not detectably released by topical application of depolarizing agents also did not appear to be released by sensory stimulation of the olfactory bulb. This result was also obtained when peptidase inhibitors (pepstatin, bestatin) were present in the superfusion stream. The circuitry of the olfactory bulb is now fairly well established (Halasz and Shepherd, 1983). Carnosine has been proposed as the primary sensory neurotransmitter (synapse 1), and should therefore be released both in response to topically applied depolarizing agents and to sensory stimulation. The absence of any enhanced release of carnosine under these conditions, when putative amino acid neurotransmitters are showing clearly detectable patterns of release is therefore curious and unexpected (Thanki and Bradford, 1985). Others have reported a similar lack of response by carnosine during chemically induced depolarization of olfactory bulb *in vivo* employing the dialysis technique for neurotransmitter collection (Jacobson and Hamberger, 1984). These results from *in vivo* studies

Table 3 — *In vivo* release of amino acids (glutamate, aspartate, GABA) from rat olfactory bulb surface following smell stimulus.

Amino acid	Response (% control)	
	Ethyl acetate (smell) $n = 11$	Toluene (smell) $n = 6$
Glutamate	224 ± 97 ★★★★	195 ± 90 ★★
Aspartate	250 ± 100 ★★★★	252 ± 70 ★★★
GABA	131 ± 55 ★	166 ± 65.0 ★
Behavioural response	+++	++

Release of amino acids from olfactory bulb surface was determined in 10 min samples (0.2 ml) of superfusate collected immediately prior to (control) or during exposure of the rat to smell (ethylacetate or toluene) stimulus. Values represent percentage changes relative to unstimulated levels. Values are mean ± SEM for the number of stimulations indicated.

See caption to Fig. 9 for absolute values of basal levels of amino acid release.

The intensity of the behavioural response to smell stimulus conssisting of increased locomotion, sniffing and grooming behaviour was scored using behavioural rating.

scale: 0 = normal, control
+ = present, mild
++ = present, moderate intensity
+++ = intense
(Student's *t*-test)
★★★★ $p < 0.0005$
★★★ $p < 0.0025$
★★ $p < 0.025$
★ $p < 0.05$

contrast with those from *in vitro* work employing crude synaptosome preparations where large, readily detectable, increases in carnosine efflux follow application of depolarizing agents such as veratridine or high-K^+ (Rochel and Margolis, 1982; Thanki *et al.,* 1985).

The lack of accelerated efflux of carnosine from *in vivo* preparations following chemical or sensory stimulation could be due to tight control by intact neural feedback inhibitory pathways , and this is being investigated. Theoretically this could substantially limit the extent of any release so that detection is not possible by the methods so far employed. The sensitivity of the method used to detect carnosine in the present studies (i.e. ion-exchange chromatography) was employed at its limit (1—5 pmol) to monitor the basal *in vivo* release of this peptide, and this could be contributory to the difficulty experienced in detecting increased carnosine release. However, in other preliminary experiments in which carnosine in the olfactory bulb was substantially labelled with [^{14}C-] β-alanine delivered via the nasal sensory nerve, no increased efflux of [^{14}C]-carnosine to superfusion fluid was detected (Thanki and Bradford, 1985), Iontophoretic investigations of the neuroactivity of carnosine in olfactory bulb *in vivo* have indicated that this peptide does not serve any classical neurotransmitter role in this brain region (Nicoll *et al.*, 1980). Our own demonstration of the absence of evoked release of endogenous carnosine *in vivo* would tend to support this conclusion.

4. CONCLUSIONS

The chronic cortical cup technique has the advantage of being non-invasive in the sense that it is not pushed into brain tissue, and unlike dialysis, push—pull, or electrochemical methods, does not damage the tissue in the region from which it is collecting neurotransmitters, nor does it interfere with neural pathways connecting with that brain structure (Abdul-Ghani *et al.*, 1981). Like these other techniques, it relies on diffusion of neurotransmitters/metabolites to its collecting site and the precise extent of the 'collection area' is unknown for most of these methods. The disadvantage of the cortical cup is its restriction to the cortical surface, though as evidenced here, it can be used with great effect in several localized cortical regions to collect neurotransmitters and related metabolites from the brain surface of awake, behaviourally normal, animals both at basal levels and during periods of enhanced neural activity. Moreover, the cortical cup remains usable for periods of at least 6 to 8 weeks after implantation.

REFERENCES

Abdul-Ghani, A. S., Bradford, H. F., Cox, D. W. G. and Dodd, P. R. (1978). Peripheral sensory stimulation and the release of transmitter amino acids *in vivo* from specific regions of cerebral cortex. *Brain Res., 171*, 55—66.

Abdul-Ghani, A. S., Coutinho-Netto, J. C. and Bradford, H. F. (1980a). *In vivo* release of acetylcholine evoked by brachial plexus stimulation and tityustoxin. *Biochem. Pharmacol., 29*, 2179—2182.

Abdul-Ghani, A. S., Coutinho-Netto, J. C. and Bradford, H. F. (1980b). The action of γ-vinyl-GABA and γ-acetylenic-GABA on the resting and stimulated release of GABA *in vivo. Brain Res., 191*, 471—481.

Abdul-Ghani, A. S., Coutinho-Netto, J. C. and Bradford, H. F. (1981). *In vivo* superfusion methods and the release of glutamate. In: *Glutamate: Transmitter in the Central Nervous System.* Roberts, P. J., Johnston, G. A. R. and Storm Mathisen, J. (eds.), John Wiley, New York, pp. 155—203.

Coutinho-Netto, J. C., Abdul-Ghani, A. S., Norris, P. J., Thomas, A. J. and Bradford, H. F. (1980). The effects of scorpion venom toxin on the release of amino acid neurotransmitters from cerebral cortex *in vivo* and *in vitro*. *J. Neurochem.,* **35**, 558–565.

Dodd, P. R., Pritchard, M. J., Adams, R. C. F., Bradford, H. F., Hicks, G. and Blanshard, K. C. (1974). A method for the continuous, long-term superfusion of the cerebral cortex of unanaesthetised, unrestrained rats. *J. Scientific Inst.,* **7**, 897–901.

Halasz, N. and Shepherd, G. M. (1983). Neurochemistry of the vertebrate olfactory bulb. *Neuroscience,* **10**, 579–619.

Jacobson, I. and Hamberger, A. (1984). Veratridine-induced release *in vivo* and *in vitro* of amino acids in the rabbit olfactory bulb. *Brain Res.,* **299**, 103–112.

Jhamandas, K., Pinsky, C. and Phillis, J. W. (1970). Effects of morphine and its antagonists on release of cerebral cortical acetylcholine. *Nature,* **228**, 176–177.

Jhamandas, K. and Sutak, M. (1974). Modification of brain acetylcholine release by morphine and its antagonists in normal and morphine-dependent rats. *Br. J. Pharmac.,* **50**, 57–62.

Lippert, B., Metcalf, B. W., Jung, M. J. and Casara, P. (1977). 4-Amino-hex-5-enoic acid, a selective catalytic inhibitor of 4-aminobutyric-acid aminotransferase in mammalian brain. *Eur. J. Biochem.,* **74**, 441–445.

Matthews, J. D., Labrecque, G. and Domino, E. F. (1973). Effects of morphine, nalorphine and naloxone on neocortical release of acetylcholine in the rat. *Psychopharmacologia,* **29**, 113.

Nicoll, R. A., Alger, B. E. and Jahr, C. E. (1980). Peptides as putative excitatory neurotransmitters: carnosine, enkephalin, substance P and TRH. *Proc. R. Soc.,* **B210**, 133–149.

Norris, P. J., Smith, C. C. T., de Belleroche, J. Bradford, H. F., Mantle, P. G., Thomas, A. J. and Penney, R. H. C. (1980). Actions of tremorgenic fungal toxins on neurotransmitter release. *J. Neurochem.,* **34**, 33–42.

Oldendorf, W. (1970). Measurement of brain uptake of radiolabelled substances using tritiated water internal standard. *Brain Res.,* **24**, 372–376.

Rochel, S. and Margolis, F. L. (1982). Carnosine release from olfactory bulb synaptosomes is calcium-dependent and depolarization-stimulated. *J. Neurochem.,* **38**, 1505–1513.

Thanki, C. and Bradford, H. F. (1985). Transmitter release from the olfactory bulb *in vivo*: amino acids and carnosine (in preparation).

Thanki, C., Norris, D. and Bradford, H. F. (1985). *In vitro* release of endogenous carnosine and amino acids from olfactory bulb synaptosome preparations (in preparation).

CHAPTER

9

Commentary: The search for approaches to monitor molecular events of cerebral neurotransmission *in vivo*

Jakob Korf
Department of Biological Psychiatry, Oostersingel 59, 9713 EZ Groningen, The Netherlands.

1. INTRODUCTION

Both clinical and experimental research on the putative relationship between behaviour and central neurotransmission rely heavily on the examination of brain tissue obtained post mortem. Besides ethical questions and the high costs of most of the laboratory animals, the data thus obtained are of only limited value as they do not allow conclusive statements on individual aspects of brain and behaviour or prognostic interventions.

In spite of these limitations much of our current knowledge on the molecular aspects of central transmission is based on post-mortem analysis of the brains of groups of rodents treated with drugs. It is only in the last 15 years that substantial progress has been made in the development of methods that are useful in the living and thus behaving animal. Some of these approaches have clinical potentials. In this chapter several available methods are discussed, in particular in terms of specificity, reproducibility and applicability.

2. PERIPHERAL BODY FLUIDS

In the late 1960s and the early 1970s a major emphasis in clinical investigations on cerebral neurotransmitters and their metabolites was on the chemical analysis of body fluids, urine, blood and cerebrospinal fluid.

There is no doubt that the urinary excretion of the metabolites of nor-adrenaline, adrenaline, dopamine and 5-hydroxytryptamine (MHPG, normetane-phrine, VMA, HVA, DOPAC, 5-HIAA, and their possible conjugates) reflect total metabolism of the parent amine. In fact, urine is the only body fluid, which provides absolutely quantitative data on the total body turnover of amines (although there may be some contribution from bacteria in the intestines), as the excretion of the amine metabolites is mainly, if not exclusively through the renal route. The catecholamine metabolites, especially VMA, MHPG and HVA, are used to characterize neurogenic tumours; neuroblastoma, ganglio-neuroblastoma and phaeochromocytoma. In addition carcinoids produce in-creased excretion of 5-hydroxyindoles (Ruthven and Sandler, 1979; Robinson, 1980).

Claims have been made for the use of MHPG and conjugates as a predictor for the success of antidepressant therapy. However, these findings are still controversial (e.g. Schildkraut, 1974; Gaertner et al., 1982). The urinary excre-tion of catecholamines and metabolites are often monitored in stress and cir-cadian rhythm research (e.g Åkerstedt and Gilberg, 1983; Frankenhaeuser, 1971). The origin of the catecholamine metabolites in urine is still not satis-factorily established. There is little doubt that peripheral tissue contributes to a major extent, although suggestions for a high central contribution have been published (for a summary, see Korf, 1979). As an example Aizenstein and Korf (1979) calculated that in the rat less than 10% of the urinary 5-hydroxyindole-acetic acid originates in the central nervous system.

Because of its quantitative nature, urinary excretion of amine metabolite can possibly be used as an index of drug responses. It is to be expected that monoamineoxidase inhibitors can thus be monitored or the precursor meta-bolism could thus be quantified. Surprisingly few experimental data are avail-able to compare central and peripheral drug effects. If such relationships exist, then urinary data provide a rather simple index to quantify molecular drug responses.

With the advent of highly sensitive assays for catecholamines and in parti-cular for their metabolites, attempts have been made to quantify cerebral metabolism by measuring levels of metabolites in the circulation. Thus arterio-venous differences of HVA and MHPG were determined and the cerebral produc-tion calculated under normal conditions and during drug treatments (Maas et al., 1979a, b).

Because of their invasive character, such approaches, although sophisticated, will not easily become applicable on a routine clinical basis. A more practical approach is the measurement of blood levels of MHPG and HVA as indices of noradrenaline and dopamine metabolism (e.g. Charney et al., 1982a, b; Kopin et al., 1983; Bacopoulos et al., 1978). As in the case of the urinary excretion of these metabolites, the levels in the circulation reflect predominantly peripheral metabolism of the parent amines. These circulating metabolites have been used to assess the effects of drugs on amine metabolism (Kendler et al., 1982; Pickar et al., 1984).

3. CIRCULATING HORMONES

Because of its close association with the brain and its reactivity to environmental and behavioural conditions pituitary function is often considered as a 'window on the brain'. The function of the hypophysis-hypothalamus is recognized by the excretion of hormones, such as adrenocorticotrophic hormone (ACTH), prolactin and growth hormone. In the context of this chapter it should be recalled that prolactin levels have often been used as an index of dopamine receptor blockade, because dopamine produces suppression of the excretion of the hormone (for a summary see Korf, 1979).

A major effort has been made to use circulating cortisol (originating in the adrenal cortex in response to ACTH) for diagnostic purposes in psychiatric practice. Accordingly a failure to suppress cortisol in response to the synthetic corticosteroid dexamethasone has been proposed as a marker of endogenous depression (e.g. Carrol et al., 1981; Health and Public Policy Committee, 1984; Berger et al., 1982). Stressful conditions do not only enhance adrenal activity (increase in adrenalin and cortisol levels) but produce also enhanced release of several pituitary hormones, including endorphines (e.g. Berkenbosch et al., 1983). Growth hormone may serve as an index for α-receptor activity (e.g. Charney et al., 1982a; Rudolf et al., 1980). If the precise neuronal circuitry becomes known, then these responses can serve as indices for the function of the constituting neuronal pathways.

In summary, circulating hormones have a demonstrated and future potential to follow cerebral neurotransmission. Needless to say, more detailed knowledge is required to relate pituitary hormones to specific central events. The advantage of the approach with hormones is its almost non-invasive character, permitting long-term studies.

4. CEREBROSPINAL FLUID

Analysis of cerebrospinal fluid is one of the most direct approaches to study cerebral metabolism. There is no doubt that most, if not all, CSF metabolites of the catecholamines and serotonin are derived from central tissue (but see Kopin et al., 1983). Using this approach both clinical and experimental observations have been made, but it is only recently that quantitative studies on the relationship of cerebral and/or spinal metabolism and cerebrospinal fluid levels and kinetics have appeared.

Moreover by using a serial sample technique to obtain cerebrospinal fluid from the rat cisterna, simultaneous biochemical and behavioural observations are possible (see contributions of Curzon and co-workers., Part III, Chapter 5, this volume and references therein). A major question raised by Elghozi et al. (1983) is whether the level of 5-hydroxyindoleacetic acid in the cerebrospinal fluid, or its enhancement following the administration of probenecid, does indeed reflect tissue rate of formation. In this respect data published by Elghozi et al. (1983) and those of Curzon and coworkers (this volume) were discrepant. Arguments such as differences in experimental protocols (for instance: anaesthetized versus conscious rats; ventricular versus cisternal sampling) may be relevant here, but development of a descriptive model clarifies also some of the dilemmas. Our model assumes first order kinetics and single compartments.

$$\text{blood} \xleftarrow{k_b} \text{brain} \underset{k_a}{\overset{k_c}{\rightleftarrows}} \text{cerebrospinal fluid} \xrightarrow{k_e} \text{blood}$$

In this scheme fractional rate constants are indicated by k. The k_b refers to transport from brain to blood; k_c from brain to the cerebrospinal fluid compartments (which are considered as a single compartment; this assumption is possibly a simplification); k_a is the rate constant in the reverse direction, and finally k_e is the rate constant of the cerebrospinal fluid compartment to blood. Under steady state (and without the use of egress-inhibiting drugs such as probenecid) we assume that $k_a \ll k_c$ and that the levels in cerebrospinal fluid are substantially lower than tissue levels. For any metabolite A (such as 5-hydroxy-indoleacetic acid, homovanillic acid or 3,4-hydroxyphenylacetic acid and possible conjugates) the transport out of the brain or spinal tissue can be described as

$$A_b = \frac{TR_A}{k_b + k_c} \tag{1}$$

In which A_b = brain levels of A at steady state conditions and TR_A = turnover rate of A. In the cerebrospinal fluid compartment, where A_c is the concentration of A

$$\frac{dA_c}{dt} = k_c A_b - k_e A_c \tag{2}$$

By giving high doses of probenecid our model shows directly that the rate of accumulation of A in the cerebrospinal fluid is not exclusively dependent on the turnover rate. In the ideal experiment with probenecid k_b, k_e and also in the early phase k_a are zero. Using equation (2) to describe the increase in the levels of A_c

$$\frac{dA_c}{dt} = k_c A_b = k_c \, TR_A \cdot t \tag{3}$$

and

$$A_{c_t} = \frac{1}{k_e} \cdot \frac{k_c}{k_b + k_c} \cdot TR_A + \tfrac{1}{2} k_c \, TR_A \cdot t^2 \tag{4}$$

in which A_{c_t} is the concentration of A_c at t min (or h) following probenecid medication.

The equation shows that the CSF-levels of a metabolite is only a reflection of the turnover rate at a fixed time following probenecid medication. In particular at early time intervals following probenecid the increase in the CSF-levels of HVA may be only related in part to either steady state levels of CSF or to the rate of central formation. This may explain why in some cases significant relations were found between baseline CSF levels and probenecid induced accumulations of a metabolite in one study, but not in another (Elghozi *et al.*, 1983; Curzon and co-workers, Part III, Chapter 5, this volume).

This model indicates that after probenecid administration the fraction of centrally formed metabolites that enter the cerebrospinal fluid compartment is different (larger) than without probenecid. Indeed, this prediction was confirmed in perfusion experiments with anaesthetized rats (Aizenstein and Korf, 1978, 1979).

5. IMAGING OF CEREBRAL PROCESSES

In the last 15 years techniques have emerged aiming to detect and localize cerebral processes *in vivo*. These techniques, of which the computer assisted X-ray tomography was a forerunner, enable not only metabolic events but also receptors to be studied. For these in particular single and positron emission tomography and nuclear magnetic resonance spectroscopy and imaging are suitable. Recent examples are the visualization of dopaminergic pathways with ^{18}F-6-fluoro 3,4-dihydroxyphenylalanine (^{18}F-DOPA) and receptors with spiperone derivatives (e.g. Garnett *et al.*, 1983; Wagner *et al.*, 1983) with positron emission tomography. Cerebral muscarinic acetylcholine receptors were visualized with (^{123}I)3-quinuclidinyl 4-iodobenzilate (Eckelman *et al.*, 1984) and dopamine receptors with ^{76}Br or ^{77}Br-spiperone (Owen *et al.*, 1983; Mazière *et al.*, 1984) with single photon emission tomography. Application of nuclear magnetic resonance includes energy metabolism, neurotransmitters and sodium (e.g. Budinger, 1984; Hila *et al.*, 1985), which may eventually be shown to depend at least in part upon central neurotransmission. Moreover the latter may become important to monitor neural lesions. The potentials and limitations of these techniques are not discussed here in detail and the reader is referred to recent surveys (e.g. Oldendorf, 1980; Brownell *et al.*, 1982; Budinger and Lauterbur, 1984.

6. VOLTAMMETRY

Based on differences in electrochemical oxidation/reduction properties, several constituents can be detected *in vivo*. Applications of voltammetry *in vivo* have been described for biogenic amines (catecholamines, 5-hydroxytryptamine), some of these metabolites and of compounds such as ascorbic acid (Maidment and co-workers, Part III, Chapter 1, this volume; Fillenz and co-workers, Part III, Chapter 7, this volume). A major problem is still the unequivocal determination of the specificity. In particular discrimination of the amines and the metabolites is often problematic.

When specificity is established, voltammetry is particularly attractive for the detection of short-lasting alterations. Examples of this are the short-lasting release of dopamine in the striatum, as the consequence of electrical stimulation of the nigro-striatal pathway (Kruk, Part V, this volume; Kuhr *et al., 1984;*

Ewing and Wightman, 1984). Questions such as tissue reaction to the electrodes used in this technique have not yet been investigated in any detail.

7. SUPER- AND PERFUSION METHODS

To monitor the release of tissue constituents directly, two techniques have been described. The superfusion technique (often with cups placed on the cerebral cortex; see also Bradford and co-workers, Part III, Chapter 8, this volume) enables the release of transmitter substances from the more peripheral brain structures to be studied. The perfusion technique, employing push–pull cannulae, allows also the perfusion of deeply situated brain (and spinal cord) regions.

Push–pull perfusion is also useful in freely moving animals. An example of such an approach is described by Philippu and co-workers, who monitored transmitter release in the hypothalamus in the free moving animals (Philippu et al., 1983, 1984; Tuomisto et al., 1983). This technique is also the subject of recent reviews (Philippu, 1984a, b, 1985). In the anaesthetized animals the push–pull cannula technique is in particular useful to monitor transmitter release and the effects of drugs thereon (for examples, see Gaddum, 1961; Van der Heyden et al., 1979; Canzek et al., 1981; Nieoullon et al., 1977).

The perfusion rate of the push–pull cannula technique is often in the range of 10–30 μl min^{-1}. Such a high perfusion rate suppresses the specific transmitter uptake and the perfused tissue is rather efficiently drained, so that systematically applied drugs do not concentrate at the site of perfusion. Implantation of even the smallest push–pull cannulas always produces tissue damage and in our experience holes of several hundred micrometres were observed after a 2 h perfusion.

In an attempt to relate tissue levels of amino acids and the output from push–pull cannulas, it was observed that there was a high correlation between them, suggesting the tissue origin of the amino acids (Korf and Venema, 1985).

8. DIALYSIS

A major recent approach to monitor molecular events in the central nervous system is the application of dialysis. Stimulating investigations of this technique were initiated by Delgado and co-workers (1972, 1984), Ungerstedt and co-workers (Ungerstedt and Pycock, 1974; Sharp and co-workers, Part III, Chapter 2, this volume), Marsden and co-workers (Maidment and co-workers, Part III, Chapter 1, this volume) and Hamberger and his group (1983). Both cortical and sub-cortical brain areas can be perfused. Some of the methodological aspects and potentials have been described by the above authors, but little data have appeared to compare the dialysis technique with push–pull perfusions.

We (Korf and Venema, 1985) compared the output of the dialysis probe (implanted in the rat striatum) and the push–pull cannula efflux. Essentially similar output of amino acids was found in both techniques (correlation coefficient $r = 0.99$, 15 amino acids). The dialysate content of the amino acids correlated highly with tissue levels, when the putative transmitter amino acids (taurine, γ-aminobutyric acid, glutamic acid and aspartic acid) were excluded from the calculation.

These transmitter amino acids were less efficiently dialysed from the tissue, presumably because of highly efficient recapture from the extracellular space. The conclusion from these findings is that transmitter molecules, because of specific uptake processes, do not reach the dialysis probe. This conclusion is in line with the results with dopamine and its metabolites (Imperato and DiChiara, 1984; Zetterström *et al.*, 1983). In this case much more metabolites than dopamine were detected; in the dialysed brain area – the striatum – the levels of the amine are at least five times those of the metabolites.

These observations together suggest that dialysis is more useful to monitor metabolic events than neurotransmission. In this respect the application of dialysis *in vivo* to measure, for example, brain energy metabolism and electrolyte movements should be considered. Recent examples are (a) our observation that electroconvulsive shock increases the dialysate content of alanine presumably formed by transamination of pyruvic acid (Korf and Venema, 1985), (b) the alterations of extracellular Ca^{2+} during ischaemia and verapamil treatment (Hagberg *et al.*, 1984), (c) the possible interrelation between extracellular taurine and phosphoethanolamine (Lehmann and Hamberger, 1984) and (d) influence of neurotoxic compounds on amino acid release (Lehmann *et al.*, 1983).

The dialysis probe remains in place and open for several weeks, but we observed changes over time both in the basal output levels as well as in the responsiveness to stimuli. In contrast the responsiveness of alanine to these stimuli (local infusion of high K or electroconvulsive shocks) was rather stable.

All these observations and suggestions emphasize the possible usefulness of dialysis for long-term observations in the same animals. Whether, as is at present the case, this technique should then be applied predominantly to monitor cerebral neurotransmission, is open to question.

9. CONCLUDING REMARKS

The brain is an organ with spatiotemporal organization with slow and fast molecular events. As is clear from the above sections none of the currently available techniques enables the fast events to be monitored, and only relatively slow processes can be analysed or certain static features can be shown. Fast cyclic voltammetry (Armstrong-James, 1984; Kruk, Part V, this volume) shows the most promise for monitoring fast events. In addition, none of the techniques is quantitative, in the sense that exact numbers can be given to the cerebral processes studied. In the end, any *in vivo* technique should indicate exactly how much transmitter is metabolized or released or how many functional receptors are present in particular brain areas, etc. Despite these enormous gaps in our present knowledge, the progress in *in vivo* methodology during the last 5 years is remarkable.

REFERENCES

Aizenstein, M. L. and Korf, J. (1978). Aspects of influx and efflux of homo-vanillic acid of rat cerebrospinal fluid. *Brain Res.,* **149**, 129–140.

Aizenstein, M. L. and Korf, J. (1979). On the elimination of centrally formed 5-hydroxyindoleacetic acid by cerebrospinal fluid and urine. *J. Neurochem.,* **32**, 122&1233.

Åkerstedt, T. and Gilberg, M. (1983). Circadian variation of catecholamine excretion and sleep. *Eur. J. Appl. Physiol.,* **51**, 203–215.

Armstrong-James, M. and Millar, J. (1984). High-speed cyclic voltammetry and unit recording with carbon fibre microelectrodes. In: Marsden, C. A. (ed.), *Measurement of Neurotransmitter Release in vivo.* John Wiley, Chichester, pp. 209–224.

Bacopoulos, N. G., Heninger, G. R. and Roth, R. H. (1978). Effects of halo-peridol and probenecid on plasma and CSF dopamine metabolites in the rhesus monkey (*Macacca mulatta*). *Life Sci.,* **23**, 1805.

Berger, M., Doerr, P., Lund, P., Bronisch, T. and Von Zerssen, D. (1982). Neuro-endocrinological and neurophysiological studies in major depressive dis-orders: are there biological markers for the endogenous type? *Biol. Psychiat.,* **17**, 1217–1242.

Berkenbosch, F., Tilders, F. J. H. and Vermes, I. (1983). Beta-adrenoceptor activation mediates stress-induced secretion of beta-endorphin related peptides from intermediate but not anterior pituitary. *Nature,* **305**, 237–239.

Brownell, G. L., Budinger, T. F., Lauterbur, P. C. and McGeer, P. L. (1982). Positron emission tomography and nuclear magnetic resonance imaging. *Science,* **215**, 619–624.

Budinger, T. F. and Lauterbur, P. C. (1984). Nuclear magnetic resonance tech-nology for medical studies. *Sciences,* **226**, 288–298.

Canzek, V., Wolfensberger, M., Amsler, U. and Cuénod, M. (1981). *In vivo* release of glutamate and aspartate following optic nerve stimulation. *Nature,* **293**, 572–574.

Carrol, B. J., Feinberg, M., Greden, J. F., Tarika, J., Albala, A. A., Haskett, R. F., James, N. M., Kronfol, Z., Lohr, N., Steiner, M., De Vigne, J. P. and Young, E. (1981). A specific laboratory test for the diagnosis of melan-cholia: standardization, validation and clinical utility. *Arch. Gen. Psychiat.,* **38**, 15–22.

Charney, D. S., Heninger, G. R., Sternberg, D. E., Hafstad, K. M., Giddings, S. and Landis, D. H. (1982a). Adrenergic receptor sensitivity in depression: effects of clonidine in depressed patients and healthy subjects. *Arch Gen. Psychiat.,* **39**, 290–294.

Charney, D. S., Heninger, G. R. and Sternberg, D. E. (1982b). Assessment of α_2-adrenergic autoreceptor for function in humans: effects of oral yohim-bine. *Life Sci.,* **30**, 2033–2041.

Delgado, J. M. R., De Feudis, F. V., Roth, R. H., Ryugo, D. K. and Mitruka, B. M. (1972). Dialytrode for long term intracerebral perfusion in awake monkeys. *Arch. Int. Pharmakodyn.,* **198**, 9–21.

Delgado, J. M. R., Lerma, J., Martin, del Rio, R., Solis, J. M. (1984). Dialy-trode technology and local profiles of amino acids in the awake cat brain. *J. Neurochem.*, **42**, 1218–1228.

Eckelman, W. C., Reba, R. C., Rzeszotarski, W. J., Gibson, R. E., Hill, T., Holman, B. L., Budinger, T., Conklin, J. J., Eng, R. and Grissom, M. P. (1984). External imaging of cerebral muscarinic acetyl choline receptors. *Science*, **223**, 291–293.

Elghozi, J. L., Mignot, E. and Le Quai-Bui, K. H. (1983). Probenecid sensitive pathway of elimination of dopamine and serotonin metabolites in CSF of the rat. *J. Neural Transmission*, **57**, 85–94.

Ewing, A. G. and Wightman, R. M. (1984). Monitoring the stimulated release of dopamine with *in vivo* voltammetry. II: Clearance of released dopamine from extracellular fluid. *J. Neurochem.*, **43**, 570–577.

Frankenhaeuser, M. (1971). Behavior and circulating catecholamines. *Brain Res.* **31**, 241–262.

Gaddum, J. H. (1961). Push–pull cannulae. *J. Physiol. (Lond.)*, **155**, 1P–2P.

Gaertner, H. J., Golfinopoulos, G. and Beyer-Pfaff, U. (1982). Responses to maprotiline treatment in depressive patients: relationships to urinary MHPG excretion and plasma drug level. *Pharmacopsychiat.*, **15**, 170–174.

Garnett, E. S., Firneau, G. and Nahmias, C. (1983). Dopamine visualized in the basal ganglia of living man. *Nature*, **305**, 137–138.

Hagber, H., Lehmann, H. and Hamberger, A. (1984). Inhibition by verapamil of ischemic Ca^{2+} uptake in the rabbit hippocampus. *J. Cereb. Blood Flow Metabol.*, **4**, 297–300.

Hamberger, A., Berthold, C.-H., Karlsson, B., Lehman, A. and Nyström, B. (1983). Extracellular GABA, glutamate and glutamine; in vivo perfusion-dialysis of the rabbit hippocampus. In: *Glutamine, Glutamate and GABA in the Central Nervous System*, Hertz, L., Kvamme, E., McGeer, E. G. and Schousboe, A. (eds.). Liss, New York, pp. 473–492.

Health and Public Policy Committee (1984). The dexamethasone suppression test for the detection, diagnosis and management of depression. *Ann. Int. Med;.* **100**, 307–308.

Hilal, S. K., Maudsley, A. A., Ra, J. B., Simon, H. E., Roschmann, P., Witte-koek, A., Cho, Z. H. and Mun, S. K. (1985). *In vivo* NMR imaging of sodium-23 in the human head. *J. Comp. Ass. Tomog.*, **9**, 1–7.

Imperato, A. and DiChiara, G. (1984). Trans-striatal dialysis coupled to reversed phase high performance chromatography with electrochemical detection: a new method for the study of the *in vivo* release of endogenous dopamine and metabolites. *J. Neuroscience*, **4**, 966–977.

Kendler, K. S., Heninger, G. R. and Roth, R. H. (1982). Influence of dopamine agonists on plasma and brain levels of homovanillic acid. *Life Sci.*, **30**, 2063–2069.

Kopin, I. J., Gordon, E. K., Jimerson, D. C. and Polinsky, R. J. (1983). Relation between plasma and cerebrospinal fluid levels of 3-methoxy-4-hydroxy-phenylglycol. *Science*, **219**, 73–75.

Korf, J. (1979). Clinical aspects of dopaminergic processes. In: *Neurobiology of Dopamine*, Horn, A. S., Korf, Westerink, B. H. C. (eds.). Academic Press, London, pp. 619–632.

Korf, J. and Venema, K. (1985) Amino acids in rat striatal dialysates: methodological aspects and changes after electro convulsive shock. *J. Neurochem.*, **45**, 000–000.

Korf, J. (1979). Clinical aspects of dopaminergic processes. In: *Neurobiology of Dopamine*, Horn, A. S., Korf, K., Westerink, B. H. C. (eds.). Academic Press, London, pp. 619–632.

Kuhr, W. G., Ewing, A. G., Caudill, W. L. and Wightman, R. M. (1984). Monitoring the stimulated release of dopamine with *in vivo* voltammetry. I: Characterization of the response observed in the caudate nucleus of the rat. *J. Neurochem.*, **43**, 560–569.

Lehmann, A. and Hamberger, A. (1984). A possible interrelationship between extracellular taurine and phosphoethanolamine in the hippocampus. *J. Neurochem.*, **42**, 1286–1290.

Lehmann, A., Isacsson, H. and Hamberger, A. (1983). Effects of *in vivo* administration of kainic acid on the extracellular aminoacid pool in the rabbit hippocampus. *J. Neurochem.*, **40**, 1314–1320.

Maas, J. W., Hattox, S. E., Green, N. M., Landis, N. M. (1979a). MHPG production by human *in vivo*. *Science*, **205**, 1025–1027.

Mass, J., Hattox, S. E., Martin, D. M. and Landis, D. H. (1979b). A direct method for determining dopamine synthesis and output of dopamine metabolites from brain in awake animals. *J. Neurochem.*, **32**, 839–843.

Mazière, B., Loc'h, C., Hantraye, P., Guillon, R., Duquesnoy, N., Soussaline, F., Naquet, R., Comar, D. and Mazière, M. (1984). [76]Br-bromospiroperidol: a new tool for quantitative *in vivo* imaging of neuroleptic receptors. *Life Sci.*, **35**, 1349–1356.

Nieoullon, A., Chéramy, A. and Glowinski, J. (1977). An adaptation of the push–pull cannula method to study the *in vivo* release of ^{3}H-dopamine synthesized from ^{3}H-tyrosine in the cat caudate nucleus: effect of various physical and pharmacological treatments. *J. Neurochem.*, **28**, 819–828.

Oldendorf, W. H. (1980). *The Quest for an Image of Brain*. Raven Press, New York.

Owen, F., Poulter, M., Mashall, R. D., Crow, T. J., Veall, N. and Zanelli, G. D. (1983). [77]Br-p-bromospiperon: a ligand for *in vivo* labelling of dopamine receptors. *Life Sci.*, **33**, 765–768.

Philippu, A. (1984a). Use of push–pull cannalae to determine the release of endogenous neurotransmitters in distinct brain areas of anaesthetized and freely moving animals. In: *Measurement of Neurotransmitter Release in Vivo*, Marsden, C. A. (ed.). John Wiley, Chichester, pp. 3–37.

Philippu, A. (1984b). Hypothalamic neurotransmitters: patters of release and involvement in blood pressure regulation; In: Flemming, W. W., Langer, S. Z., Graefe, K. H. and Weiner, N. (eds.). *Neuronal and Extraneuronal Events in Autonomic Pharmacology*. Raven Press, New York, pp. 83–92.

Philippu, A. (1985). The use of push–pull cannulae for superfusing various hypothalmic areas in anaesthetized and conscious, freely moving animals. In: Drucker Colin, R. and Bayon, A. (eds.). *In Vivo Perfusion and Release of Neuroactive Substances: Methods and Strategies.* Raven Press, New York (in press).

Philippu, A., Hagen, R., Hanesch, U., Waldmann, U. (1983). Changes in the arterial blood pressure increase the release of endogenous histamine in the hypothalamus of anaesthetized cats. *Naunyn Schmiedeberg's Arch. Pharmacol.,* **323**, 162–167.

Philippu, A., Bald, M., Kraus, A. and Dietl, H. (1984). *In vivo* release by histamine agonists and antagonists of endogenous catecholamines in the cat hypothalamus. *Naunyn Schmiedeberg's Arch. Pharmacol.,* **326**, 116–123.

Pickar, D., Labarea, R., Linnoila, M., Roy, A., Hommer, D., Everett, D. and Paul, S. (1984). Neuroleptic-induced decrease in plasma homovanillic acid and antipsychotic activity in schizophrenic patients. *Science,* **225**, 954–957.

Robinson, R. (1980). *Tumours that Secrete Catecholamines: Their Detection and Clinical Chemistry.* John Wiley, Chichester, pp. 1–132.

Rudolf, C. D., Kaplan, S. L. Ganong, W. F. (1980). Sites at which clonidine acts to affect blood pressure and the secretion of renin, growth hormone, and ACTH. *Neuroendocrinology,* **31**, 121–128.

Ruthven, C. R. J. and Sandler, M. (1979). Neurogenic amines and secreting tumours. In: *Chemical Diagnosis of Disease,* Brown, S. S., Mitchell, F. L., Young, D. S. (eds.). Elsevier North-Holland Biomedical Press, Amsterdam, pp. 1217–1291.

Schildkraut, J. J. (1974). Biochemical criteria for classifying depressive disorders and predicting responses to pharmacotherapy: preliminary findings from studies of norepinephrine metabolism. *Pharmacopsychiat.,* **7**, 98–107.

Tuomisto, L., Yamatodani, A., Dietl, H., Waldmann, U. and Philippu, A. (1983). *In vivo* release of endogenous catecholamines, histamine and GABA in the hypothalamus of Wistar Kyoto and spontaneously hypertensive rats. *Nauny-Schmiedeberg's Arch. Pharmacol.,* **323**, 183–187.

Ungerstedt, U. amd Pycock, C. J. (1974). Functional correlates of dopamine neurotransmission. *Bull. Schweiz. Akad. Med. Weis.,* **30**, 44–55.

Van der Heyden, J. A. M., Venema, K. and Korf, J. (1979). The *in vivo* release of endogenous GABA from rat substantia nigra measured by a novel method. *J. Neurochem.,* **32**, 469–476.

Wagner, Jr., H. H., Burns, D., Dannals, R. F., Wong, D. F., Langström, B., Duelfer, T., Frost, J. J., Ravert, H. T., Links, J. M., Rosenblom, S. R., Lukas, S. E., Kramer, A. V. and Kuhar, M. J. (1983). Imaging dopamine receptors in the human brain by positron emission tomography. *Science,* **221**, 1264–1265.

Zetterström, T., Ungerstedt, U. (1984). Effects of apomorphine on the *in vivo* release of dopamine and its metabolites, studied by brain dialysis. *Europ. J. Pharmacol.,* **97**, 29–36.

Part

IV

Workshop:
Recent developments in HPLC
analysis of transmitters and
related compounds

Report:

Recent developments in HPLC analysis of transmitters and related compounds

M. H. Joseph[†]

Division of Psychiatry, MRC Clinical Research Centre, Watford Road, Harrow HA1 3UJ, UK

C. A. Marsden

Department of Physiology and Pharmacology, University of Nottingham Medical School, Clifton Blvd., Nottingham, NG7 2UH, UK

The following general discussion centres on recent developments in the measurement of neurotransmitters and related compounds, using HPLC with electrochemical detection. It reflects the needs of research workers who wish to relate transmitter release and metabolism to function. We have solicited short articles (designated 'Communication' in the text) on particular applications which represent, in our view, important developments. The oral and poster presentations are referenced as far as possible; in other cases the addresses of the workers involved are appended so that further details can be obtained from them. The arrangement of this report follows the sequence in which HPLC determination is performed; a general section is followed by sections on developments in electrochemical detection, and on specific analytical applications.

1. GENERAL TOPICS

1.1 Sample preparation
Although the sensitivity and specificity of HPLC with electrochemical (EC)

---

†Present address: Departments of Psychology and Biochemistry, Institute of Psychiatry, Denmark Hill, London, SE5 8AF, UK.

detection have drastically simplified the work up of samples prior to the determination of catecholamines and metabolites in brain, the very low concentrations found in plasma and urine still require a degree of pre-separation. This has most commonly been brought about by absorption on alumina, and acid elution, before HPLC analysis.

D. M. Lake and I. A. Macdonald (Communication 1, Part IV) describe a new procedure for the isolation of catecholamines from plasma, involving complexation with diphenyl borate and ion pair extraction into an organic phase. The use of this method is described in the communication by Caligura *et al.*, (see section 1.3, below). R. Calverley described a procedure based on similar principles of complex formation but using phenyl boronate immobilized on small columns for isolating catecholamines from urine. A simple suction device enabled a number of samples to be treated in parallel, and set up ready for analysis.

The increasing appreciation of the extent to which catecholamines and their metabolites are conjugated during metabolism *in vivo* has led to a demand for HPLC determinations of these conjugates, which are not in themselves electroactive at accessible potentials. While many conjugates can be hydrolysed prior to HPLC under controlled acid conditions (see Hutson *et al.*, 1984), in the case of MHPG-sulphate, the principal metabolite of noradrenaline in rat brain, this is difficult because of interfering reactions. Enzymic hydrolysis on the other hand tends to introduce many interfering peaks. D. S. Walter and M. J. Haynes (Communication 2, Part IV) describe the use of small silica columns (Waters' Sep-Paks) to clean up enzymically hydrolysed MHPG from rat brain prior to HPLC analysis.

1.2 Mobile phase composition
A problem with the reverse-phase HPLC analysis of catecholamines is the difficulty in resolving noradrenaline unambiguously from the unretained peak in simple extracts such as the supernatant from deproteinized brain tissue. This is usually achieved by addition of alkyl sulphates as ion-pair agents to the mobile phase. However, sufficient retardation is often achieved only at the cost of excessively long retention times for other amines, notably 5HT. M. H. Joseph (Communication 3, Part IV) describes another application of the boronate pairing mentioned above; the addition of butane boronic acid (BuB) to a phosphate buffer mobile phase. This has the effect of retarding catechols specifically, but of accelerating the elution of non-catechols, in particular the 5-hydroxyindoles 5HT and 5HIAA. Another mobile phase which appears to be particularly useful for amines and metabolites, as well as other species, is ammonium acetate buffer; its application to CSF analysis was described by T. Bottiglieri (Bottiglieri *et al.,* 1984; Lim and Peters, 1984).

The modification of mobile phases to retard particular compounds may lead to problems if samples are injected in substantial volumes of solutions very different from the mobile phase (e.g. acid extracts of tissue). Thus using the BuB containing mobile phase mentioned above, it was important to bring the brain extract to the composition of the mobile phase before injection. This was achieved by using phosphoric acid to precipitate tissue protein and neutralizing with a BuB containing solution. The effectiveness of a high concentration of methanol as a protein precipitant may also be useful where low pH is to be avoided (see, for example, Joseph and Davies, 1983). I. C. Kilpatrick, M. J. Jones and O. T. Phillipson avoided this problem by deproteinizing brain samples directly in the mobile phase prior to HPLC analysis (see also Saller and Salama, 1984; Walter and Haynes, Commun. 3; Bennett *et al.*, Commun. 8).

1.3 Column

Microbore columns are attractive in HPLC because of the economies of runtime, of mobile phase consumption, and of column packing material. E. Caligura and co-workers (Communication 4, Part IV,) describe the use of microbore columns for the measurement of catecholamines. It appears that technical problems can be overcome, and indeed the plumbing arrangements actually simplified by slurry packing $1/16''$ tubing as the column with 3 μm particles, and connecting it directly into the injector and detector (metal top of Bioanalytical Systems electrode). Injection volumes are limited to 5 microlitres, but the increase in sensitivity is about 20-fold, owing to elution in a smaller volume, so that this is not a major restriction. Matching the injectate and mobile phase may again be advantageous.

2. DEVELOPMENTS IN ELECTROCHEMICAL DETECTION

The question of increasing the sensitivity of glassy carbon electrodes for EC detection by cleaning procedures (e.g. chromic acid, see Anton, 1984) requires more study although there is general agreement that the stability and sensitivity of modern glassy carbon electrodes has improved so that they are suitable for most applications.

A major advance in electrochemical detection has come from the use of multiple working electrodes whose potential can be independently controlled. This enables small amounts of easily oxidisable compounds to be detected at one electrode, operated at a low potential to reduce noise and maximize selectivity, while compounds oxidizing at a higher potential are detected at another electrode. Judicious choice of suboptimal potentials enables a higher degree of analytical specificity to be achieved for compounds oxidizing at both potentials, since the ratio of peak heights at the two potentials is characteristic of the species being detected. A third possibility is the detection of compounds which are oxidized reversibly (such as catecholamines and 5-hydroxyindoles) in the presence of compounds which are oxidized irreversibly (such as ascorbic and uric acids). This is achieved by setting the first electrode to an oxidizing potential, and the second to a reducing potential. The irreversible substances will not be 'seen' at the second electrode.

The multiple-electrode approach was developed from an early description by Blank (1976). Multiple electrode detectors are now commercially available from Bioanalytical Systems (BAS) and from Environmental Sciences Associates (ESA). Those from the former company are based on the thin layer amperometric detector cells used in their single working electrode design. G. P. Cellerino described the development of the ESA Coulochem 5100A multiple electrode detector. The use of porous graphite working electrodes results in almost complete conversion of oxidizable species at a suitable potential (coulometric detection), resulting in a greater signal for a given amount of electroactive substance eluting from the column. While this should increase the signal 10- to 20-fold over amperometric detection, the analytical sensitivity will depend on signal to noise ratio. The true gain in sensitivity will thus depend upon the extent to which noise increases with effective surface area.

The coulochem detector also offers control of a third electrode, without current detection; this opens up further possibilities. It can be used to 'pre-oxidize' the mobile phase before the injector to reduce background, or it can be used to control a conditioning electrode between the column and the detector electrodes. In this way a species of interest can be fully oxidized, and then quantified by potential-dependent re-reduction at the two detector electrodes, as mentioned above. An application of this is described by P. J. Langlais, W. R. Matson and E. D. Bird (Communication 5, Part IV); ascorbate can be screened out of the determination of noradrenaline in brain extract by pre-oxidation at $+0.4$ V followed by re-reduction successively at -0.1 and -0.4 V. The current at the latter two electrodes is monitored by the detector and different compounds give different ratios of current at these two voltages. This is therefore a combination of selectivity towards reversibly oxidizable species, and species identification by peak ratio.

Another example of on-line electrochemical modification of a species to permit subsequent detection, in this case fluorimetric, is the conversion of dihydrobiopterin to biopterin mentioned below (section 3.2). Chemical modification of a species to permit subsequent EC detection is also possible. Examples of this are given in sections 3.4 and 3.5 below.

3. APPLICATIONS

3.1 5HT in blood

Three posters covered the measurement of 5HT in blood, nearly all of which is contained in the platelets. This is of interest in connection with a number of neurological and psychiatric states, including migraine, depression, autism, mental retardation and Down's syndrome. Problems in the measurement of 5HT in blood arise at the extraction stage; many protein precipitants give poor recovery, in addition 5HT is liable to oxidation by oxyhaemoglobin.

D. P. Geaney, C. L. Davies and P. C. Tagari solved this problem by prior separation of platelets (Tagari *et al.*, 1984). Incomplete recovery of platelets may be a problem with this approach. E. F. Marshall and W. N. Kennedy measured 5HT in whole blood using zinc hydroxide precipitation of proteins; addition of ascorbate to protect 5HT during deprotienization was not found to be necessary. M. H. Joseph and R. Lofthouse adopted a similar approach, but found that ascorbate addition to the blood before freezing and subsequent deproteinization was essential. All these groups used HPLC with EC detection to determine the 5HT; where ascorbate was added to whole blood its effect could be screened out using the multiple electrode mode on the coulochem detector (see section 2 above) or fluorescence detection was used.

3.2 Catecholamines

See communications mentioned above, and included in this Part IV, by: Lake and Macdonald (1); Joseph (3); Caliguri, Capella, Bottari and Mefford (4); Langlais, Matson and Bird (5). See also Hjemdahl, Part II, Chapter 1, this volume.

3.3 Amine metabolites and related compounds including pterins

See Communications mentioned above, and included in this Part IV by: Joseph (3); Caliguri, Capella, Bottari and Mefford (4); Langlais, Matson and Bird (5); Walter and Haynes (2).

Two posters described methods for HPLC-EC determination of the dopamine metabolite 3-methoxytyramine. C. L. Davies and D. J. Heal, and also F. Ponzio and co-workers agreed that 3-methoxytyramine could only be readily detected by this method in rat brain after MAO inhibition, and explored the possibility that it might reflect dopamine release under these circumstances.

K. Hyland, I. Smith and D. Howells (Communication 6, (Part IV) describe the use of sequential coulometric EC and fluorescence (F) detectors for the detection of tyrosine and tryptophan (F), oxidized and reduced forms of the pterin cofactors for biogenic amine synthesis (F) and biogenic amine metabolites (HVA, 5HIAA and MHPG by EC) in CSF. The detectors are also used in series in a novel way in that dihydrobiopterin was oxidized at the EC detector, and subsequently determined as its fluorescent product, biopterin. Series multiple electrodes can also be used to distinguish and measure the different redox states of biopterin (Lunte and Kissinger, 1984).

3.4 Acetylcholine

R. E. Shoup described the method of Potter *et al.* (1983) by which choline and acetylcholine can be determined in neuronal tissue. This involves separation of choline and acetylcholine by reversed phase HPLC, and mixing the effluent on-line with acetyl-cholinesterase and choline oxidase. The action of choline oxidase on endogenous choline, and on choline generated by hydrolysis of acetylcholine, produces hydrogen peroxide, which is then detected on-line at a platinum electrode. Binding of suitable enzymes onto a solid matrix would offer considerable economies of enzyme material; the same group have recently (Meek and Eva, 1984) described such a modification in which these enzymes are adsorbed onto a short column of weak anion exchange resin placed between the analytical column and the detector.

3.5 Amino acids

The majority of amino acids do not have intrinsic electrochemical activity. Nonetheless, the full range of amino acids can be determined by HPLC-EC because their *o*-phthalaldehyde/mercaptoethanol (OPT/ME) derivatives are electroactive (Joseph and Davies, 1983). Derivatization consists of a simple mixing at room temperature before injection into the HPLC; the derivatives themselves chromatograph well on reversed phase. One problem is the relative instability of the OPT products when ME is used as the thiol, so that accurate timing is required. W. A. Jacobs *et al.* (Communication 7, Part IV) explore the use of sterically bulky thiols in place of ME. The best seemed to be t-butyl thiol (Allison *et al.,* 1984); this improved stability of the derivatives, with relatively little effect on their electrochemical properties. The practical significance of this is that large numbers of samples could be derivatized at the same time, and then placed in an autosampler.

3.6 Peptides

Peptides can be well resolved by HPLC, and this is often used preparatively prior to quantification by radioimmunoassay. An attractive alternative is on-line detection of peptides; those that contain tyrosine and tryptophan will have intrinsic electrochemical activity. Even these amino acids require a relatively high EC detector potential resulting in increased background and noise, and reduced specificity. G. W. Bennett *et al.* (Communication 8, Part IV), report marked improvements in the sensitivity of peptide detection; their HPLC separation used the Waters Z module radial compression system for the column in combination with the ESA Coulochem 5100A detector, enabling substances oxidizing at a lower potential to be screened out. Vasopressin, met- and leu-enkephalin, oxytocin and angiotensin I are resolved, and the responses of vasopressin and oxytocin to adrenalectomy were monitored in the neuro-intermediate lobe, the median eminence and specific hypothalmic nuclei of the rat.

An alternative approach to the EC detection of peptides is to form derivatives. OPT-ME can be used pre- or post-column to form derivatives as described above for amino acids. OPT-ME derivatives of peptides are much less fluorescent than those of amino acids, but their electrochemical activity is not so severely reduced (Joseph and Davies, 1983). Thus OPT derivatization holds some promise, especially for peptides which lack amino acids with intrinsic EC activity.

4. CONCLUSION

Recent developments in HPLC-EC have resulted in its extension to a wider range of transmitter-related compounds and in a higher degree of sensitivity and specificity. More than ever it seems to be an ideal complement to the *in vivo* sampling techniques described in other parts of this book.

REFERENCES

Allison, L. A., Meyer, G. S. and Shoup, R. E. (1984). *o*-Phthalaldehyde derivatives of amines for high-speed liquid chromatography/electrochemistry. *Anal. Chem.,* **56**, 1089–1096.

Anton, A. H. (1984). A simple, reliable and rapid method for increasing the responsiveness of the glassy carbon electrode for the analysis of biogenic amines by HPLC with electrochemical detection. *Life Sci.,* **35**, 79–85.

Blank, C. L. (1976). Dual electrochmical detector for liquid chromatography. *J. Chromatogr.,* 117, 35–46.

Bottiglieri, T., Lim, C. K. and Peters, T. J. (1984). Isocratic analysis of MHPG, 5HIAA and HVA in CSF by HPLC with amperometric detection. *J. Chrotog.,* **311**, 354–360.

Hutson, P. H., Sarna, G. J., Kantamaneni, B. D. and Curzon, G. (1984). Concurrent determination of brain dopamine and 5-hydroxytryptamine turnovers in individual freely moving rats using repeated sampling of cerebrospinal fluid. *J. Neurochem.,* **43,** 151–159.

Joseph, M. H. and Davies, P. (1983). Electrochemical activity of OPT-mercaptoethanol derivatives of amino acids. Application to HPLC determination of amino acids in plasma and other biological materials. *J. Chromatogr.,* **277,** 125–136.

Lim, C. K. and Peters, T. J. (1984). Ammonium acetate; a general purpose buffer for the clinical applications of HPLC. *J. Chromatogr.,* **316,** 397–406.

Lunte, C. E. and Kissinger, P. T. (1984). Determination of quinonoid dihydrobiopterin by LC–EC. *J. Chromatogr.,* **317,** 407–412.

Meek, J. L. and Eva, C. (1984). Enzymes adsorbed on an ion exchanger as a post-column reactor: application to acetylcholine measurement. *J. Chromatogr.,* **317,** 343–347.

Potter, P. E., Meek, J. L. and Neff, N. H. (1983). Acetylcholine and choline in neuronal tissue measured by HPLC with electrochemical detection. *J. Neurochem.,* **41,** 188–194.

Saller, C. F. and Salama, A. I. (1984). Rapid automated analysis of biogenic amines and their metabolites using reversed-phase HPLC with electrochemical detection. *J. Chromatog.,* **309,** 287–298.

Tagari, P. C., Boullin, D. J. and Davies, C. L. (1984). Simplified determination of serotonin in plasma by LC-EC. *Clin. Chem.,* **30,** 131–135.

AFFILIATIONS AND ADDRESSES OF CONTRIBUTORS

R. Calverley	Jones Chromatography Ltd.,
	(for Analytichem Int.)
	Colliery Road, Llanbradach,
	Mid-Glamorgan, CF8 3QQ, UK
G. P. Cellerino	ESA Inc.,
	Bedford, MA, 01730, USA
	British Agents:
	Severn Analytical
	36 Brunswick Road,
	Gloucester, GL1 1JJ, UK
C. L. Davies and D. J. Heal	MRC Unit and Department of Clinical Pharmacology,
	Radcliffe Infirmary,
	Woodstock Road, Oxford, UK
M. H. Joseph* and	Division of Psychiatry,
R. Lofthouse	Clinical Research Centre,
	Watford Road, Harrow,
	Middlesex, HA1 3UJ, UK
*Present address	Departments of Psychology and Biochemistry,
	Institute of Psychiatry,
	Denmark Hill, London, SE5 8AF, UK

I. C. Kilpatrick[†]   Departments of Pharmacology[†] and Anatomy,
M. W. Jones and   University of Bristol, Bristol BS8 1TD, UK
O. T. Phillipson

E. F. Marshall and   Department of Psychiatry,
W. N. Kennedy   University of Newcastle upon Tyne,
                                       Newcastle upon Tyne, NE2 4AL, UK

F. Ponzio, G, Achilli,   Istituto di Recerche Farmacologie, 'Mario Negri',
M. Di Lallo, C. Pergeo,   Via Eritrea 62,
G. Sacchelli and   I-20157 Milano, Italy.
S. Algin

R. E. Shoup   Research Laboratories,
                                       Bioanalytical Systems Inc.,
                                       1205 Kent Avenue,
                                       West Lafayette,
                                       IN 47906, USA

1

A two-stage procedure for extracting catecholamines, from plasma or urine, prior to separation and quantification by LCEC

D. M. Lake and **I. A. Macdonald**

Department of Physiology and Pharmacology, University of Nottingham
Medical School, Nottingham, NG7 2UH, UK

There are many descriptions of the use of high performance liquid chromatography with electrochemical detection (LCEC) to measure the levels of catecholamines in plasma or urine. Although some methods involve the use of strong cation-exchange chromatography (SCX) to separate the catecholamines, most techniques use reverse-phase, ion-pair (RP-IP) separations. However, in almost all cases the catecholamines are initially extracted from the biological fluid onto alumina, even though this method is not specific for the catecholamines. This non-specificity is not critical when SCX chromatography is used, because the other compounds extracted onto the alumina are not retained by the SCX and appear in the solvent front. However, the much more efficient RP-IP chromatography can lead to the other compounds extracted onto the alumina then co-eluting from the RP-IP column with the catecholamines. This can lead to complex chromatograms which are difficult to interpret and probably underlies the poor results recently obtained with RP-IP based methods in an inter-laboratory evaluation of techniques for measuring plasma catecholamines (Hjemdahl, 1984, and Part II, Chapter 1, this volume).

In order to overcome the problem of selectivity of the extraction technique, we have developed a two-stage extraction process which involves the initial extraction of the cations in the sample, followed by the extraction from those cations of any catechol (dihydroxyphenyl) molecules. Our basic approach is similar to that used by Frayn and Maycock (1983), except that we have used the more selective, organic, extraction technique of Smedes, Kraak and Poppe (1982) rather than alumina extraction. The detail of our technique, including an evaluation of the extraction conditions we have developed, is described elsewhere (Macdonald and Lake, 1985). However, the method involves the following steps:

(i)   50 mg of Sepralyte SCX (Analytichem International Inc.) are activated with 1 ml of 0.2 M Na_2HPO_4 buffer (pH 7.5), by shaking for 1 min then centrifuging and discarding the buffer.

(ii) The plasma (0.5 to 2 ml) or urine (0.25 to 0.5 ml) sample is then mixed with the internal standard (e.g. 10 pmol of 3,4-dihydroxybenzylamine) and, if necessary, the pH adjusted to be 7.5 to 8.0 before the cations are extracted onto the SCX by mixing for 2 min. After centrifugation, the supernatant is discarded and the SCX washed twice with 1 ml water, before the cations are eluted into 1 ml of 1 M NaH_2PO_4 buffer (pH 2.9) by mixing for 1.5 min.

(iii) After centrifugation, this eluate is transferred to a screw-topped glass tube, sufficient NH_4OH (concentrated stock solution, approx. 8 mol/l) is added to raise the pH to 8 (this usually requires 90–100 μl of NH_4OH) before 0.5 ml of 2 M NH_4OH/NH_4Cl buffer (pH 8.5, containing 3.5 g diphenylborate-ethanolamine complex and 5 g ethylenediamine tetraacetic acid per L) is added to form a diphenylborate-catechol complex. Then, 2.5 ml of a mixture of heptane/octanol (1 vol octanol/99 vols heptane), containing 2.5 g tetraoctylammonium bromide per L, is added and the teflon-lined screw caps are applied to the tubes which are then shaken for 2 min to extract the borate-catechol complex into the organic phase, forming an ion-pair with the tetraoctylammonium bromide.

(iv) After centrifugation, 2 ml of the heptane/octanol supernatant are transferred to a glass centrifuge tube, 1 ml of octanol and 0.2 ml 0.08 M CH_3COOH are added before the mixture is vortex mixed for 1 min to back-extract the catecholamines into the CH_3COOH. After centrifugation, the CH_3COOH layer is removed from below the organic supernatant, and stored in Eppendorf tubes on ice prior to injection onto the RP-IP system.

This two-stage process excludes most, if not all, of the additional peaks seen on the chromatogram of an alumina extract of plasma. We use this method to measure basal levels of noradrenaline (NA) and adrenaline (A) in 2 ml samples of human plasma and obtain intra-assay coefficients of variation (CV) of 8% for both amines (NA levels 2 nmol/l, A levels 0.19 nmol/l), whilst the interassay CV is less than 10% for NA and less than 20% for A.

REFERENCES

Frayn, K. N. amd Maycock, P. F. (1983). Sample preparation with ion-exchange resin before liquid chromatographic determination of plasma catecholamines. *Clin. Chem.,* **29**, 1426–1428.

Hjemdahl, P. (1984). Interlaboratory comparison of plasma catecholamine determinations using several different assays. *Act Physiol. Scand. Suppl.,* **527**, 43–54.

Macdonald, I. A. and Lake, D. M. (1985). An improved technique for the extraction of catecholamines from body fluids. *J. Neurosci. Methods,* **13**, 239–248.

Smedes, F., Kraak, J. C. and Poppe, H. (1982). Simple and fast solvent extraction system for selective and quantitative isolation of adrenaline, noradrenaline and dopamine from plasma and urine. *J. Chromatogr.,* **231**, 25–39.

2

Synergism between idazoxan and desipramine on MHPG levels in rat cortex

Donald S. Walter and **Margaret J. Haynes**
Pharmacology Department, Reckitt and Colman plc, Dansom Lane, Hull, HU8 7DS, UK

1. INTRODUCTION

In the brain, α_2-blockade with idazoxan or yohimbine increases the turnover rate of NA (Walter *et al.*, 1984; Scatton *et al.*, 1983) whereas no increase occurs following acute dosage of uptake blockers such as desipramine (DMI) (Sugrue, 1981). The latter would be expected since α_2-feedback would increase proportionally with the synaptic NA concentration. Similarly the observed increase in NA turnover produced by α_2-blockade would probably be an underestimate of the amount of released NA because of re-uptake. The effect of simultaneously blocking reuptake with DMI and α_2-adrenoceptors with idazoxan has been studied here, using MHPG as a measure of NA turnover.

2. METHODS

An HPLC method for MHPG has been developed which uses Silica Sep-Paks (Waters). Dry Sep-Paks absorb up to 1.8 ml of aqueous solution. These were loaded with 1.5 ml of an aqueous MHPG extract and the sample eluted from the Sep-Paks with successive 0.5 ml aliquots of distilled water (Fig. 1). MHPG was routinely eluted with 2 ml of distilled water from dry Sep-Paks loaded with 1.5

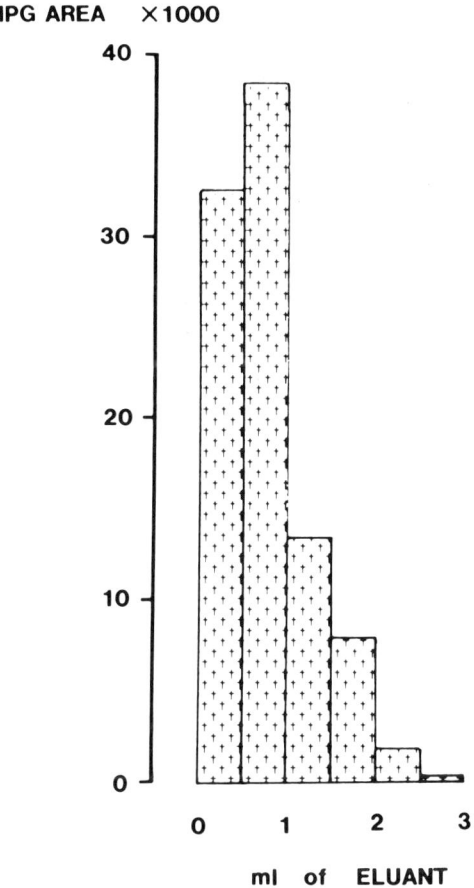

Fig. 1 – Elution of MHPG from a Silica SEP-PAK. MHPG (1.5 ml, 10 ng ml⁻¹ in distilled water) was applied to the SEP-PAK and eluted with successive 0.5 ml aliquots of distilled water. The amount of MHPG eluted was determined from the peak area following HPLC.

ml of brain extract. The detector response to 10 ng MHPG was measured over the oxidation potential range 500–1000 mV. A working potential of 700 mV was chosen and the detector response to MHPG was found to be linear over the range 0.15–10 ng on column.

DMI (2–15 mg.kg⁻¹) or saline was dosed i.p. 1 h before idazoxan (2.5–40 mg.kg⁻¹) or water dosed orally. The rats (male SD, 180–200 g) were killed 1 h following idazoxan or water. Rat cortex was homogenized in 0.4 M HClO₄ (3 ml.g⁻¹) and centrifuged (9000 g, 4 min). Supernatant (0.9 ml), 1.0 M sodium acetate buffer pH 5.2 (0.15 ml) and 1.0 M KOH (~ 0.2 ml) were mixed, final pH 5.2, brought to 0°C (10 min) and centrifuged to remove KClO₄. Sulphatase (20 μl, H2, Sigma) was added to the supernatant and incubated (20 h, 37°C).

The mixture was pipetted onto Silica Sep-Paks and MHPG eluted under reduced pressure with distilled water (2 ml). 1.0 M sodium acetate buffer pH 5.2 (0.1 ml) and ethyl acetate (Rathburn, 3.5 ml) were added and the tubes vortex mixed (15 s) and centrifuged. Ethyl acetate extract (3 ml) was removed and blown to dryness (N_2, 60°C) and reconstituted in mobile phase (70 μl). MHPG was resolved by HPLC on a column of 3 μm Shandon ODS (10 cm × 0.4 cm) equilibrated with 70 mM NaH_2PO_4, 1 mM sodium EDTA and 2 mM sodium heptane sulphonic acid pH 6.4 (1.5 ml/min). Detection was with a BAS TL5 flow cell and glassy carbon electrode maintained at +700 mV versus a silver/silver chloride electrode. Using these conditions the run time was 12–15 min. The extraction of MHPG from rat brain homogenate was linear and the recovery between 40% and 50%.

3. RESULTS AND DISCUSSION

DMI (2–15 mg.kg^{-1}, i.p.) followed by water p.o. produced no statistical change in the MHPG concentration whereas idazoxan (2.5–40 mg.kg^{-1}, p.o.), following

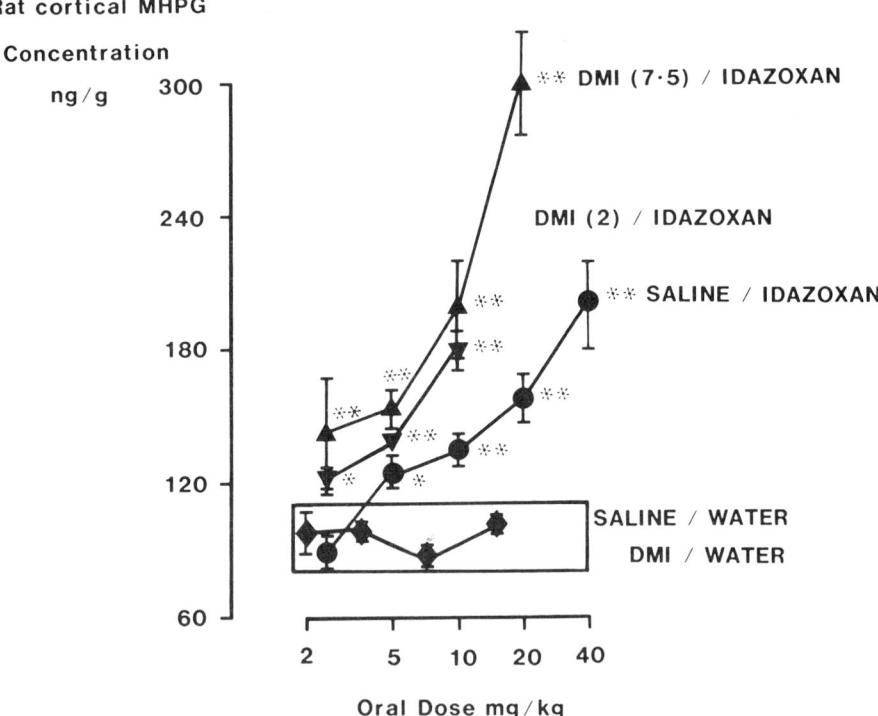

Fig. 2 – Effects of DMI and idazoxan dosed alone or in combination on the concentration of MHPG in rat cortex. Points are mean ± SEM for 4–6 rats per group. The rectangular box shows the mean concentration of MHPG ± SEM for saline/water-treated rats. *$p < 0.05$; $p < 0.01$ vs saline/water control in each experiment.

saline i.p., produced a dose-related rise. When idazoxan was dosed 1 h following either 2 or 7.5 mg.kg^{-1} DMI i.p., the log dose response lines were steeper and shifted 2- or 4-fold to the left (Fig. 2). The data show synergism between DMI and idazoxan and suggest that low doses of an uptake blocker and an α_2-antagonist given in combination may be an efficient way of increasing the turnover rate of NA in the CNS. The effects of such a combination on the sympathetic system, however, should not be ignored.

REFERENCES

Walter, D. S., Flockhart, I. R., Haynes, M. J., Howlett, D. R., Lane, A. C., Burton, R., Johnson, J. and Dettmar, P. W. (1984). Effects of idazoxan on catecholamine systems in rat brain. *Biochem. Pharmacol., 33,* 2553–2557.

Scatton, B., Dedek, J. and Zivkovic, B. (1983). Lack of involvement of α_2-adrenoceptors in striatal dopaminergic transmission. *Eur. J. Pharmacol., 86,* 427–433.

Sugrue, M. F. (1981). Effects of acutely and chronically administered antidepressants on the clonidine-induced decrease in rat brain 3-methoxy-4-hydroxyphenylethylene glycol sulphate content. *Life Sci., 28,* 377–384.

3

Catecholamine analysis using butane boronic acid as a group-specific pairing agent in the mobile phase

Michael H. Joseph

Division of Psychiatry, MRC Clinical Research Centre, Watford Road, Harrow, HA1 3UJ, UK

Present address: Departments of Psychology and Biochemistry, Institute of Psychiatry, De Crespigny Park, Denmark Hill, London, SE5 8AF, UK[*]

1. INTRODUCTION

HPLC-EC is the method of choice for analysis of the catecholamines. Reversed phase columns are convenient, and give excellent resolution, but obtaining sufficient retention of noradrenaline to resolve it from the unretained peak is often a problem. The retention of amines cannot be controlled by pH, since they remain charged through the available pH range for reversed phase columns (pH 2 to 8), and catecholamines are also liable to spontaneous oxidation at alkaline pH. The usual solution adopted is the addition of ion-pairing agents such as alkyl sulphonates ($R.SO_3H$) or sulphates ($R.SO_4H$), e.g. sodium octyl sulphate, to the mobile phase. This, however, can result in undesirably long overall run times, especially in simple tissue extracts in which the unretained peak is likely to be large, and other amines, e.g. 5HT, 3MT are present. (For another example of this problem, and an alternative solution see Communication 5, Part IV).

Alkyl boronates ($R.B(OH)_2$) are used as derivatization reagents for GLC analysis of molecules with hydroxyl groups on adjacent carbon atoms such as carbohydrates, steroids and catecholamines (Poole and Zlatkis, 1980). Boric acid has been used in the form of gel columns for separating catechols (Higa *et al.,* 1977), and in buffers to stabilize catechols against oxidation. It seemed possible that an alkyl boronate added to the mobile phase for HPLC might act analogously to an ion-pairing agent, but pair specifically with catechols (and possibly glycols). This would result in increased retention of the catecholamines and their catecholic metabolites, but not of non-catecholic amines and metabolites, in particular 5HT.

2. MATERIALS AND METHODS

Butane boronic acid (BuB; Sigma or Aldrich) was added to 0.05 or 0.1 M sodium phosphate buffers. HPLC was carried out on a Gilson gradient system, using a Rheodyne injector with 200 μl sample loop, and a 15 cm $\times$ 4.6 mm column of Hypersil ODS 5 with guard column (Chrompack). Fluorescence (Kratos 950; mercury line excitation, interference filter at 254 nm; emission at 365 nm bandpass) and electrochemical (Bioanalytical systems, LC4 with TL5) detectors were used in series as previously described (Joseph and Davies, 1983). Elution was either isocratic, without addition of organic modifier, or a gradient of methanol was used.

3. RESULTS AND DISCUSSION

n-Butane boronic acid (BuB; Sigma or Aldrich), as the longest chain alkyl boronate readily available, was used as a test compound by addition to a sodium phosphate buffer. At the usual pH of 3 to 6 for separating amines and metabolites (Cross and Joseph, 1981) the retarding effect was small, but at around neutral pH (7.0 to 7.5) a greater effect was seen, as might be expected from previous work (Higa *et al.,* 1977). Fig. 1 shows that increasing concentrations of BuB in phosphate buffer, pH 7.5, led to increased retention of catechols, but decreased retention of 5-hydroxyindoles, presumably due to BuB acting as an organic modifier with respect to the latter. 5 mM BuB and 0.1 M phosphate were selected as conditions to study a larger series of standards (Table 1). The retarding effect seems to be greatest for the catecholamines, followed by the catechol metabolite DOPAC. The retention of other compounds is reduced, by a factor of about two-thirds in most cases. The retention of methylated metabolites (HVA, MHPG) is reduced less, and VMA is paradoxically retarded as strongly as DOPAC, perhaps due to its α-hydroxy acid structure. The particularly marked effect on the catecholamines may relate to the addition of a hydroxyl ion to the boronate in solution, resulting in an ion-pairing as well as a catechol-paring interaction.

These conditions can then be applied to the analysis of brain samples (Fig. 2). At this relatively high pH, retention of amine metabolites is much reduced. However, at 5 mM BuB in 0.1 M phosphate, pH 7.5, NA is eluted between DOPAC and 5HIAA. The retentions of 5HT and DA can be usefully shortened, and peak shape improved by running a gradient of 0% to 20% methanol over 10 minutes after NA has eluted.

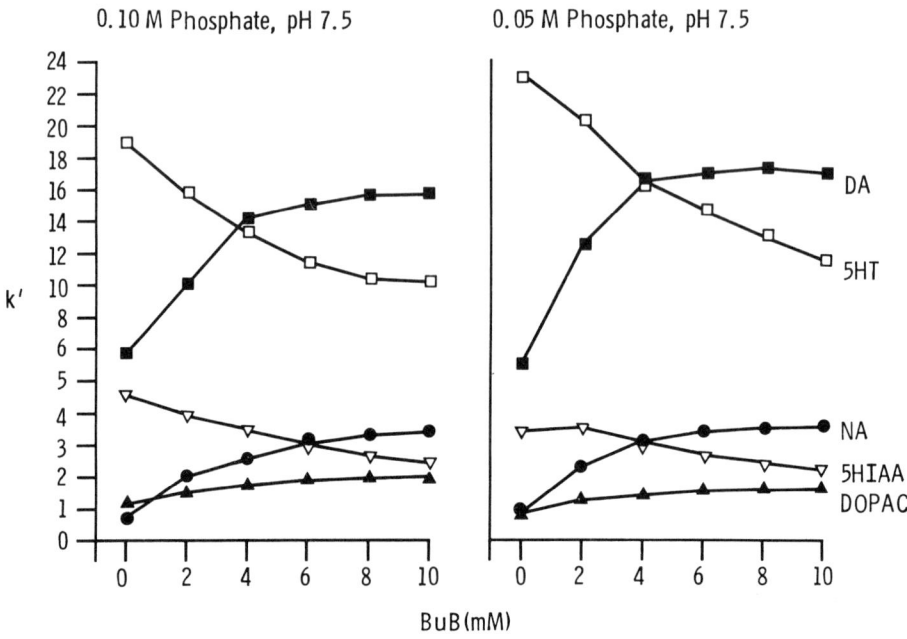

Fig. 1 — Effect of increasing concentrations of butane boronic acid on the retention of catechols and 5-hydroxyindoles. Capacity factors are plotted against final
BuB concentration in phosphate eluting buffer, pH 7.5, at (a) 0.1 M, (b) 0.05 M.

Table 1 — Effect of addition of butane boronic acid (5 mM) to 0.1 M phosphate
buffer pH 7.5 on capacity factors for catechols and other compounds.

	k'		
BuB concentration	0 mM	5 mM	Ratio $\dfrac{\text{with BuB}}{\text{without BuB}}$
Noradrenaline	0.4	2.15	5.38
Dopamine	3.35	11.8	3.52
DOPAC	0.93	1.55	1.68
VMA	0.5	0.8	1.60
MHPG	7.0	6.18	0.882
HVA	5.0	3.6	0.720
Tyrosine	1.55	1.03	0.661
Tryptophan	14.15	9.6	0.678
5HIAA	4.2	2.8	0.666
5HT	15.0	9.35	0.623
5Hydroxytryptophol	37.4	22.75	0.608

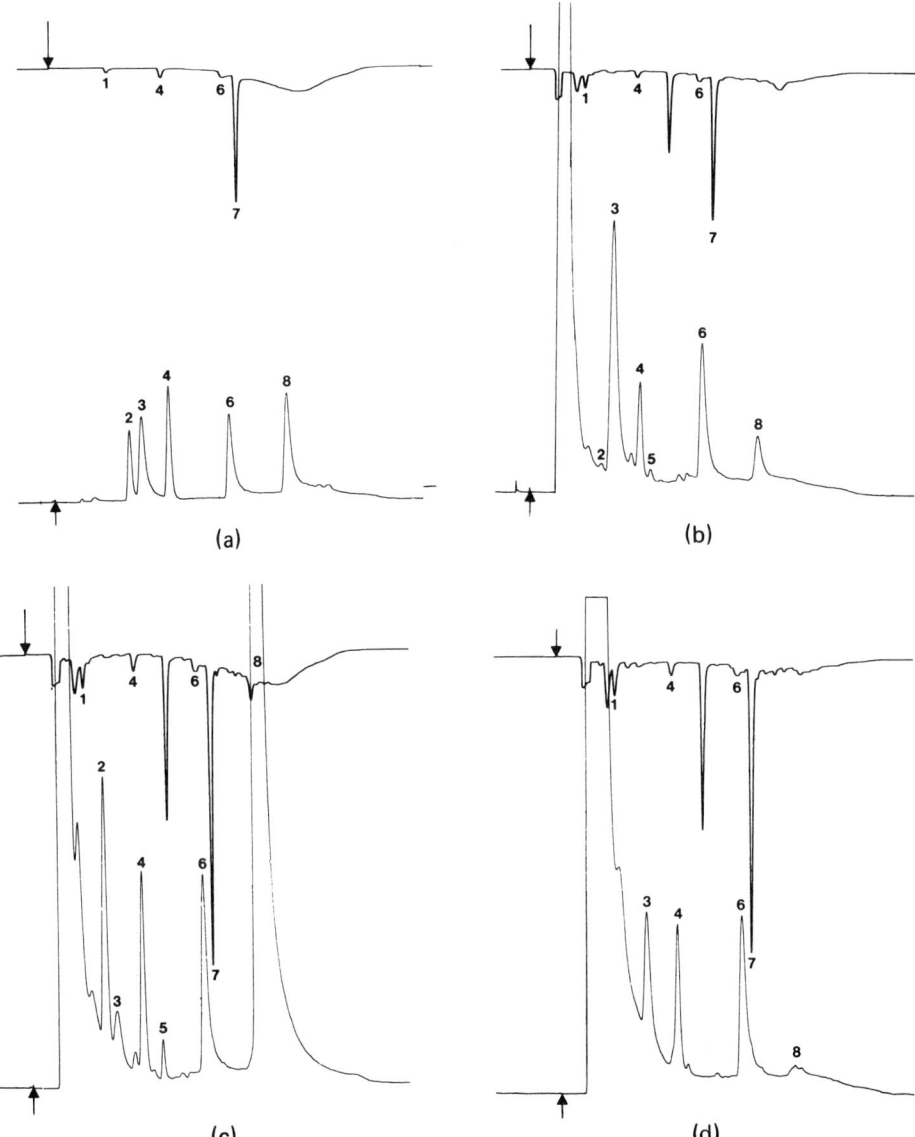

Fig. 2 — Separation of amines and related compounds; standards and brain samples. Running buffers are 0.1 M phosphate, pH 7.5, containing 5 mM BuB (final). A gradient of 0–20% methanol was run as described in methods. The upper of each pair of traces is F detector, sens. 0.1, 254/365 nm. The lower is EC detector operated in series at 0.4 V, 20 nA full scale. Injection is indicated by arrows. Peaks are 1. Tyrosine; 2. DOPAC; 3. NA; 4. 5HIAA; 5. HVA; 6. 5HT; 7. Tryptophan; 8. DA.

(a) Standards corresponding to 250 ng/g of amines and metabolites and 2.5 μg/g of amino acids carried through the method.
(b) Rat brain hypothalamus.
(c) Rat brain striatum.
(d) Rat brain hippocampus.

Standards were made up to final dilution in the initial running buffer. Brain tissue was deproteinized in about 10 volumes of 0.1 M phosphoric acid and the supernatant neutralized with an equal volume of 0.1 M phosphate buffer containing 10 mM BuB. This gave a final pH and BuB concentration equal to that of the initial eluting buffer; after a further brief centrifugation, 200 μl of the neutralized extract was injected into the HPLC system. It is important to inject samples in the equivalent of the running buffer, since otherwise a reduction in retention and resolution, especially of noradrenaline, is seen, presumably due to the disturbance of the equilibrium between the BuB and the column. The presence of BuB will also help to stabilize catechols against spontaneous oxidation at this relatively high pH.

The working voltage of the EC detector was reduced to 0.4 V so that the unretained peak did not interfere with DOPAC detection. Note that use of a buffer at higher pH results in a downward shift of the oxidation potentials relative to that in the usual pH range (Kissinger *et al.,* 1979). Thus HVA and MHPG, which are also resolved with this system (as expected from Table 1), can be detected even at this potential, although sensitivity is greater if a higher working voltage (ca 0.7 V) is used. Peaks for tyrosine, 5HIAA, 5HT and tryptophan are observed on the fluorescence detector (the amino acids being electrochemically inactive at these working potentials). Fig. 2 also demonstrates the application of the method to various rat brain areas. Marked variations, particularly in catecholamine and metabolite levels, between brain areas are seen, in general agreement with those in the literature. These are reported in more detail elsewhere (Joseph, 1985).

4. CONCLUSIONS

Butane boronic acid can be used as a pairing agent in an HPLC mobile phase at around neutral pH to selectively retard the elution of catechol compounds, in particular the catecholamines It is likely that the series of alkyl boronic acids will have similar properties. This provides an extra parameter of mobile phase composition which can be manipulated to optimize the separation of complex mixtures of biogenic amines, precursors and metabolites such as are obtained from biological materials. As an example of a group-specific, pairing agent being used in an HPLC mobile phase, BuB may also provide a model for a wide range of applications of other group specific modifiers.

ACKNOWLEDGEMENTS

I wish to thank Dennis Risby for skilful technical assistance, and Dr. Lila Tsaltas for collaboration on the rat brain dissection. Figures and table reproduced from Joseph (1985) with permission.

REFERENCES

Cross, A. J. and Joseph, M. H. (1981). The concurrent estimation of the major monoamine metabolites in human and non-human primate brain by HPLC with electrochemical and fluorescence detection. *Life Sci.,* **28**, 499–505.

Higa, S., Suzuki, T., Hayashi, A., Tauga, I. and Yamamura, Y. (1977). Isolation of catecholamines in biological fluids by boric acid gel. *Anal. Biohchem.,* **77**, 18–24.

Joseph, M. H. (1985). Alkyl boronates as catechol-specific mobile phase pairing agents; application to HPLC analysis of biogenic amines, precursors and metabolites in brain tissue. *J. Chromatogr.,* **342**, 370–375.

Joseph, M. H. and Davies, P. (1983). Electrochemical activity of *o*-phthalaldehyde mercaptoethanol derivatives of amino acids: application to HPLC determination of amino acids in plasma and other biological materials. *J. Chromatogr.,* **277**, 125–136.

Kissinger, P. T., Bratin, K., Davis, G. C. and Pachla, L. A. (1979). The potential utility of pre and post column chemical reactions with electrochemical detection in liquid chromatography, **17**, 137–146.

Poole, C. F. and Zlatkis, A. (1980). Cyclic derivatives for the selective chromatographic analysis of bi-functional compounds. *J. Chromatogr.,* **184**, 99–180.

4

Analysis of plasma and CSF catecholamines using high-speed microbore LCEC following a two-stage extraction procedure

Edward J. Caliguri, Peter Capella, Leo G. Bottari and **Ivan N. Mefford**
Department of Chemistry, Boston College, Chestnut Hill,
Massachusetts 02167, USA

1. INTRODUCTION

Analysis of catecholamines in blood plasma or CSF has been fraught with a variety of technical difficulties. Concentrations of catecholamines range from 0 to 250 pg per millilitre in rested normals. As a result, measurement of these compounds in small volumes of fluid requires selective extraction and preconcentration with efficient chromatographic separation and operation of the electrochemical detector at or near the limit of detection.

We have attempted to simplify measurement of these compounds by taking advantage of the inherent increased mass sensitivity which can be obtained with microbore HPLC (Scott and Kucera, 1979). This is coupled with an extremely selective two-stage extraction procedure (Macdonald and Lake, 1985) which allows preconcentration of the extracted catecholamines into a very small volume suitable for application to a microbore HPLC system.

Numerous methods have been developed for determination of plasma catecholamines using HPLC with electrochemical detection. These methods have generally used an extraction with aluminium oxide as a cleanup/preconcentration step (Keller *et al.*, 1976). Chromatographic separation has been either by cation exchange or reverse phase HPLC (Hallman *et al.*, 1978). Electrochemical detection has been accomplished by either amperometric (Mefford, 1981) or coulometric (Goto *et al.*, 1981) oxidation of the separated catechols. The Al_2O_3 extraction is not completely satisfactory when reverse phase HPLC is used as numerous compounds may be extracted which are electroactive and which may co-chromatograph with catecholamines. Uric acid has often been found to interfere with analysis of norepinephrine (Davis *et al.*, 1981) and unknown peaks frequently are found to chromatograph near epinephrine and/or the internal standard. Cation exchange chromatography, while offering less chromatographic efficiency, offers additional selectivity with fewer chromatographic interferences (Hjemdahl, 1984, and this volume).

Smedes *et al* (1982) recently developed a solvent extraction using diphenylborate complexation. This selective procedure takes advantage of the catechol moiety, as does the Al_2O_3 extraction. Macdonald and Lake (1985, and Communication 1, Part IV) have modified this procedure to include an initial cation exchange extraction. When coupled, these two isolation steps take advantage of the selectivity offered by both cation exchange and the diphenylborate complexation. We have modified this procedure to take advantage of the smaller volumes which may be injected onto microbore chromatography columns.

Microbore chromatography offers a marked decrease in on-column sample dilution. The peak volume of eluting species is related to the column volume. In the case of a 1 mm i.d. column, compared to a 4.6 mm i.d. column of the same length, with the solvent maintained at the same linear valocity and using the same packing material, the peak volume decrease is the same as the decrease in column volume or the ratio of the radii squared;

$$\frac{(\text{radius of conventional column})^2}{(\text{radius of microbore column})^2} = \frac{(2.3 \text{ mm})^2}{(0.5 \text{ mm})^2} = 21.2$$

or a 20-fold decrease in peak volume. As a result, the same quantity of material applied to both columns is twenty times more concentrated in the eluant of the microbore system. Microbore HPLC requires decreased flowrates proportional to the decrease in column volume. This results in a longer residence time in the electrochemical detector cell. For an amperometric detector this provides an increased coulometric yield, as more material may be oxidized. By preparing short microbore columns packed with 3 μm reverse phase material, we have been able to obtain efficient resolution of catecholamines with short analysis times, while taking advantage of the increased sensitivity found with microbore HPLC.

2. PREPARATION OF HIGH SPEED MICROBORE COLUMNS

A commercial slurry packing pump (Chemco model 124A) was used to pack columns. A slurry reservoir was prepared from a 25 cm length $\times$ 4.6 mm i.d. column blank. The exit end of this blank was counter drilled to accommodate a 1/16″ stainless steel tube. The slurry solvent and packing solvent was isopropanol. The slurry was prepared to be about 45 mg/ml using 200 mg of

Shandon Hypersphere 3 μm ODS in 4.5 ml of degassed isopropanol. The micro-bore column blank consisted of a 1/16″ o.d. stainless steel tube, 10 cm in length and 1.2 mm i.d. The column exit was fritted with a 0.5 μm pore, 1/16″ dia. × 1/32″ stainless steel frit and seated into the stainless steel auxiliary block (MF1018, BioAnalytical Systems, Inc., West Lafayette, Indiana) of an electro-chemical detector cell. The slurry was delivered at 700 bar (10,000 PSI) for four hours and the system allowed to equilibriate with atmospheric pressure (about 30 minutes). Columns prepared in this manner gave typical plate counts of 45,000 to 65,000 per metre, for separation of catecholamines, comparable to conventional bore, 3 μm columns.

3. EXTRACTION OF CATECHOLAMINES

(1) 50 mg of strong cation exchange resin, 40 μm in diameter (SCX-P, Analyti-chem International) is placed in a 1.5 ml polypropylene centrifuge tube. 1.0 ml of 0.2 M Na phosphate, pH 8.0, is added and the tube vortexed for 1 minute, centrifuged and the supernatant discarded.

(2) A 1.0 ml volume of sample, either plasma or CSF is placed over the SCX-P. 10 μl of 10^{-6} M dihydroxybenzylamine (in 0.050 M H_3PO_4, internal stan-dard) and about 500 μl of 0.2 M Na phosphate, pH 8.0, is added to fill the tube. The contents of the tube are thoroughly mixed for 2.5 minutes, centrifuged and the supernatant discarded.

(3) 750 μl of 1.0 M Na phosphate, pH 2.9, is added to elute catecholamines from the SCX-P. The tube and contents are shaken for about 2 minutes and centrifuged. The supernatant is carefully transferred to a fresh 1.5 ml polypropylene tube.

(4) To this is added 500 μl of diphenylborate solution. (0.2% (w:v) diphenyl-borate ethanolamine and 0.5% (w:v) EDTA in 3 M ammonium chloride buffer, pH 8.6) along with 75 μl of fresh concentrated NH_4OH. It is critical that the pH of the solution at this point is 8.6 ± 0.3. To this aqueous solution is added 200 μl of an organic extractant containing ion-pairing reagent (1% octanol (v:v) and 0.35% (w:v) tetraheptyl ammonium bromide in n-heptane). The mixture is shaken vigorously for two minutes, then centrifuged to separate the organic layer. The organic layer is then care-fully transferred to a 400 μl capacity polypropylene centrifuge tube.

(5) To the organic solution, total volume 200 μl, is added 80 μl of octanol and 10 μl of 0.4 M acetic acid. This mixture is then vigorously shaken for 2 minutes and centrifuged. The acetic acid, containing the extracted cate-cholamines, can be seen as a small droplet at the bottom of the tube. This droplet is taken up by syringe, and injected onto the chromatographic column. Extreme care must be taken to avoid contamination with the organic solvent.

4. CHROMATOGRAPHIC APPARATUS

In order to minimize sample dispersion, several modifications to the standard chromatographic system were made for use with microbore columns.

(1) The column was placed directly into the injection port to eliminate band-broadening in connecting tubing.

(2) The column was packed into the stainless steel auxiliary block and the 51 μm spacer provided by BAS was replaced with a 10 μm spacer with a 3 mm channel width.

(3) A microbore injection valve, Rheodyne model 7413, with a 5 μl loop was used for sample injection.

(4) Pulseless solvent delivery was accomplished using a model 400-02 pump, (Applied Chromatography Systems, Inc.) at a flow rate of 200–250 μl/minute. The column arrangement is shown in Fig. 1.

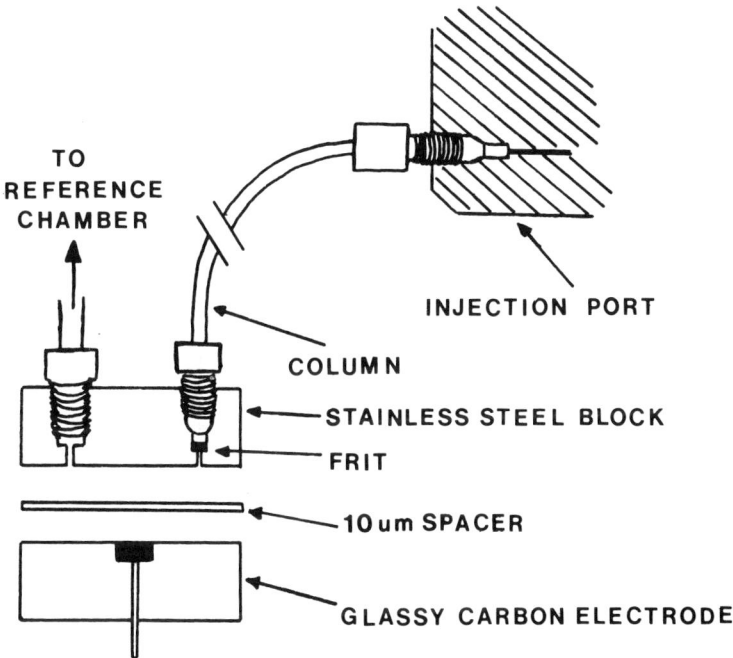

Fig. 1 – Column/detector hardware arrangement used to minimize band-broadening for high speed microbore LCEC.

Separation of catecholamines was accomplished with a solvent of 0.2 M NaH_2PO_4, 30 mg/l sodium octyl sulphate and 1% methanol or acetonitrile and 50 mg/l EDTA, adjusted to pH 3.3 Amperometric detection was at a glassy carbon electrode (BAS) with an applied potential of +0.60 volts vs Ag/AgCl using a model LC-2A amperometric detector (BAS). The detector was modified to have a time constant of 0.3 seconds.

5. RESULTS AND DISCUSSION

Separation of standards and extracts of both plasma and CSF are shown in Fig. 2. Unknown peaks seen in these chromatograms are found in blanks and are

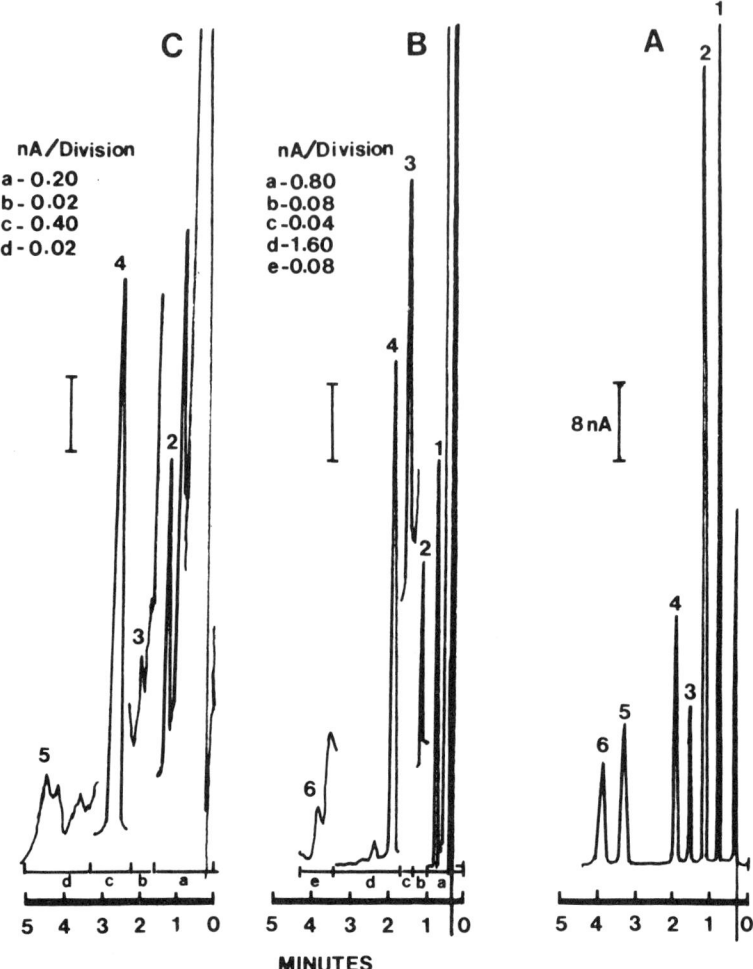

Fig. 2 – High speed microbore resolution of catecholamines. (A) Standards, peak identities, 1. norepinephrine 2.06 ng, 2. dopa 3.31 ng, 3. epinephrine 0.79 ng, 4. DHBA (internal standard), 5. 3,4 dihydroxyphenylacetic acid, 1.34 ng, 6. Dopamine 0.97 ng. (B) Plasma catecholamines extracted from 1.0 ml into 10 μl, peak identities, 1. norepinephrine, 212 pg/ml, 2. dopa, 3. epinephrine, 43 pg/ml, 4. DHBA, 5. dopamine 22 pg/ml. (C) CSF catecholamines extracted from 2.0 ml into 10 μl. Peak identities, 2. norepinephrine 109 pg/ml, 3. epinephrine 14 pg/ml, 4. DHBA, 5. dopamine 7.5 pg/ml. (Chromatogram C was obtained with an acetate–citrate buffer, pH 5.1, 120 mg/l sodium octyl sulphate, 5% methanol.)

apparently a product of diphenylborate degradation. In a given series of extractions these peaks are reproducible and always present. Plasma or CSF blanks (allowed to stand at room temperature for several days, or heated) show no peaks at the retention times of norpinephrine, epinephrine or dopamine. As described, the extraction procedure yields recoveries of 40–45% for each catecholamine of which half may be applied to the column. Relative recoveries

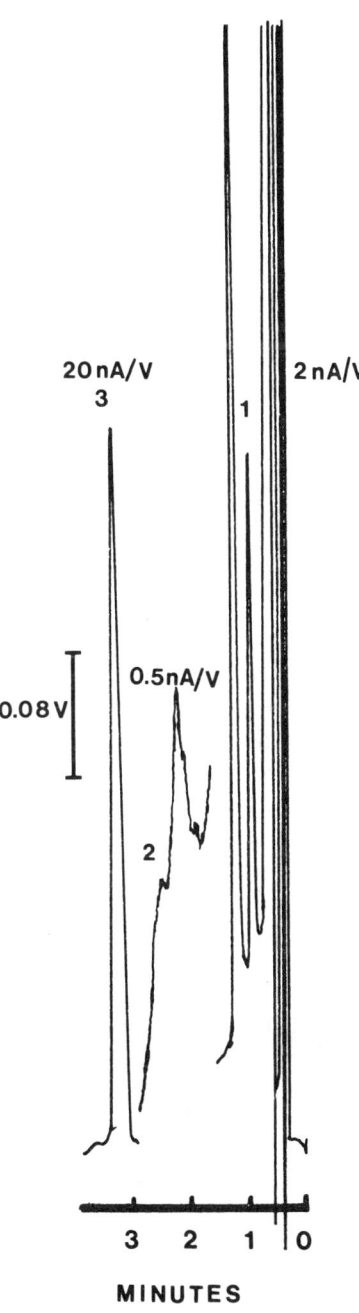

Fig. 3 – Chromatogram of catecholamines extracted from 100 μl of human plasma. Peak identities, 1. norepinephrine, 440 pg/ml, 2. epinephrine, 3. DHBA.

of each compound compared to the internal standard, dihydroxybenzylamine are between 0.90 and 1.1. A more detailed account of the extraction procedure is described elsewhere (Lake and Macdonald, Communication 1, Part IV, and Macdonald and Lake (1985)).

The limit of detection for the system as described is less than one picogram for each catecholamine. One millilitre of plasma or CSF is quite satisfactory for analysis. Much smaller volumes of plasma may be used as seen in Fig. 3. Reproducibility of multiple analyses of a pooled sample is quite good, less than ± 10% for each catecholamine (standard deviation) in the 20–200 pg/ml range.

There are several advantages to the use of microbore HPLC. Solvent consumption is roughly 10% of a conventional chromatographic system. If columns are prepared in the laboratory, the cost is minimal, around ten dollars in the USA. Perhaps most important for the present application is the lower limit of detection which these columns provide. In our hands, the limit of detection for catecholamines is approximately 200 femtograms, a 20- to 50-fold improvement.

The extraction procedure we have employed gives further signal enhancement due to the pre-analysis concentration into 10 μl. This extraction procedure also adds specificity to the determination of catecholamines through both cation exchange and diphenylborate complexation.

REFERENCES

Davis, G. C., Kissinger, P. T. and Shoup, R. E. (1981). Strategies for determination of serum or plasma norepinephrine by reverse phase liquid chromatography, *Anal. Chem.*, **53**, 156–159.

Goto, M., Nakamura, T. and Ishii, D. (1981). Micro high performance liquid chromatographic system with micro precolumn and dual electrochemical detector for direct injection analysis of catecholamines in body fluids, *J. Chromatogr.*, **181**, 287–294.

Hallman, H., Farnebo, L. O., Hamberger, B. and Jonsson, G. (1978). A selective method for the determination of plasma catecholamines using liquid chromatogrpahy with electrochemical detection, *Life Sci.*, **23**, 1049–1052.

Hjemdahl, P. (1984). Catecholamine measurements by high performance liquid chromatography, *Am. J. Physiol.*, **247**, E13–E20.

Keller, R., Oke, A., Mefford, I. and Adams, R. N. (1976). Liquid chromatographic analysis of catecholamines. Routine assay for regional brain mapping, *Life Sci.*, **19**, 995–1004.

Macdonald, I. A. and Lake, D. M. (1985). An improved technique for extracting catecholamines from body fluids, *J. Neurosci. Methods,* **13**, 239–248).

Mefford, I. N. (1981). An application of high performance liquid chromatography with electrochemical detection to neurochemical analysis: Measurement of catecholamines, serotonin and metabolites in rat brain, *J. Neurosci. Methods,* **3**, 207–224.

Scott, R. P. W. and Kucera, P. J. (1979). Mode of operation and performance characteristics of microbore columns for use in liquid chromatography, *J. Chromatogr.*, **169**, 51–72.

Smedes, F., Kraak, J. C. and Poppe, H. (1982). Simple and fast solvent extraction system for selective and quantitative isolation of adrenaline, noradrenaline and dopamine from plasma and urine. *J. Chromatogr.*, **231**, 25–39.

5

An automated series coulometric electrochemical detection method for the simultaneous HPLC assay of monoamines and metabolites in crude tissue extracts or CSF

Philip J. Langlais, Wayne R. Matson[†] and **Edward D. Bird**
Brain Tissue Resource Center, McLean Hospital, Belmont, MA 02178,
and Harvard Medical School, Boston, MA, USA

[†]ESA, Inc., 45 Wiggins Avenue, Bedford, MA 01730

1. INTRODUCTION AND PURPOSE

Several high performance liquid chromatographic (HPLC) amperometric single electrode detection (EC) methods are currently used in the separation and quantitation of the monoamines, their precursors and metabolites in urine, blood, cerebrospinal fluid (CSF) and brain. The combination of a thin-layer amperometric detector with reverse-phase HPLC separation techniques has proved to be a major technical advance in the analyses of monoamine neuro-transmitters and has enhanced our understanding of their role in the control of behavioural, cognitive and motor activities. Through several years of experience with developing and applying single-cell HPLC-EC methods for monoamine determination (Langlais *et al.*, 1980, 1982, 1984a, b), certain limitations and areas for improvement have become apparent. Major shortcomings and problems include detection limits in the high picogram to low nanogram range, the inability to adequately detect the presence of co-eluting substances, and the use of one or more internal standards with varying and inadequate control of recoveries which place serious limits on their analytical accuracy and reproducibility. In addition, the number of samples which can be processed each day (throughput) is generally low, owing to extensive sample preparation procedures, the small number of compounds measured with each analytical assay and the inability to totally automate the analyses due to baseline drift and a gradual decline in detector response.

Several investigators have reported on the measurement of monoamines by direct injection of unprocessed CSF and perchloric acid (PCA) brain extracts onto a reverse-phase, single or dual electrode detection system. This approach reduces sample preparation to a single step, thereby greatly increasing sample throughput. Evaluation and calculation of recovery rates are also eliminated by direct injection procedures, thereby increasing analysis efficiency through elimination of tedious post-analysis calculations. While certain advantages are possible with this approach, a number of inherent problems exist. The 'void volume' signal generated in single electrode electrochemical detector assays of direct injections of CSF or PCA extracts is very large, completely obscuring or grossly interfering with the analysis of early eluting compounds such as 3-methoxy-4-hydroxy-phenylglycol (MHPG), 3,4-dihydroxyphenylglycol (DOPEG) and norepinephrine (NE). Secondly, the electrode surface quickly becomes coated with proteinaceous material present in CSF and PCA extracts, resulting in significant and rapid reductions in detector response. Most important, with direct injection, the probability of co-elution error increases dramatically.

Series dual amperometric detectors have been employed to record at different potentials and thereby permit the user to examine different segments of the current/voltage curve of each compound separated by the liquid chromatograph (Kissinger, et al., 1977; Blank, 1976). However, because of the low efficiency (2–5%) inherent in amperometric detectors, a large portion of the compound presented to the first electrode remains unchanged and is therefore present at the second electrode. Hence, series amperometric detectors have limited resolution by virtue of the fact that the observed current/voltage curves are cumulative. We have recently developed a novel, HPLC, series coulometric detection method for the simultaneous analysis of the catecholamines, indoleamines, their major metabolites and precursors in unprocessed (centrifuged only) CSF and crude 0.1 M PCA extracts of brain (Langlais et al., 1984a, b; Matson et al., 1984). This method utilizes recently developed high efficiency (approximately 99% conversion) flow-through coulometric detectors (Andrews et al., 1982). This type of series coulometric detection with its inherent capability for quantitative conversion or removal of compounds offers several strategies that enhance selectivity and anlytical reliability.

2. METHOD

2.1 Apparatus

The original method developed employed a Model 5100A Coulochem® Detector (ESA, Inc., Bedford, MA) consisting of three coulometric cells in series

(Langlais *et al.*, 1984a). This method has been recently improved by the addition of a fourth cell (second conditioning cell). The apparatus is detailed schematically in Fig. 1. The first high efficiency conditioning cell is set at $+400$ mV, this oxidizes all material eluting from the column up to this potential. This improves selectivity by eliminating the detection of a significant proportion of non-reversible compounds at subsequent electrodes operated in the reductive mode. That is, all compounds that can be completely oxidized at $+1$ to $+400$ mV and cannot be subsequently reduced (non-reversible) will not appear in the analysis at the two recording electrodes set at -150 and -400 mV, respectively. Secondly, oxidation of the column effluent greatly reduces baseline drift and virtually eliminates the large 'void' currents routinely observed with amperometric detectors following direct injections of crude samples onto an HPLC apparatus. The second conditioning cell is set at a -80 mV potential and was introduced into the system to eliminate the detection at subsequent recording electrodes of reversible compounds which are frequently found in CSF and PCA brain extracts as a function of the particular disorder being studied (Matson *et al.*, 1984). In the three-electrode system, the presence of these compounds occasionally produced unacceptable sample T_2/T_1 compound signatures (see below).

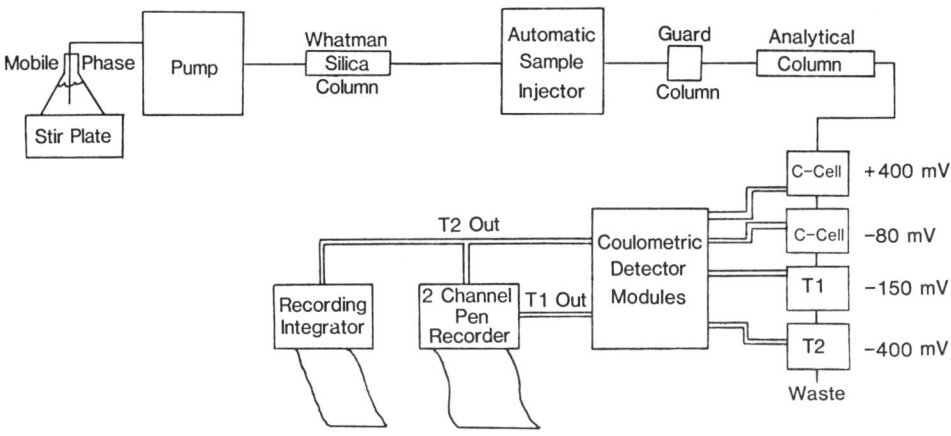

Fig. 1 – System schematic.

The third and fourth electrodes are set at two different reductive potentials beyond that of the second conditioning cell. The response of these two recording electrodes yields a specific ratio (T_2/T_1) or signature which is characteristic and unique for each monoamine, metabolite and precursor, thereby providing important qualitative information about peak composition and purity. The HPLC system consists of a Model 6000A pump, WISP automatic sample injector, a guard column packed with C_{18} Corasil, a C_{18} μBondapak column (30 cm $\times$ 4.6 cm) (Waters Assoc., Milford, MA) and a silica saturation precolumn (Whatman Corp.). Data analysis is performed by an HP 3390A reporting integrator (Hewlett Packard, Lexington, MA) connected to T_2. Quantitation of sample peaks is performed by comparison of sample peak heights to those of standard peak heights stored in a calibration table. Initial identification of a sample peak is performed on the basis of retention time and subsequently verified by comparison of the sample peaks T_2/T_1 signature, measured from an Omniscribe (Texas Instruments) dual channel recorder, to the signature obtained with authentic standards.

2.2 Reagents
The mobile phase is prepared by adding 210 ml methanol and 80 ml acetonitrile to 2 litres 0.1 M phosphate—citrate buffer containing sodium heptane sulphonic acid (1.21 gm/l) and disodium EDTA (0.50 gm/l), filtered, degassed, adjusted to final pH 3.0 and delivered at a 1.6 ml/min flowrate. All separations are accomplished at ambient temperature.

2.3 Sample preparations
To obtain brain extracts for direct injection, frozen post-mortem human brain tissue (25–75 mg wet wt.), dissected as previously described (Langlais *et al.*, 1983) is sonicated at 4°C in disposable microcentrifuge tubes. Extractions are carried out in 1.0 ml of 0.1 M PCA solution containing 0.4 mmol/l sodium metabisulphite and 0.1 mmol/l disodium EDTA, previously flushed with N_2 for 5 min prior to use. A clear supernatant is obtained by centrifuging the homogenate at 30,000 $\times$ g, for 45 min at 4°C and stored at −70°C until analysis. Human cerebrospinal fluid (CSF) stored at −70°C *without* the addition of antioxidants such as ascorbic acid (Langlais *et al.*, 1982) is thawed at 4°C (crushed ice), vortexed and a 300 ml aliquot centrifuged at 6,000 $\times$ g for 10 min at 4°C.

3. DESCRIPTION OF AUTOMATED ANALYSIS AND ASSAY CHARACTERISTICS
Representative chromatograms obtained by direct injection of a 0.1 M PCA solution of standards and a 0.1 M PCA extract of human post-mortem n. accumbens tissue are shown in Figs. 2 and 3, respectively. Notice the absence of any large 'void' signal typically observed in conventional one-cell amperometric assays. With this new assay procedure, individual peaks can be readily identified in the first 2–3 minutes of the separation in which polar and neutral compounds are eluting from the reversed phase column. The retention time (R_t), capacity factor (k') and signature (T_2/T_1) of several of the monoamines, metabolites, precursors and related compounds are given in the table.

Table 1 — Retention time (R_t), capacity factor (k'), T_2/T_1 signature of mono-amines and related compounds.

	R_t (mins)	k'	$T_2/T_1{}^a$	Adequate separation from Preceding peak	Following peak
Kynurenine	1.65	0.03	–	–	+
3,4-Dihydroxyphenylglycol (DHPG)	2.49	0.60	2.30	+	+
3-Methoxy-4-hydroxyphenyl-glycol (MHPG)	3.45	1.20	3.08	+	+
L-3-4-dihydroxyphenyl-alanine (L-DOPA)	3.67	1.30	1.61	+	+
Homogentisic acid	3.81	1.40	22.60	+	+
Norepinephrine (NE)	3.94	1.50	1.69	+	+
Epinephrine (EP)	4.67	1.90	2.01	+	+
Acetaminophen (Paracetamol)	5.28	2.30	0.55	+	+
3,4-Dihydroxyphenylacetic acid (DOPAC)	5.55	2.50	0.77	+	+
Normetanephrine	6.00	2.80	1.86	+	–
Vanillyl alcohol	6.10	2.80	2.44	–	+
3.4-Dihydroxymandelic acid (DOMA)	7.18	3.50	1.00	–	–
Dopamine (DA)	7.23	3.50	1.16	–	+
Metanephrine	7.69	3.80	2.00	+	–
5-Hydroxytryptophol (5-HTP-ol)	7.78	3.90	∞^b	–	+
5-Hydroxytryptophan (5HTP)	8.16	4.10	∞^b	+	+
5-Hydroxyindoleacetic acid (5HIAA)	8.97	4.60	∞^b	+	+
Homovanillylalcohol (HVA-ol; MOPET)	9.69	5.10	2.00	+	+
Homovanillic acid (HVA)	11.69	6.30	1.60	+	–
n-Acetyl-5-hydroxytrypt-amine (n-Acetyl-5HT)	11.69	6.30	∞^b	–	+
3-Methoxytyramine (3MT)	14.84	8.30	1.21	+	–
5-Hydroxytryptamine (5HT)	16.94	9.60	∞^b	+	+
Tyramine			No peak observed		
Octopamine			No peak observed		
L-tryptophan			No peak observed		
Vanillic acid			No peak observed		
Valnillymandelic acid			No peak observed		

^{a} T_2/T_1 values obtained with four-electrode configuration: $C_1 = +400$ mV; $C_2 = -80$ mV; $T_1 = -150$ mV; $T_2 = -400$ mV.
^{b} The indole compounds reduce only at T_2; therefore $T_1 = 0$ and $T_2/T_1 = \infty$.

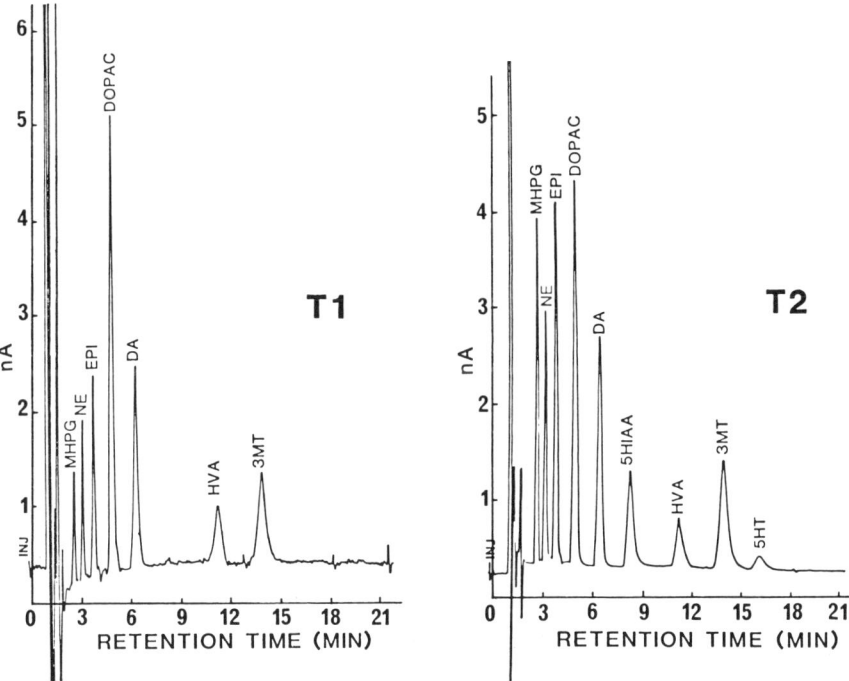

Fig. 2 – Chromatogram obtained from a 10 μl injection of a 0.1 M PCA standard solution (100 ng/ml except NE, 50 ng/ml).

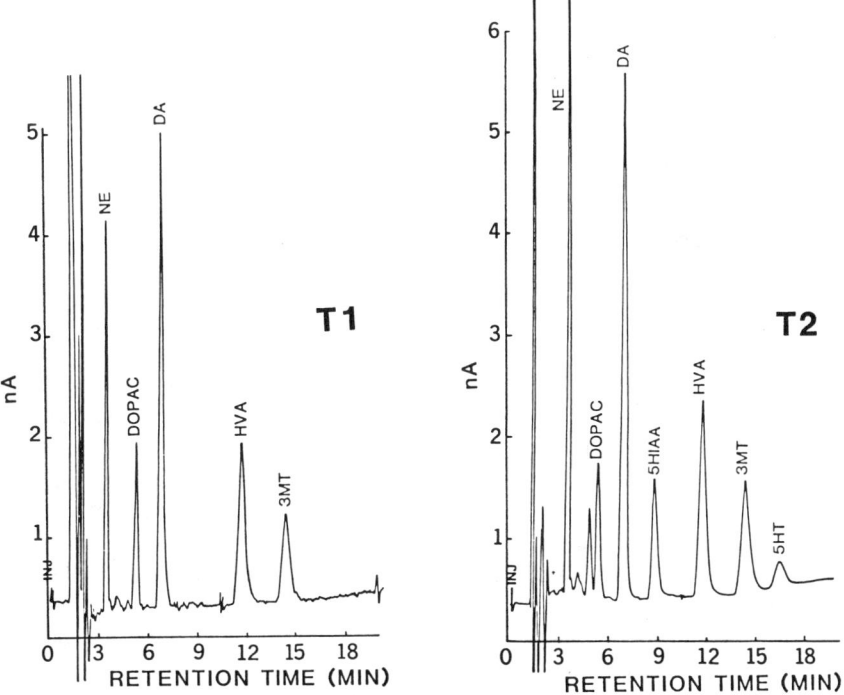

Fig. 3 – Chromatogram obtained from a 10 μl injection of 0.1 M PCA extract of frozen post-mortem human n. accumbens.

Typical operating detection limits of this method are compound dependent, ranging from 1.0 pg for dopamine (DA), 3,4-dihydroxyphenylacetic acid (DOPAC), epinephrine (EPI), NE, 3-methoxytyramine (3MT) to 50 pg for homovanillic acid (HVA) and serotonin (5HT). Linear responses are obtained from 1.0 to 50 pg to 50 ng. Within run coefficient of variation (% C.V.) ranges from 0.85 (DOPAC) to 10.54 (5HT) for standards ($N = 15$, 1.0 ng) and 2.27 (HVA, 1.998 ng) to 21.90 (MHPG, 0.073 ng. $N = 15$) for brain tissue extracts and CSF specimens. For a more detailed description of the method's precision for each compound, see Table 1 (Matson *et al.,* 1984).

To perform a routine automated analysis, the HP 3390A integrator is calibrated and the retention time of the various compounds identified by repeated injection of 10, 20 and 30 µl of a 0.1 M PCA extraction solution containing 50 or 100 ng/ml of each or the authentic monoamines, metabolite and precursor compounds. The automatic injector sample tray is assembled with the placement of the 0.1 M PCA standard solution after every fifth brain tissue extract or CSF specimen. A total of 40 separate tissue or CSF samples can be routinely assayed during a 13.5–15.0 hour automated run, either attended during the day or unattended overnight. If analyses are to be performed overnight and either the run will be completed or the mobile phase will be exhausted before anyone can attend to the apparatus, then a programmable timer is employed which can be preset to turn off the instrument's power to avoid damaging pumps, detectors or simply wasting mobile phase.

All of the catecholamines and their metabolites in both 0.1 M PCA standard solutions and tissue extracts have been found to be quite stable during a 13.5–15.0 hour automated analysis conducted at room temperature. A linear reduction is observed in the indoles which is identical in both 0.1 M PCA standard solutions and tissue extracts with a maximum 25% loss at the end of a 13.5 hour analytical run. The calculation of tissue extract indole content is normalized using the measured reduction in standards interspersed within the analytical run.

4. CONCLUSIONS

This brief report describes an automated single chromatographic method which is capable of separating over 20 of the major monoamines, metabolites and precursors. The use of new coulometric electrochemical detectors has greatly enhanced the resolution, separation and sensitivity of monoamine analysis. Four coulometric cells in a series configuration permit the initial oxidation at a high voltage (+400 mV) of the majority of compounds eluting from the column and their subsequent reduction at three separate and sequentially higher reductive potentials (−80 mV, −150 mV and −400 mV). The initial oxidation at +400 mV has allowed for a significant reduction in the 'void' signal and enhanced the resolution and detection of more polar compounds, e.g. DHPG and MHPG, and the virtual elimination of non-reversible compound interference at the two recording electrodes (−150 mV and −400 mV), and greatly stabilized baseline signal, thereby eliminating drift and allowing totally automated, unattended operation. The analytical accuracy of monoamine analysis has been improved with this new method for several reasons, First, the ability to directly inject unprocessed CSF or 0.1 M PCA extracts into the system eliminates error due to variabilities inherent in sample preparation, corrections based in internal standard recoveries and tedious post-analysis calculations. Secondly, comparison of tissue sample peak signatures to those obtained with authentic standards permits validation of peak purity and detection of co-eluting substances. Comparison of monoamine metabolite CSF concentrations obtained with one-cell amperometric and three-cell coulometric HPLC-EC methods have produced data indicating that significant overestimations of CSF, MHPG, 5HT, 5HTP and DOPAC concentrations are obtained with one cell amperometric detection methods (Matson *et al.*, 1984).

ACKNOWLEDGEMENTS

This work was supported in part by a grant from AFAR, Inc., by the E. G. Cale and L. Seidel Research Funds, the Veterans Administration Hospital in Bedford, MA 01730 and under NIH, DRR, SBIR Phase I Grant # 1 R43 RR02566-01.

REFERENCES

Andrews, R. W., Schubert, C. W., Morrison, J., Matson, W. R. and Zink, E. W. (1982). Dual electrode cells for LCEC: Recent developments. *Am. Lab.*, **14**, 140–151.

Blank, C. L. (1976). Dual electrochemical detector for liquid chromatography. *J. Chromatogr.*, **117**, 35–46.

Kissinger, P. T. (1977). Amperometric and coulometric detectors for high performance liquid chromatography. *Anal. Chem.*, **49**, 447–456.

Langlais, P. J., McEntee, W. J. and Bird, E. D. (1980). Rapid liquid chromatographic measurement of 3-methoxy-4-hydroxyphenylglycol and other monoamine metabolites in human cerebrospinal fluid. *Clin. Chem.*, **26**, 786–788.

Langlais, P. J., Bird, E. D. and McEntee, W. J. (1982). Stability of monoamine metabolites in human cerebrospinal fluid. *Ann. Neurol.*, **12**, 48–51.

Langlais, P. J., Walsh, F. X., Stevens, T. J. and Bird, E. D. (1983). Decreased catecholamine conntent caused by slicing of frozen human postmortem brain with an electric blade. *Neurosci. Lett.*, **41**, 99–103.

Langlais, P. J., Bird, E. D. and Matson, W. R. (1984a). An automated HPLC, three cell electrochemical method for the simultaneous assay of monoamines and metabolites in crude brain extracts. *Clin. Chem.*, **30**, 1046.

Langlais, P. J., Rothschild, A. J., Schatzberg, A. F., Cole, J. O. and Bird, E. D. (1984b). Dexamethasone elevates dopamine in human plasma and rat brain. *Psychopharmacol. Bull.*, **20**, 365–370.

Langlais, P. J., Walsh, F. X., Bird, E. D. and Levy, H. L. (1985). CSF neurotransmitter metabolites in neurologically normal infants and children. *Pediatrics*, **75**, 580–586.

Matson, W. R., Langlais, P. J., Volicer, L., Gamache, P. H., Bird, E. D. and
Mark, K. A. (1984). n-Electrode three dimensional liquid chromatography
with electrochemical detection for determination of neurotransmitters. *Clin.
Chem.*, **30**, 1477–1488.

6

An isocratic high performance liquid chromatographic system for the investigation of abnormalities of neurotransmitter amine, biopterin, and aromatic amino acid metabolism in CSF using sequential coulometric electrochemical and fluorescence detection

Keith Hyland, Isabel Smith and **David Howells**

Institute of Child Health, 30 Guildford Street, London WC1N 1EH, UK

In the study of abnormalities of neurotransmitter amine metabolism it is desirable to locate the underlying cause of the amine disturbance. We have developed an isocratic HPLC method to determine aromatic amino acids, neurotransmitter amine metabolites, and the pterin cofactors of the aromatic amino acid hydroxylases.

1. METHODS

Mobile phase was prepared by the addition of sodium acetate (6.8 g), citric acid (1.05 g), and EDTA (20 mg) to 900 ml distilled water. The pH was adjusted to 5.22 with NaOH and the volume made up to 1 litre with distilled water. Flow rate was 1.4 ml/min. Temperature was 35°C.

The column was an Apex 5μ reverse phase ODS. Detection was by an ESA dual cell coulometric electrochemical (EC) detector with electrodes set at +0.05 V and +0.45 V respectively. A Perkin Elmer LS3 spectrofluorimeter was connected in series after the EC detector.

2. MEASUREMENT OF THE NEUROTRANSMITTER AMINE METABOLITES

Homovanillic acid (HVA), 5-hydroxyindolacetic acid (5HIAA), and 3-methoxy-4-hydroxyphenylglycol (MHPG) were detected electrochemically (+0.45 V).

3. MEASUREMENT OF PTERINS

All three oxidation states of the biopterins may be measured by fluorescence (Ex Max=348, Em Max=444 nm). Biopterin (B) by its natural fluorescence, 7,8-dihydrobiopterin (BH_2) by fluorescence following post-column electrochemical oxidation (Hyland, 1985) and tetrahydrobiopterin (BH_4) indirectly by subtracting these values ($B + BH_2$) from the total biopterin ($B + BH_2 + BH_4$) found after MnO_2 oxidation (Niederweiser *et al.*, 1984). Oxidation of the pterins was performed by the addition of 5 μl 6 M HCl and 1 mg of MnO_2 to 200 μl of CSF. After 10 min, MnO_2 was removed by centrifugation.

4. MEASUREMENT OF AMINO ACIDS

Fluorescence settings were changed during the chromatographic run in order to achieve maximum sensitivity, although this is not necessary if only tryptophan and tyrosine are to be measured. Tyrosine: Ex Max=277, Em Max=303. Tryptophan: Ex Max=280, Em Max=350. Phenylalanine: Ex Max=255, Em Max=281.

5. RESULTS AND DISCUSSION

Fig. 1(a) shows a chromatogram of a mixture of neopterin (N), monapterin (M), BH_2, B, MHPG, 5HIAA and HVA. BH_2 is not naturally fluorescent but has been converted to a fluorescent compound following post-column electrochemical oxidation (Hyland, 1985). This is demonstrated in Fig. 1(b) where the EC detector is switched off and the peak correponding to BH_2 is no longer seen.

Fig. 2(a) shows a chromatogram obtained from a CSF sample from a patient with dihydropteridine reductase (DHPR) deficiency. DHPR is the enzyme required to recycle quinonoid-BH_2 to BH_4 which is the cofactor of the aromatic amino acid hydroxylases (Kaufman *et al.*, 1975). Quinonoid-BH_2 spontaneously rearranges to BH_2 (Benkovic, 1980). A large peak corresponding to BH_2 is seen in the chromatogram which disappears when the EC detector is switched off Fig. 2(b). By determining the amount of total biopterin after MnO_2 oxidation of the CSF from the DHPR deficient patients we have shown that over 90% is present as BH_2 (results not shown). Fig. 2 also demonstrates that in DHPR deficiency there are greatly reduced concentrations of the neurotransmitter amine metabolites when compared to age-matched controls (Fig. 2(c)) owing to lack of BH₄ and hence reduced activity of the aromatic amino acid hydroxylases.

Fig. 3(a) is the chromatogram of the aromatic amino acids obtained from the CSF of a healthy person and Fig. 3(b) that obtained from a patient with DHPR deficiency showing increased phenylalanine.

We are using this method to investigate CSF from patients in whom a primary or secondary defect in aromatic amino acid, biopterin or neurotransmitter amine metabolism is suspected.

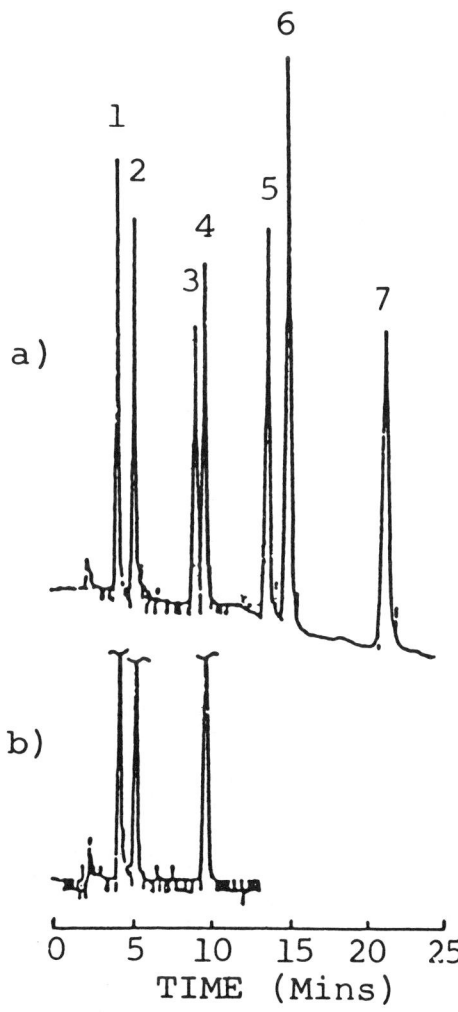

Fig. 1 – Fluorescence and electrochemical chromatogram of pterins (250 pg) and neurotransmitter metabolites (2.5 ng). (a = EC detector on: b = EC detector off). 1 = neopterin; 2 = monapterin; 3 = dihydrobiopterin; 4 = biopterin; 5 = MHPG; 6 = 5HIAA; 7 = HVA. Chromatogram shows fluorescence output for 12 min and EC output until the end of the run.

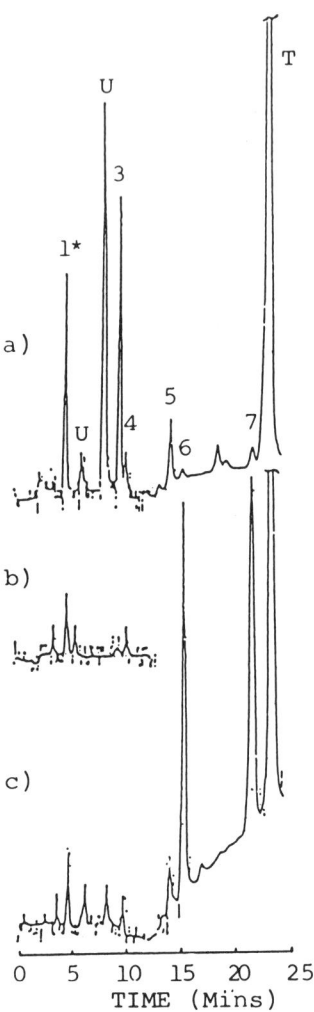

Fig. 2 – Analysis of pterins and neurotransmitter amine metabolites in CSF from
(a) DHPR-deficient patient (EC detector on), (b) same CSF sample (EC detector
off), (c) control CSF (EC detector on). Peak identification as in Fig. 1 except:
1* = neopterin + dihydroneopterin, U = unidentified, T = tryptophan.

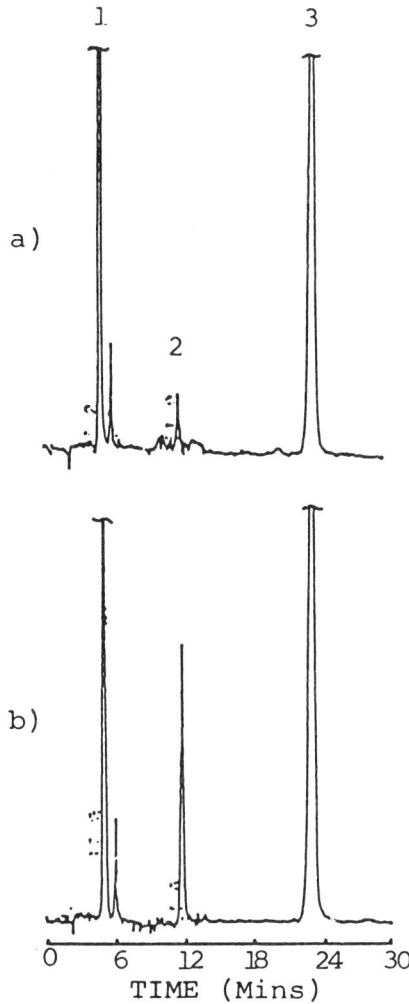

Fig. 3 — Fluorescence chromatogram of aromatic amino acids in CSF. (a) Control CSF, (b) CSF from DHPR deficient patient; 1 = tyrosine, 2 = phenylalanine, 3 = tryptophan.

REFERENCES

Benkovic, S. J. (1980). On the mechanism of action of folate- and biopterin-requiring enzymes. *Ann Rev. Biochem.,* **49**, 227–253.

Hyland, K. (1985). The estimation of tetrahydro-, dihydro- and fully oxidised pterins by high performance liquid chromatography using sequential electrochemical and fluorometric detection. *J. Chromatogr.,* **343**, 35–41.

Kaufman, S., Holtzman, N. A., Sheldon, M., Butler, I. J. and Krumholz, A. (1975). Phenylketonaria due to a deficiency of dihydropteridine reductase. *N. Engl. J. Med.,* **293**, 785–790.

Niederwieser, A., Staudenmann, W. and Wetzel, E. (1984). High performance liquid chromatography with column switching for the analysis of biogenic amine metabolites and pterins. *J. Chromatogr.,* **290**, 237–246.

7

Modified *o*-phthalaldehyde derivatization of primary amines for determination by LCEC

W. A. Jacobs, G. S. Mayer, P. J. Harrington, M. L. Leburg and **R. E. Shoup**

Technical Center, Bioanlytical Systems, Inc., West Lafayette,
IN 47906, USA

Primary amines react with *o*-phthalaldehyde (OPA) in the presence of a thiol to produce 1-*S*-substituted isoindoles. In addition to being fluorescent, the resulting derivatives are easily oxidized and provide convenient electrochemical access to an important class of generally electroinactive compounds (Joseph and Davies, 1983). Current emphasis, consistent with rapid improvements in reverse phase column technology, is on precolumn OPA derivatization. With the shift from postcolumn to precolumn methods, the variable stability of OPA/2-mercapto-ethanol (OPA/2-ME) derived isoindoles has been a continuing problem which has made obtaining good analytical precision difficult. The problem is frequently cited in the literature (Simons and Johnson, 1976, 1977; Stobaugh *et al.,* 1983), but no completely satisfactory explanations have appeared. In many cases accurate timing of the derivatization reaction is required in order to achieve acceptable precision. Accordingly, studies were undertaken to identify the factors responsible for the observed instability, the ultimate goal being the implementation of procedural modifications capable of alleviating this complication.

Preliminary studies using the standard OPA/2-ME reagent and selected amine substrates indicated a significant effect of amine structure on derivative stability (Table 1). The structure–stability relationship appeared to relate to the steric bulk of the amine side chain, as well as its proximity to the isoindole ring. Stability increased in proportion to both bulk and ring proximity, a relationship that was subsequently verified in detailed studies utilizing a wide selection of amines. Electronic substituent effects were determined to be of little importance.

Table 1 – Apparent first order rate constants for decay of isoindoles derived from ethanethiol and selected primary amines ($R-NH_2$).

R	k_{app} $(min^{-1}) \times 10^2)$	$t_{1/2}$ (min)
a. $-CH_3$	31.6 ± 0.6	2.2
b. $-CH_2CH_3$	12.0 ± 0.4	5.8
c. $-CH(CH_3)_2$	0.33 ± 0.03	210
d. $-C(CH_3)_3$	a	–
e. $-CH_2CH_2CH_3$	5.69 ± 0.04	12.2
f. $-CH_2CH(CH_3)_2$	2.3 ± 0.2	30
g. $-CH_2C(CH_3)_3$	0.33 ± 0.06	210

a No detectable change after 3 hours.

In keeping with the above observations, it was reasoned that the use of a bulky thiol may provide similar stabilization. Initial experiments using t-butyl-thiol supported this proposition with resulting isoindole derivatives exhibiting dramatic improvements in stability (e.g. for 4-aminobutyric acid derivatized with OPA/2-ME, $t_{1/2} = 8.0$ min; using OPA/t-BT, $t_{1/2} = 410$ min). This, too, was subsequently verified in more detailed experiments where thiol bulk was varied systematically. Interestingly, the substitution of ethanethiol, as suggested by others (Simons and Johnson, 1983), resulted in only modest stabilization (for 4-aminobutyric acid using OPA/ET $t_{1/2} = 11.6$ min).

In agreement with recent reports (Stobaugh *et al.*, 1983), excess OPA in the reaction mixture was found to catalyse the degradation of isoindole derivatives. In the absence of catalytic degradation, the stability of all derivatives was excellent. Furthermore, the catalytic activity of OPA was influenced by a number of parameters including thiol structure, amine structure, thiol concentration, solvent composition, and pH. A mechanism was formulated to explain the observed results. We suggest that OPA acts essentially as a water transfer agent, but perhaps more significant is its concurrent role of assisting thiol removal by forming a favourable leaving group (Jacobs and Leburg, 1985). Based on simplifying assumptions, the following relationship was derived from decomposition of the isoindole (denoted here as A):

$$\frac{-dA}{dt} = k[A] + k_c [A] [OPA]$$

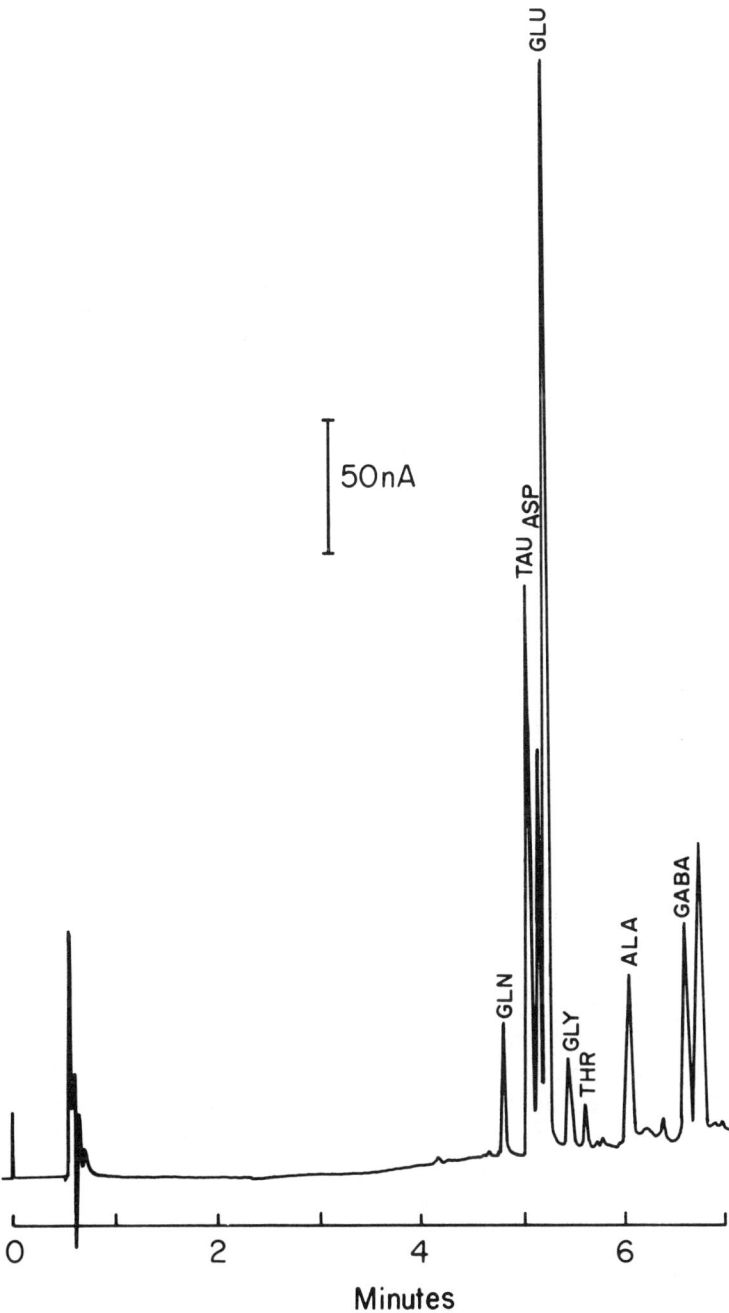

Fig. 1 – Gradient elution of OPA/t-BT derivatives from rat brain homogenate. Concentrations: GLN, 216 μM; TAU 808 μM; ASP, 726 μM, GLU, 1.63 mM; GLY, 241 μM, GABA, 501 μM. Detector: BAS LC-4B/17 at 0.80 V vs Ag/AgCl. Gradient (in linear segements): 0 min, 67.2% 0.05 NaClO₄/0.005 sodium citrate buffer (pH 5.0), 30.8% MeOH, 2% THF, 2 min, 33.6% buffer, 64.4% MeOH, 2% THF; 5 min, 20% buffer, 45% MeOH, 35% THF; 8 min, hold conditions. Flow rate: 1.5 ml/min. Stationary phase: 100 × 4.6 mm reverse phase (3 micron, C₁₈). (From Allison *et al.* (1984).

Based on the mechanism, structural modifications were presumed to influence stability by altering the fundamental rate constants controlling intermediate formation and breakdown.

The mechanistic studies demonstrated that sufficient steric bulk would stabilize any OPA-catalysed hydrolysis of the derivative. For this reason we selected t-butylthiol as a model thiol in determining the analytical properties of these alternate substitution derivatives. Hydrodynamic voltammograms for the derivatives were generated. Substitution of t-BT for 2-ME only slightly increased the derivative's redox potential. Data obtained from rapid-scanning staircase hydrodynamic voltammetry also reflected a trend of increasing oxidation potential with greater hydrophobicity. Using LCEC, we also monitored the conversion of tyrosine to its corresponding derivative; essentially all of the tyrosine was reacted and the product peak was maximal in 2 minutes. A percentage conversion of 94% for derivatizing t-butylamine to product was determined; the reaction is nearly quantitative.

The merits of fluorescence vs amperometric detection for the detection of these OPA/RSH amino acid derivatives depend on the nature of the thiol involved. Fluorescence spectra were obtained on methionine and GABA derivatives using 2-ME and TBT. Excitation and emission wavelengths were virtually unchanged with substitution, but relative emission intensity decreased 6–10-fold. Using liquid chromatography and tandem detection, minimum detectable concentrations of S-t-butyl-N-butylisoindole as a test solute were also nearly 20-fold better via electrochemistry. The limiting factor was the baseline noise of the fluorescence detector.

TBT/OPA reagent was applied to the detection of brain pool amino acids (Allison *et al.,* 1984). Rats were decapitated, and the freshly dissected brain was homogenized in methanol/H_2O. The supernatant was derivatized with OPA/TBT reagent for detection of GLU, taurine, ASP, GLN, GLY, and 4-aminobutyric acid (GABA). Many of these amino acids were the poorest in stability using OPA/2-ME, so utilizing the OPA/TBT reagent for this determination is advantageous. A typical run is presented in Fig. 1. Since the OPA/RSH reaction is generally applicable to primary amines, we have also investigated its utility in the detection of biogenic diamines. For example, cancer patients often have elevated levels of spermidine, cadaverine and putrescine, and there is interest in using these levels as a way to evaluate the effectiveness of various methods of therapy. Preliminary work to measure these compounds in pediatric CSF samples is under way.

REFERENCES

Allison, L. A., Mayer, G. S. and Shoup, R. E. (1984). o-Phthalaldehyde derivatives of amines for high-speed liquid chromatography/electrochemistry, *Anal. Chem.,* **56**, 1089–1096.

Jacobs, W. A. and Leburg, M. W., (Bioanalytical Systems, Inc.) (1985). Studies on the degradation of o-phthalaldehyde derived isoindoles, manuscript in preparation.

Joseph, M. H. and Davies, P. (1983). Electrochemical activity of o-phthalaldehyde-mercaptoethanol derivatives of amino acids: application to HPLC determination of amino acids in plasma and other biological materials, *J. Chromatogr.*, **277**, 125–136.

Simons, S. S., Jr. and Johnson, D. F. (1976). The structures of the fluorescent adduct formed in the reaction of o-phthalaldehyde and thiols with amines, *J. Am. Chem. Soc.*, **98**, 7098.

Simons, S. S., Jr., and Johnson, D. F. (1977). Preparation of a stable fluorescent 1-Alkylthio-2-alkylisoindole. *J. Chem. Soc., Chem. Commun.*, 374–375.

Stobaugh, J. F., Repta, A. J., Sternson, K. W. and Garreu, K. W. (1983). Factors affecting the stability of fluorescent isoindoles derived from reaction of o-phthalaldehyde and hydroxyalkylthiols with primary amines, *Anal. Biochem.*, **135**, 485–504.

8

HPLC-ECD of neuropeptides in neural and endocrine tissues

G. W. Bennett, Janel V. Johnson and **C. A. Marsden**
Department of Physiology and Pharmacology, Queen's Medical Centre,
Clifton Boulevard, Nottingham NG7 2UH, UK

1. INTRODUCTION

We have reported previously (Bennett *et al.*, 1981) that biologically active neuropeptides which contain one or more of the amino acids, tyrosine, tryptophan or cysteine, are electroactive and can be assayed in brain and other tissues by means of an electrochemical detector coupled with a suitable HPLC system. Such neuropeptides include arginine vasopressin (AVP), oxytocin, neurotensin, somatostatin, luteinizing hormone-releasing hormone, cholecystokinins (CCK-4,-8), corticotrophin and various opioid peptides. Reports from other groups have described the use of the HPLC-ECD technique to detect Met- and Leu-enkephalins and endorphin (Meek *et al.*, 1977) and CCK-4,-8 (Sauter and Frick, 1983) whilst our own group has concentrated on the measurement of the neurohypophyseal peptides (particularly AVP) and the enkephalins in brain and adrenal tissue samples respectively (Johnson *et al.*, 1984a, b).

Neuropeptides are more commonly quantified by radioimmunoassay (RIA) techniques which achieve sensitivities in the picomolar to femtomolar range. However, many antibodies used in RIAs show significant cross-reactivity with closely related peptides, resulting in false-positive measurements. The HPLC-ECD technique avoids such specificity problems enabling the rapid assay of several peptides in common samples, but generally does not achieve the high sensitivity of a good RIA. With the latter disadvantage in mind therefore, we have more recently improved the sensitivity of the HPLC-ECD technique as a result of a number of modifications. Using the improved HPLC-ECD procedure we have measured levels of AVP (and other peptides) in discrete unilateral brain regions and pituitary of the rat and studied changes in brain and pituitary AVP levels following acute and chronic adrenalectomy (Johnson *et al.*, 1984a, b). In the present studies HPLC-ECD peptide measurements have been compared with levels measured by RIA and this clearly demonstrates the improved accuracy and specificity of the ECD method in comparison with the immunological technique.

2. METHODS

2.1 HPLC technique
Reverse phase isocratic HPLC separation of various neuropeptides was carried out using a Waters Z module radial compression separation system containing a radial-pak C18, 10 μ cartridge. The mobile phase used was 0.15 M NaH_2PO_4/methanol (60:40 v/v), pH 5.8, delivered at a constant flow rate of 1.5 ml/minute by a Waters 510 pump.

2.2 ECD method
The detector used was an ESA Coulochem 5100A dual channel detector with 2 porous graphite in-line working electrodes. A current/voltage curve for AVP (20 pmol injected) was determined: increasing the voltage at detector electrode 2 led to an increased peak height (nanoamps) up to a plateau level of 800 nA between 0.80 V and 0.90 V. It was decided therefore to select a working potential of 0.85 V at detector electrode 2 and a screen potential of 0.40 V at detector 1 as this value was at the foot of the current voltage curve at 100 nA. Similar electrode conditions were found to be optimum for other peptides investigated. The system also incorporated a guard cell electrode prior to the injector and this was set at 0.90 V to act as a scrubber for the mobile phase.

2.3 Detection of neuropeptide standards
Using the above conditions the retention times (min) of the series of peptide standards (20 pmol injected) were as follows: AVP (5.0), Met-enkephalin (6.0), Leu-enkephalin (7.5), oxytocin (11.0), angiotensin II (12.5), neurotensin (15.5) and angiotensin III (17.5). Calibration curves for each of the above neuropeptides were constructed between 0.2 to 200 pmol injected by measuring peak area in nA$\times$min. The limit of detection for each peptide at a signal to noise ratio of 3:1 was less than 200 fmol.

2.4 Measurement of neuropeptides in tissues
Brain, pituitary or adrenal tissues were dissected and homogenized by sonication (Ultrasonics Rapides Ltd, 100 W for 1 min) in 1 M acetic acid. The supernatants were separated by centrifugation (4000 g $\times$ 20 min) dried down in a vortex evaporator (Buchler) and stored at $-20°C$. The pellet was stored at

−20°C until protein was determined by the method of Lowry *et al.* (1951). Samples were taken up in mobile phase prior to injection.

Tentative identification of peaks observed in brain tissue extracts was made by comparing their HPLC retention times (R_T) with the R_T of pure synthetic standards and confirmed by adding similarly extracted standards to the tissue extract ('spiking'). To test that each peak was made up of only one peptide and not a mixture of peptides with similar R_T, two oxidation peaks were generated for each peptide and the ratio of the two peak heights measured. For example, AVP standards were injected onto the column, detector electrode 1 was set at 0.60 V and detector 2 at 0.90 V. Some AVP was oxidized at detector 1 and the remainder at detector 2, the ratio of the two peak heights was recorded. This procedure was repeated for AVP in extracts of neurointermediate lobe (NIL) and the two ratios compared. The peak height ratio for AVP standard was 1.255 ± 0.005 ($n = 10$) and for AVP in the NL extract $1,300 \pm 0.020$ ($n = 10$). There is no significant difference between these two values ($p > 0.05$) confirming that the AVP peak measured in the tissue extracts does not include other peptides with similar R_T. Similar procedures were repeated with other brain tissue extracts for other peptides before their identification was accepted.

2.5 Comparison of AVP levels measured by HPLC-ECD and radioimmunoassay (RIA)

Rats were adrenalectomized and AVP measured in brain and pituitary regions by HPLC-ECD (Johnson *et al.*, 1984b). Aliquots of identical samples were stored at −80°C for parallel measurement by RIA using the method of Jenkins *et al.* (1983) with minor modifications. The antibody was a gift from Dr. D. J. Perkin, St. George's Hospital Medical School, London. AVP standards were similarly extracted and stored at −80°C and the AVP levels were shown not to alter significantly during storage (up to 7 months) when measured either by HPLC-ECD or RIA. Selected groups of tissue extracts were run through the HPLC prior to RIA, using HPLC conditions identical to those for HPLC-ECD. Fractions (1 min) were collected with the ECD detector switched off and in fractions of the mobile phase, AVP content was measured by RIA. The constituents of the mobile phase were shown not to alter antibody binding in the RIA.

3. RESULTS AND DISCUSSION

The major improvements to the present HPLC-ECD system for measurement of neuropeptides, compared with those described previously, are associated with (a) the Z module chromatographic system, and (b) the dual channel coulometric detector.

(a) The use of the Z module offers a number of advantages compared with the conventional column. Firstly, the uniformly compressed cartridge improves peak separation and reduces peak 'tailing' due to surface properties which are characteristic of column separation. Secondly, the reduced resistance to flow of the mobile phase through the cartridge compared with a column (with equivalent packing material) enables more rapid analysis at lower back pressures.

Finally, the Z module cartridge contributed towards improvements in the signal-to-noise ratio and consequently in the overall improvement in sensitivity.

(b) The use of the dual coulometric detector has also improved the signal to noise ratio. This detector enables operation in the 'screen mode' whereby the first detector can be set to oxidize substances at a lower potential (0.4 V) in order to remove background and unwanted peak currents at the second detector (set at 0.85 V). Thus peptide oxidations are monitored within the range 0.40 to 0.85 V. This screening is possible since the large surface area graphite-porous detectors oxidize almost all of the analyte in contrast with more conventional amperometric detectors. Furthermore a guard cell was present in the system prior to the injector and set at a potential above the working range of detector 2 in order to oxidize and eliminate any contaminants in the mobile phase. This further contributed towards an increased signal-to-noise ratio. The coulometric detector also offers improvements in sensitivity and reproducibility since much of the large electrode surface area of the detectors is not inactivated by neuropeptide adsorption to the electrode surface as occurs with small surface amperometric detectors.

Adrenalectomy (10 day) caused regional specific changes in AVP content as measured by HPLC-ECD (Table 1) (Johnson et al., 1984b). In the present

Table 1 – Comparison of AVP levels in pituitary and hypothalamic tissues of sham ($n=8$) and 10 day adrenalectomized (Adx) rats ($n=12$) as measured by HPLC-ECD and RIA.

		HPLC-ECD[a]	RIA
		(ng/gland)	
Neurointermediate lobe	Sham	502 ± 46	1532 ± 163
(NIL)	Adx	390 ± 34	1093 ± 103
		(pg/µg protein)	
Median eminence	Sham	315 ± 19	895 ± 72
(ME)	Adx	409 ± 32	1231 ± 102
		(pg/µg protein)	
Supraoptic nucleus	Sham	206 ± 14	225 ± 18
(SON)	Adx	139 ± 9	159 ± 7
Suprachiasmatic nucleus	Sham	31 ± 5	55 ± 7
(SCN)	Adx	65 ± 16	77 ± 19
Paraventricular nucleus	Sham	62 ± 11	91 ± 13
(PVN)	Adx	56 ± 9	–

NB. AVP levels measured by RIA in the NIL and ME were significantly greater ($p < 0.01$) then the HPLC-ECD measurements. AVP levels measured by RIA in the SON, SCN and PVN were also higher than levels measured by HPLC-ECD but did not reach significance.
[a]HPLC-ECD data from Johnson et al. (1984b) (with permission).

study parallel measurement of the same tissue samples by RIA showed qualitatively similar changes in AVP content. The quantitative levels measured by RIA, however, were approximately 2–3 times those measured by HPLC-ECD in the neurointermediate lobe (NIL) and median eminence (ME) and also higher (although not significantly) in the supraoptic nuclei (SON), suprachiasmatic nuclei (SCN) and paraventricular nuclei (PVN). The most likely explanation for a difference in levels measured by RIA and HPLC-ECD may be false-positive measurements by RIA due to the antibody binding non-specifically to 'AVP-like' peptides present in the NIL and ME. The finding that AVP levels measured by RIA in the SON, SCN and PVN were not significantly higher than those measured by HPLC-ECD may indicate the presence of fewer non-specific cross-reacting peptides in these regions, where peptide processing has not occurred to the same degree as in the terminal regions (NIL and ME).

The AVP content of samples of ME extract was further assayed by RIA following separation by HPLC (Table 2). This enabled (a) a more direct comparison with HPLC-ECD measurements of similar aliquots, and (b) an assessment of the recovery of AVP-like immunoreactivity from the HPLC. Table 2 shows that AVP measured by HPLC-ECD in ME extracts occurs as a sharp peak at 5 min

Table 2 – Comparison of AVP levels in median eminence tissue extracts ($n = 6$) measured by HPLC-ECD and HPLC-RIA.

HPLC fraction (min)	HPLC-ECD (pg AVP)	HPLC-RIA
0–1	[Precolumn AVP levels by RIA: 2234 ± 126]	
1–2		
2–3		
3–4		
4–5		232 ± 19
	917 ± 69	
5–6		953 ± 158
6–7		248 ± 18
7–8		
8–9		
9–10		
TOTAL	917 ± 69	1704 ± 208

250 µl aliquots of median eminence tissue extracts were separated by HPLC and measured using ECD or by RIA in 1-min fractions collected with the detector switched off (see section 2).
NB. The main peak identified as AVP by HPLC-ECD (see text) peaked at 5 min whereas AVP by HPLC-RIA was measured as a more broad peak within three separate 1-min fractions.

(917 ± 69 pg; $n = 6$). In contrast, significant AVP immunoreactivity was measured in 3 HPLC fractions (4–7 min) as a large, broad, peak, but, interestingly, the peak fraction of immunoreactivity (5–6 min) was not significantly different from that measured by ECD (953 ± 158 pg; $n = 6$). Furthermore, the total AVP immunoreactivity eluted from the HPLC in the 10-min collection period was 1,704 ± 208 pg ($n = 6$) and this represented only 75% of the AVP immunoreactivity present in the sample before HPLC (2,234 ± 126; $n = 6$). These results suggest that non-specific 'AVP-like' immunoreactivity in acetic-acid extracts of rat ME is due to natural or generated molecules chemically similar to AVP, which separate on HPLC closely associated with 'true-AVP', and also other 'AVP-like' material, possibly larger precursor molecular forms, which do not elute from the present HPLC during a 10-min collection period.

Since one can be confident that using a dual channel detector the AVP peak measured by HPLC-ECD (see NIL measurements, above) represents a single molecular component, it would appear that HPLC-ECD can provide a far more accurate and specific method of measuring neuropeptide levels than RIA. The recent improvements in sensitivity with HPLC-ECD as described in this paper make this technique an attractive method for measuring several peptides in common biological samples.

REFERENCES

Bennett, G. W., Brazell, M. P. and Marsden, C. A. (1981). Electrochemistry of neuropeptides: A possible method for assay and *in vivo* detection. *Life Sciences*, **29**, 1001–1007.

Jenkins, J. S., Ang, B. T.-Y., Hawthorn, J., Rossor, M. N. and Iversen, L. L. (1983). Quantitative distribution of neuropeptide hormones in human brain and spinal cord. *Progress in Brain Research*, **60**, 123–128.

Johnson, J. V., Bennett, G. W., Marsden, C. A., Gardiner, S. M. and Bennett, T. (1984a). Electrochemical measurement of neurohypophyseal peptides in hypothalamic and pituitary tissues. *Regulatory Peptides*, **9**, 335.

Johnson, J. V., Bennett, G. W., Marsden, C. A., Gardiner, S. M. and Bennett, T. (1984b). Electrochemical measurements of neurohypophyseal peptide levels in rat hypothalamic regions after adrenalectomy. *Clinical and Experimental Hypertension – Theory and Practice*, **6A**, 1993–1998.

Lowry, O. H., Roseborough, N. J., Lewis, Farr, A. and Randall, R. J. Protein measurement with the Folin Phenol Reagent. *Journal of Biological Chemistry*, **193**, 265–275.

Meek, J. L., Yang, H. Y.-T. and Costa, E. (1977). Enkephalin catabolism *in vitro* and *in vivo*. *Neuropharmacology*, **16**, 151–154.

Sauter, A. and Frick, W. (1983). Determination of cholecystokinin tetrapeptide and cholecystokinin octopeptide in different rat brain regions by high pressure liquid chromatography with electrochemical detection. *Analytical Biochemistry*, **133**, 307-313.

Part

V

Workshop:
In vivo techniques for measuring transmitter release and metabolism

Report:

In vivo techniques for measuring transmitter release and metabolism

M. Fillenz

University Laboratory of Physiology, Parks Road, Oxford, OX1 2PT, UK

R. B. Holman

Department of Physiology and Biochemistry, University of Reading, RG6 2AJ, UK

The second afternoon Workshop concentrated on a discussion of the relative merits of the various techniques for monitoring transmitter release *in vivo*. The purpose of these techniques is to monitor transmitter release in the brain (1) following the administration of drugs, (2) in the course of behaviour. The ideal technique would allow simultaneous measurement of several transmitters in more than one brain region, with a fine temporal resolution over long periods of time without interfering with brain function.

The discussion was concerned with the extent to which the various techniques available at present can satisfy these objectives, or offered promise of being able to satisfy them in the future. In the absence of a single method which fulfils these criteria, the price to be paid for achieving one or more of them was discussed as a guide to the choice for a particular purpose. In a general comparison of the perfusion (ranging from CSF sampling to dialysis) versus the electrochemical techniques, the former offer the advantage of the measurement of a wide range of released substances; however, sampling is usually restricted to a single probe, and the time resolution is coarse and limited by the frequency of sampling. However, very interesting results have been obtained with various forms of well established perfusion/sampling techniques, as illustrated in this volume by Curzon *et al.* (Part III, Chapter 5) and Bradford *et al.* (Part III, Chapter 8); and see Korf (Part III, Chapter 9). The most recent of the perfusion techniques is that of intracranial dialysis; this was therefore discussed in somewhat greater detail.

Seven different groups from the UK, the USA and Sweden presented posters with dialysis systems demonstrating the detection of the release of a variety of endogenous amino acid and monoamine neurotransmitters.

In part, this interest must be due to the concomitant developments of high performance liquid chromatography (HPLC) coupled with electrochemical detection (EC). HPLC-EC provides a means to isolate and quantitate pico or nanogram quantities of transmitter or metabolite in dialysis samples and is within the financial contraints of many laboratories. However, the dialysis system itself also offers two distinct advantages over previously available techniques. Firstly, the cannula can be implanted directly into discrete, deep brain structures. Both cortical cup and ventricular perfusion procedures are restricted to collecting from relatively large surface areas of the brain, producing an ambiguity as to the site of any alterations in neuronal activity. Although the push—pull cannula can be implanted into specific brain areas, it is an open perfusion system — the in-flow and out-flow tubes are not directly connected. Therefore continuous flow is more difficult to maintain and the system is more liable to damage tissue due to increases in intracranial pressure.

Yet despite such an apparently safe means for sampling *in vivo*, the first topic of discussion was a potential neurochemical artefact due to the *in vivo* dialysis cannula. It was reported (Holman and Snape) that the tissue content of the dopamine (DA) metabolites, 3,4-dihydroxyphenylacetic acid (DOPAC) and homovanillic acid (HVA), in the striatum containing the cannula as compared to the contralateral tissue, was significantly increased when measured at the conclusion of dialysis experiments in anaesthetized rats. This stimulation of the metabolism of DOPAC and HVA was not the result of the dialysis perfusion, as the cannula alone could elicit a similar response in the tissue. In addition, the effect appears to be specific for DA as the content of the 5-hydroxytryptamine (5HT) metabolite, 5-hydroxyindoleacetic acid (5HIAA) was unchanged. The results suggest a possible lesion, produced by the cannula, which alters ongoing DA metabolism. Whether the effect can be avoided by placement of the cannula in a different area of the striatum is not yet clear. Several other groups at the meeting apparently had not encountered these problems, as they had not observed any changes in secretion of the DA metabolites with time in dialysis samples. However, Holman and Snape noted that they did not consistently observe a dramatic increase in the DOPAC and HVA content of the first four or five samples of dialysate which are used as indicators of control or basal secretion. Thus any treatments at the end of this 'control' period could be confounded with later increases due to the artefactual formation of the metabolites, emphasizing the need for tissues analyses at the conclusion of any perfusion experiment.

These results led to further discussions as to the value of measuring monoamine metabolites in experiments designed to delineate changes in neurotransmitter release. It is generally accepted that changes in transmitter activity should be reflected by increases or decreases in the metabolite content. Yet in the experiments mentioned above, although the concentrations of DOPAC and HVA increased during the course of a dialysis perfusion, the percentage increase in the samples was never as great as the percentage increase occurring in the tissue. Justice, Michael, Wages and Neill using a combination of *in vivo* voltammetry and dialysis concluded that changes in extracellular metabolite concentrations following eating behaviour or electrical stimulation of the medial forebrain bundle occurs long after the release and re-uptake of the transmitter itself. The DOPAC concentrations did not increase until 20 minutes after a one-minute burst of stimulation, and did not return to control values until 90 minutes post-stimulation. Although the metabolite content indicated an increase in release, the time course of that release process is not accurately reflected in the results. The authors do suggest, however, that these metabolite measurements may offer a means to estimate the size of the 'functional' or 'readily-releasable' pool of DA without the need for pharmacological treatments.

Sharp, Zetterstrom and Ungerstedt also reflected the concern with the significance of metabolite measurements from their dialysis studies following administration of amphetamine or neuroleptics. They measured endogenous DA release *in vivo* and found that amphetamine elicited a rapid and short-lived increase in the extracellular content of the amine. Freed *et al.* (Part III, Chapter 6, this volume) suggest that the time course for the DA metabolite could be made to overlap that for DA, as measured by the Swedish group, by calculating the first derivative of the metabolite data. Again the data suggest that metabolite concentrations can reflect changes in release, but not their time course. Finally, however, even such limited interpretations of metabolite data may be open to error. Ungerstedt's group indicated from their results with neuroleptics, that the drugs could induce increase in DA metabolism, which was not associated with an increased release of the amine itself.

The obvious solution to this problem would be to determine the concentrations of the neurotransmitter as well as the metabolites in the same dialysis samples. At least two groups at the meeting presented just such data (Sharp, Zetterstrom and Ungerstedt; Routledge and Marsden). Although the concentrations of the DA and 5HT seemed to vary, the content of the amine tended to be about 100 times less that of the respective metabolites. Despite such low picogram concentrations, the HPLC-EC methods used by most groups should be sufficiently sensitive. Yet a number of other groups reported they were unable to detect either DA or 5HT in dialysis samples with the exception of the first few samples following positioning of the cannula (which is presumably due to mechanical disruption of the tissue). Whether the differences between laboratories in detection of the monoamine neurotransmitters is due to the different dialysis membranes used or to some other technical differences was not readily apparent. However, for the future it would seem extremely useful to define and to standardize the *in vivo* dialysis procedures in order to facilitate the comparison of results from the large number of laboratories now developing the technique.

The various forms of the *in vivo* electrochemical techniques all share certain advantages as well as disadvantages. Their spatial and temporal resolution is much finer, but detection is restricted to electroactive substances. There is still considerable controversy surrounding the identification of the various electroactive compounds. The parameter measured — the oxidation current at the electrode surface — is determined by the electrode material, electrode pretreatment and the configuration of the applied potential. Substances are characterized by their oxidation potential and preliminary investigatory tests are usually carried out *in vitro*. It has become clear, however, that both the chemical and physical characteristics are profoundly changed once electrodes are implanted in the brain. This means that electrodes have to be characterized after implantation and *in vitro* tests are of limited value. The problem of interpreting changes in the voltammogram is that the oxidation potentials of electroactive compounds in the ECF are often too close to each other to produce resolvable peaks. Examples of this are the difficulty of distinguishing ascorbic acid, catecholamines and their metabolites; the same is true of uric acid, indoleamines and their acid metabolites.

The validation of voltammogram peaks is often based on the effect of systemically administered drugs on the size of the peak. These tests have led to confusion in the past, since they were based on the assumption that the drug affected only one of the electroactive compounds. The problem of identifying and removing interfering substances is being tackled by chemical modifications of the electrode material which selectively restricts access to the electrode surface, electrical pretreatment of the electrodes, which at present is a purely empirical approach with no known theoretical basis, and modifications of the applied potential.

Merits and limitations of fast cyclic voltammetry at carbon fibre microelectrodes

Zygmunt L. Kruk

Department of Pharmacology, The London Hospital Medical College,
Turner Street, London E1 2AD, UK

1. INTRODUCTION

Fast cyclic voltammetry (FCV) was developed following a fortuitous series of events. In 1979 Armstrong-James and Millar had perfected the construction of single carbon fibre microelectrodes, suitable for unit activity recording in the CNS. At this time, we had numerous discussions about the problems associated with ionophoresis, and in particular the difficulties of getting any idea of when drug came out of the barrels, and the concentration of drug ejected. The publications of Adams and Marsden prompted me to suggest that it might be possible to use the carbon fibre electrode (hitherto only used for unit activity recording), as the working electrode for electrochemical measurement of monoamines ejected during ionophoresis from a multibarrel carbon fibre microelectrode.

Because we were working in the electrophysiology laboratory, and because we could not afford to buy any of the commercial electrochemistry equipment, apparatus which was already available was pressed into service, while other 'bits' were made from Radio Spares components. We chose cyclic voltammetry because we had function generators which would produce squarewaves, ramps and sine waves; thus we had a ready source of input voltage. For recording cyclic voltammograms a two-channel digital storage oscilloscope was used. This had the advantage of enabling us to subtract background currents from faradaic signals at the push of a button. The screen display could then be output to an X-Y pen recorder. Whereas we started making CV scans using conventional voltage sweep rates of tens of mV/s, faradaic currents were small, and when we amplified them we introduced a lot of noise. If we increased the scan rate to some 200–300 V/s however, our signal got larger and relatively quieter. So FCV was born.

2. FCV: MERITS

The first bonus we saw with FCV was that using catecholamines (usually dopamine), we always saw a reduction peak as well as an oxidation peak. Provided the voltage scan was kept constant, the positions of oxidation and reduction peaks remained constant. Using the carbon fibre microelectrodes for FCV did not affect their performance as low noise electrodes for unit activity recording. We found early on that if multibarrel electrodes were kept with the tip immersed in distilled water, they worked for up to 5 consecutive days, able both to record unit activity and detect catecholamines. By using a 'wave gate' we were able to allow through only 1.5 wave cycles from the function generator each second. At voltage scan rates of 300 V/s, we completed a FCVoltammogram in about 15 milliseconds. Complete assays could be made up to four times a second, thus events lasting less than 1 second could be investigated. The electrodes could be calibrated in standard solutions of catecholamines.

We found that we could use such *in vitro* calibrated electrodes to 'quantify' ionophoretic ejections of catecholamines and 5HT *in vitro* and *in vivo* (Armstrong-James *et al.*, 1980, 1981a; Kruk *et al.*, 1980; Millar *et al.*, 1981). NADH, NADPH and biologically interesting peptides containing tyrosine residues can be detected and quantified (*in vitro*) (Armstrong-James *et al.*, 1981b). Dopamine can be readily distinguished from DOPAC on the basis of peak oxidation and reduction voltages, as well as from the overall different shapes of the peaks. O-methylated metabolites produce unique (and changing) oxidation peaks, while adrenaline produces two oxidation and two reduction peaks (Kruk *et al.*, 1983).

Dopamine is readily distinguished from ascorbic acid, for the latter shows no reduction peak. Bicyclic voltammetry, and pressure ejection of ascorbate oxidase confirm the ability of the electrodes to distinguish dopamine from ascorbate (Stamford *et al.*, 1983). More recently we have shown that, using FCV, it is possible to detect and measure extracellular dopamine release in the striatum of the anaesthetized rat, during electric stimulation of the median forebrain bundle. The technique follows changes in concentration with a time resolution of at least 250 milliseconds. In addition to giving data on dopamine release, we also obtain data about uptake processes (Stamford *et al.*, 1984a, 1984b). Pharmacological and electrochemical experiments provide strong evidence in favour of our measuring dopamine (as opposed to ascorbic acid or DOPAC) release during electric stimulation of the median forebrain bundle (Stamford *et al.*, 1984a, 1984b).

FCV: LIMITATIONS

1. CF electrodes (especially those which have been etched in chromic acid) tend to become less sensitive both *in vitro* and *in vivo*. This is probably a form of 'poisoning'. 5HT and 5HIAA are particularly liable to cause such poisoning.
2. If electrodes are not etched in chromic acid, and no electrical conditioning is carried out, then electrodes appear to be less liable to poisoning.
3. Electrical conditioning produces electrodes which appear to absorb catecholamines, which is undesirable if they are being used to measure moment-to-moment changes in catecholamine concentration.
4. The lower limits of detection of most electrodes with FCV is in the region of 1×10^{-6} M catecholamine, or 1×10^{-5} M catecholamine acid metabolites. The electrodes have yet to be tested using pulse techniques which are claimed to be more sensitive than ramped techniques.
5. The electrodes are fragile, and we have not attempted to use them in conscious animals for electrochemical experiments. Preliminary experiments show that they can be used to record unit activity for several days following implantation.
6. Some poisoning does occur when electrodes are used *in vivo*. The sensitivity of the electrodes to dopamine is decreased by about 50% almost immediately on implantation.

4. CONCLUSIONS

FCV at carbon fibre microelectrodes is a powerful technique for use in anaesthetized animals. It can measure moment-to-moment changes in dopamine concentration, and allows dopamine to be distinguished from DOPAC or ascorbic acid. Fragility and poisoning remain problems which must be overcome if the method is to be used in conscious animals.

ACKNOWLEDGEMENTS

The work described here was done in the Pharmacology and Physiology laboratories at The London Hospital Medical College by Mike Armstrong-James, Kevin Fox, Julian Millar, Jon Stamford and the author. Selwyn Mable (Medical Physics Department) has helped with technical development of apparatus.

REFERENCES

Armstrong-James, M. and Millar, J. (1979). Carbonfibre microelectrodes. *J. Neurosci. Meth.*, **1**, 279–287.

Armstrong-James, M., Millar, J. and Kruk, Z. L. (1980). Quantification of noradrenaline ionophoresis. *Nature*, **288**, 181–183.

Armstrong-James, M., Fox, K., Kruk, Z. L. and Millar, J. (1981a). Quantitative ionophoresis of catecholamines using multibarrel carbonfibre microelectrodes. *J. Neurosci. Methods*, **4**, 385–406.

Armstrong-James, M., Fox, K., Kruk, Z. L. and Millar, J. (1981b). Electrochemical detection of enkephalins in bulk solution and following ionophoresis. *J. Physiol.,* **313**, 38 P.

Kruk, Z. L. and Stamford, J. (1983). Characterisation of catecholamines by high speed cyclic voltammetry. *Brit. J. Pharmac.,* **80**, 632 P.

Kruk, Z. L., Armstrong-James, M. and Millar, J. (1980). Measurement of the concentration of 5-HT ejected during ionophoresis using multibarrel carbonfibre microelectrodes, *Life Science,* **27**, 2093–2098.

Millar, J., Armstrong-James, M. and Kruk, Z. L. (1981). Polarographic assay of ionophoretically applied dopamine and low noise unit recording using a multibarrel carbonfibre electrode. *Brain Research,* **205**, 419–442.

Stamford, J., Kruk, Z. L. and Millar, J. (1983). A double cycle fast voltammetry technique allowing direct measurement of irreversibly oxidised species; characterisation of ascorbate in rat central nervous system. *J. Neurosci. Meth.,* **10**, 107–118.

Stamford, J., Kruk, Z. L. and Millar, J. (1984a). Measurement of stimulated striatal dopamine release by fast cyclic voltammetry. (In preparation).

Stamford, J., Kruk, Z. L., Millar, J. and Wightman, R. M. (1984b). Striatal dopamine uptake in the rat: *in vivo* analysis by fast cyclic voltammetry. *Neurosci. Lett.,* **51**, 133–138.

2

Application of *in vivo* voltammetry to the study of serotonergic function in rat hippocampus in stress

Michael H. Joseph[†] and **Guy A. Kennett**[‡]

Division of Psychatry, Clinical Research Centre, Watford Road,
Harrow, HA1 3UJ, UK

We have used voltammetric electrodes to monitor the release of 5HT in the rat hippocampus. These electrodes were fabricated from a paste made from ultra carbon powder, paraffin oil and epoxy resin, packed in a pulled glass microcapillary.Using a linear ramp from 0 to 1 V in 10 seconds (i.e. 100 mV/s) with miniature Ag/AgCl reference electrode, *in vitro* calibration indicated that the 5-hydroxyindoles including 5HT and 5HIAA, but also catechols and ascorbic acid, contributed to a single peak at 0.35 to 0.4 V. A peak at this voltage was also seen *in vivo* in the freely moving animal after prior implantation of electrodes into the dorsal hippocampus. In view of the results subsequently reported by others (Crespi *et al.*, 1983; O'Neill *et al.*, 1984; Mueller *et al.*, 1985) it would be unwise to exclude uric acid as a further possible contributor to this peak, although our preliminary *in vitro* results suggest that uric acid may oxidize at a higher potential with our electrodes.

Since we wished to use *in vivo* voltammetry (IVV) to monitor 5-hydroxy-indole release in stress, we treated this current signal as one might a bioassay

†Present address: Departments of Psychology and Biochemistry, Institute of Psychiatry, Denmark Hill, London SE5 8AF, UK.
‡Present address: Department of Neurochemistry, Institute of Neurology, 33 John's Mews, London, WC1 2NS, UK

response; that is, we observed the effect on the signal of a variety of pharmacological manipulations which should have predictable effects on 5-hydroxyindole release. Several points arise out of our experiences (Kennett and Joseph, 1982) and those of others (Cespuglio *et al.,* 1981; Echizen and Freed, 1983; Baumann and Waldmeier, 1984).

(1) Several drugs with one common effect should be used.
(2) Drugs which allow critical discriminations should be used, e.g. drugs which release 5HT, but do not change, or reduce, 5HT turnover as measured by wet biochemistry (PCA, fluoxetine) should give an increased signal.
(3) The feedback effects of changes in 5HT availability on 5HT release should be considered (MAOIs).
(4) Effects of drugs leading to a build-up of other substances which are detectable in principle, but not normally present in substantial amounts, should be considered (e.g. 5HTP or aromatic amino acid decarboxylase inhibitor administration leading to build up of 5HTP).
(5) The effect of drugs on the distribution of substances detected should be considered (e.g. reserpine).

In respect of 5-hydroxyindole measurements the contribution of uric acid to the signal should be further explored. Results reported by others suggest that the contribution may vary with electrode type or the method of voltage sweep employed (Crespi *et al.,* 1983; O'Neill *et al.,* 1984). Full resolution of this problem will, however, depend on simultaneous monitoring of ascorbic and uric acid release, by *in vivo* dialysis, or ideally, by simultaneous IVV monitoring. Specific lesioning of the 5HT system (O'Neill *et al.,* 1984) will be crucial in establishing the contribution of 5HT release to the observed baseline signal.

We have used our *in vivo* technique to observe the effects of immobilization stress on the hippocampal signal (Joseph and Kennett, 1983a). A biphasic increase is seen; this is substantially attentuated by preventing the associated rise in brain tryptophan by administering valine. Co-administration of tryptophan, but not tyrosine, with the valine completely restored the biphasic stress response.

Restricting 5HT synthesis in another way, using prior PCPA administration similarly attentuates the IVV stress response. In this second case the attenuation is not due to a limitation of tryptophan availability, since AMPT, which has a greater limiting effect than PCPA on tryptophan availability, but inhibits catecholamine rather than 5HT synthesis, does not significantly attenuate the stress-induced increase in signal (Joseph and Kennett, 1983a). Thus the increase in signal can be attenuated, not only by restricting the availability of the substrate for 5HT synthesis, but also by restricting the activity of the relevant rate limiting enzyme.

These results are consistent with the interpretation that immobilization stress increases 5HT release, and that this increase is substantially dependent upon increased 5HT synthesis. It does not seem likely, while it cannot be excluded at this time, that uric acid release would be modulated in precisely this way by altering tryptophan availability and 5HT synthesis, unless it also were released into the hippocampus in concert with the activity of serotonergic projections thereto. Our IVV results are also consistent with our results on the modulation by tryptophan availability of corticosterone release, a putatively 5HT dependent response to immobilization stress in the rat (Joseph and Kennett, 1983b).

Others have observed broadly similar effects of stress on the IVV serotonergic signal in various brain areas (Crespi and Jouvet, 1984; Baumann and Waldmeier, 1984; Ikeda *et al.*, 1984). IVV catecholaminergic responses to other stresses have also been reported in rats and monkeys (Lindsay *et al.*, 1981; Keller *et al.*, 1983; Cheney-Thamm *et al.*, 1984). The dependence of increased 5HT function on increased tryptophan availability has also been confirmed by others (Yehuda and Meyer, 1984; Kelly and Franklin, 1984).

It is important to distinguish between the interpretation of baseline IVV signals, and that of their *response* to pharmacological or physiological manipulations. It is also important not to generalize from one area of the brain to another. It will be crucial to the interpretation of our findings to explore firstly the effects of pharmacological manipulations and of stress on uric and ascorbic acid release, and secondly the effects on the hippocampal IVV response to stress of selective lesions of the serotonergic and catecholaminergic projections to this brain area.

REFERENCES

Baumann, P. A. and Waldmeier, P. C. (1984). Negative feedback control of serotonin release *in vivo*: comparison of 5HIAA levels measured by voltammetry in conscious rats and by biochemical techniques. *Neuroscience,* **11**, 195–204.

Cespuglio, R., Faradji, H. Riou, F., Buda, M., Gonon, F., Pujol, J. F. and Jouvet, M. (1981). Differential pulse voltammetry in brain tissue. II. Detection of 5HIAA in the rat striatum. *Brain Res.,* **223**, 299–311.

Cheney-Thamm, J., Reite, M., Alianello, E. A., Yamamoto, B. K., Capitanio, J. P. and Freed, C. R. (1984). Caudate electrochemical response following amphetamine administration in pigtail monkeys. *Life Sciences,* **35**, 1453–1460.

Crespi, F. and Jouvet, M. (1984). Differential pulse voltammetric determination of 5-hydroxyindoles in four raphe nuclei of chronic freely moving rats simultaneously recorded by polygraphic technique: physiological changes with vigilance states. *Brain Res.,* **299**, 113–119.

Crespi, F., Sharp, T., Maidment, N. and Marsden, C. A. (1983). Differential pulse voltammetry *in vivo* – evidence that uric acid contributes to the indole oxidation peak. *Neurosci. Lett.,* **43**, 203–207.

Echizen, H. and Freed, C. R. (1983) *In vivo* electrochemical detection of extraneuronal 5HIAA and norepinephrine in the dorsal raphe nucleus of urethane anaesthetized rats. *Brain Res.,* **277**, 55–62.

Ikeda, M., Hirata, Y., Fujita, K., Shinzato, M., Takahashi, H., Yagyu, A. and Nagatsu, T. (1984). Effects of stress on release of dopamine and serotonin in the striatum of spontaneously hypertensive rats; an *in vivo* voltammetric study. *Neurochem. Int.,* **6**, 509–512.

Joseph, M. H. and Kennett, G. A. (1983a). Stress induced release of 5HT in the hippocampus and its dependence on increased tryptophan availability; an *in vivo* electrochemical study. *Brain Res.,* **270**, 251–257.

Joseph, M. H. and Kennett, G. A. (1983b). Corticosterone response to stress depends upon increased tryptophan availability. *Psychopharmacology,* **79**, 79–81.

Keller, R. W., Stricker, E. M. and Zigmond, M. J. (1983). Environmental stimuli, but not homeostatic challenges, produce apparent increases in dopaminergic activity in the striatum; an analysis by *in vivo* voltammetry. *Brain Res.,* **279**, 159–170.

Kelly, S. J. and Franklin, K. B. J. (1984). Restraint stress potentiates morphine analgesia by increasing brain tryptophan. *Neurosci. Lett.,* **44**, 305–310.

Kennett, G. A. and Joseph, M. H. (1982). Does *in vivo* voltammetry in the hippocampus measure 5HT release? *Brain Res.,* **236**, 305–316.

Lindsay, W. S., Herndon, J. G., Blakely, R. D., Justice, J. B. and Neill, D. B. (1981). Voltammetric recording from neostriatum of behaving Rhesus monkey. *Brain Res.,* **220**, 391–396.

Mueller, K., Palmour, E., Andrews, C. D. and Knott, P. J. (1985). *In vivo* voltrammetric evidence of production of uric acid by rat caudate. *Brain Res.,* **355**, 231–235.

O'Neill, R. D., Fillenz, M., Grunewald, R. A., Bloomfield, M. R., Albery, W. J., Jamieson, C. M., Williams, J. H. and Gray, J. A. (1984). Voltammetric carbon paste electrodes monitor uric acid and not 5HIAA at the 5-hydroxyindole potential in the rat brain. *Neurosci. Lett.,* **45**, 39–46.

Yehuda, R. and Meyer, J. S. (1984). A role of serotonin in the hypothalamic–pituitary–adrenal response to insulin stress. *Neuroendocrinol.,* **38**, 25–32.

Index